Composite Materials

VOLUME 8

Structural Design and Analysis

Part II

COMPOSITE MATERIALS

Edited by

LAWRENCE J. BROUTMAN   AND   RICHARD H. KROCK

Illinois Institute of   *P. R. Mallory & Co., Inc.*
Technology   *Laboratory for Physical Science*
Chicago, Illinois   *Burlington, Massachusetts*

VOLUME 8

Structural Design and Analysis
Part II

Edited by

C. C. CHAMIS

NASA-Lewis Research Center
Cleveland, Ohio

ACADEMIC PRESS   New York   San Francisco   London   1975

A Subsidiary of Harcourt Brace Jovanovich, Publishers

ACADEMIC PRESS, INC.
111 Fifth Avenue, New York, New York 10003

United Kingdom Edition published by
ACADEMIC PRESS, INC. (LONDON) LTD.
24/28 Oval Road, London NW1

Library of Congress Cataloging in Publication Data

Chamis, Christos C
    Structural design and analysis.

    (Composite materials, v. 7-8)
    Includes bibliographies.
    1.   Composite construction.   2.   Structures, Theory
of.   I.   Title.   II.   Series.
TA664.C47   624'.17   74-12301
ISBN 0-12-136508-5 (v.8)

Contents

7 Discrete Element Analysis of Composite Structures

David M. Purdy

8 Probabilistic Design and Reliability

Brian H. Jones

v

9 Experimental Characterization of Composites

Charles W. Bert

10 Analysis of Discontinuities, Edge Effects, and Joints

Glenn C. Grimes and Lowell F. Greimann

10 Design of Composite Structural Components

C. C. Chamis

List of Contributors

Numbers in parentheses indicate the pages on which the authors' contributions begin.

CHARLES W. BERT (73), School of Aerospace, Mechanical and Nuclear Engineering, The University of Oklahoma, Norman, Oklahoma

C. C. CHAMIS (231), NASA-Lewis Research Center, Cleveland, Ohio

LOWELL F. GREIMANN (135), Department of Civil Engineering, Iowa State University, Ames, Iowa

GLENN C. GRIMES (135), Department of Structural Research, Southwest Research Institute, San Antonio, Texas

BRIAN H. JONES (33), Goldsworthy Engineering, Inc., Torrance, California

DAVID M. PURDY (1), Douglas Aircraft Company, Long Beach, California

Foreword

The development of composite materials has been a subject of intensive interest for at least 15 years, but the concept of using two or more elemental materials combined to form the constitutent phases of a composite solid has been employed ever since materials were first used. From the earliest uses, the goals for composite development have been to achieve a combination of properties not achievable by any of the elemental materials acting alone; thus a solid could be prepared from constituents which, by themselves, could not satisfy a particular design requirement. Because physical, chemical, electrical, and magnetic properties might be involved, input from investigators of various disciplines was required. In the various volumes of this treatise references to specific materials have generally only included the man-made or synthetic composites, but certainly the broad definition of composite materials must include naturally occurring materials such as wood. Chapters dealing with analytical studies of course can apply equally to synthetic or naturally occurring composites.

While composites have been used in engineering applications for many years, the severe operating conditions at which materials have to function (in the space age) led to the science of composite materials as we know it today. The efforts of scientists and engineers working on government research and development programs created entirely new materials, fabrication techniques, and analytical design tools within a short span of time to serve a limited market, but one with constantly demanding requirements. At end of the 1960s, a sharp reduction in the level of government expenditures in these areas and redistribution or re-emphasis of much of the personnel and institutions that had been involved in the development of composite materials raised the possibility that no complete reference work would be available to record many of these important developments and techniques. It was also apparent that this great bulk of technology, if properly digested and evaluated, could be employed in industrial and consumer applications for advantages of economy, performance, and design simplicity. For these reasons, the Editors and Academic Press have prepared this treatise detailing the major aspects of the science and technology of composite materials. We believe that the wide representation of contributors and the diversity of subject matters contained in the treatise assure the complete coverage of this field.

We intend that the volumes be used for reference purposes, or for text supplement purposes, but particularly to serve as a bridge in transferring the bulk of composite materials technology to industrial and consumer applications.

The Editors are indebted for the cooperation and enthusiasm they have received from the Editor of each volume and the individual contributors who worked diligently and as a unit to complete this task. We are also grateful to the staff at Academic Press who provided constant support and advice for the project.

Finally, the Editors wish to thank the management of P. R. Mallory and Co., Inc. and the administration of Illinois Institute of Technology for providing a key element in the successful completion of this work through their support and encouragement.

LAWRENCE J. BROUTMAN
RICHARD H. KROCK

Preface

The seventh and eighth volumes of *Composite Materials* are devoted to methods of structural design and analysis.

The evaluation of any design results from a requirement or desire to satisfy either a known or agreed upon need. Several decisions precede the definitization of any specific design objective. However, once the design objective has been definitized, the design becomes an iterative process employing various analysis/design disciplines. These disciplines have progressed to the point where composite components can be designed successfully.

The analysis/design disciplines employed in composite design include: continuum mechanics principles dealing with anisotropic elasticity, composite failure mechanics, structural/stress analysis for struts, plates, and shells, wave propagation and impact mechanics, stress concentrations at discontinuities and joints, reliability, automated design, and various test methods.

In order to provide a text with a balanced integration of the above disciplines and one in which the reader may acquire pertinent information by self-study, analysts/designers specializing in these disciplines were invited to contribute chapters in their major area of specialty.

Eleven major areas of specialty are covered in these two volumes. They are: (1) some topics in anisotropic elasticity, (2) failure criteria and failure analysis of composite structural components, (3) analysis of truss, beam, frame, and membrane components, (4) analysis of plates, (5) analysis of shells, (6) wave propagation and impact, (7) finite element analysis of composite structures, (8) probabilistic design and reliability, (9) experimental characterization of composites, (10) analysis of discontinuities, edge effects, and joints, and (11) design of composite structural components.

In Chapter 1, the continuum mechanics concepts employed to describe composite behavior are examined. A short summary of selected topics in the theory of anisotropic elasticity is presented. A section is devoted to the discussion of the generalized Hooke's law, its symmetry properties, and restrictions on the elastic moduli. Some elementary examples, illustrating the differences between the behavior of isotropic and anisotropic solids, are discussed. Difficulties encountered in characterizing fiber-reinforced composite materials are shown to result from the unusual behavior of anisotropic solids. The governing field equation for St. Venant torsion for an anisotropic solid possessing a plane of elastic symmetry is derived in detail. It is used to illustrate the available solution methods. Examples, applicable to composite materials, are discussed. The governing field equation for plane deformation of an anisotropic body with a plane of elastic symmetry is derived. Particular emphasis is placed on the assumptions underlying the various forms of plane deformation. A large body of literature dealing with stress concentration problems is summarized.

Chapter 2 presents a summary of the state of the art and provides working tools for failure criteria and failure analysis of composite structural components. The chapter covers two general aspects of this important area. The first is concerned with the characteristics of composite materials where laminate characterization, laminate stress–strain data, laminate stress analysis, and composite design philosophies for strength are examined in detail. The second is concerned with the discussion of failure criteria for the unidirectional composite (lamina or ply), the composite laminate, generalizations, stress–strength analysis, and future trends.

Chapter 3 examines the structural analysis methods of truss, beam, frame, and membrane composite components. Specifically, this chapter presents a pertinent summary and review of the state of the art in structural analysis including analysis philosophies, techniques, and methods of approach. Static, dynamic, and stability methods are considered. Analysis deficiencies are identified and growth areas are indicated. The discussion of the various topics is supplemented with appropriate hardware examples.

Chapter 4 is an in-depth review of the static, stability, and dynamic analysis of composite plates. The topics covered are macroscopic constitutive relations of unidirectional composite plates loaded in their plane, composite stiffness matrix for thin laminate plates, small-deflection theory of thin laminate plates, large-deflection theory of thin laminate plates, thick laminate plates, and sandwich plates. For each one of these topics the underlying assumptions, the general theory, and various special cases are discussed in detail. The treatment is limited to composite plates with linearly elastic material behavior. Cases for which this assumption could be violated are identified.

Chapter 5 is an in-depth review of the static, stability, and dynamic analysis of composite shells. The topics covered are genealogy of shell theories, linear theory of thin laminated shells, doubly curved shell of revolution, conical shells of revolution, circular cylindrical shells, noncircular, conical, and cylindrical shells, large deflection and finite strain theory of thin shells, thick laminated shells, and sandwich shells. The underlying assumptions, the general theory, and various special cases are discussed in detail for each topic. The effects of transverse-shear-flexibility is also examined.

Chapter 6 provides an extensive review of the mechanics of wave propagation and impact in composites. This area is currently receiving considerable attention in both theory and experiment from the composites community. The author presents a summary of the results to date (May, 1973) that seem to be accepted in the field and that might be of use to the structural dynamics analyst. The specific topics examined are anisotropic waves in composite structures, dispersion effect on waves, scattering and absorption of waves, shock waves in composites, experimental results, and the effects of impact.

Chapter 7 summarizes the basic methods of discrete element analysis and demonstrates how these methods may be applied to composite structures. The basic methods are discussed in general terms. For greater detail, the reader is referred to any of the excellent books available on the subject. The basic methods can be subdivided into two basic categories: element theory and methods of analyzing the multielement representation of the structure normally called the idealization. The methods of analyzing the idealization remain unchanged between isotropic and nonisotropic structures, but the element properties must be modified to account for the nonisotropic behavior. Several examples are given in which the discrete (finite) element analysis method was applied to composite structures.

Probabilistic design and component reliability are becoming prominent in structural design in general and structural design of composite components in particular.

Chapter 8 examines the concepts of probabilistic design and reliability as it pertains to composites. Considerable detail is devoted to the topics of statistical aspects of strength and loads, macro- and micromechanical aspects of statistical strength, design applications of the Weibull and normal distributions, and factors of safety and reliability. A discussion on structural reliability is also included. The relationship between structural reliability and various design factors is brought out whenever possible.

Chapter 9 provides an in-depth examination of the experimental methods for characterizing composites and composite components. Both the experimental techniques and their corresponding analytical parts (if available) are described. Considerable discussion is devoted to static testing for uniaxial tension, compression, bending, and shear; static multiaxial loading; how to systematize experimental programs for complete characterization of composite properties; and various testing methods for dynamic properties. Whenever possible, advantages, disadvantages, and special pitfalls are pointed out for the various available test methods. Due to volume space limitation, the details of standard tests and experimental results are not covered. However, numerous references are cited wherein such details are described.

Chapter 10 is an extensive review of the state of the art of the analysis of discontinuities, edge effects, and joints in composites. The discontinuities covered are partly a macrofracture mechanics problem and partly one of a micromechanical discontinuity. The edge effects examined are found to be closely related to the lamination sequence and are usually significant only within one laminate thickness distance of the free edge. Attachment efficiency and cost and adhesive bonded joint analysis techniques are presented showing that nonlinear analysis techniques accurately predict bonded joint strengths. Mechanically fastened joints are reviewed describing typical experimental behavior and the lack of research in this area. In some respects, discontinuities and edge effects are closely related to joints and their behavior under load; thus incorporating them into a single chapter is logical. The equations that describe the stress/strain behavior at discontinuities, free edges, or joints are given, and graphical representation of the corresponding responses is presented.

Chapter 11 summarizes the methodology for designing composite structural components. The various design procedures and the several steps within each procedure are described. The various design procedures covered include evolution of design, sources and types of design data, conventional and automated design including structural synthesis, simultaneous component and material design, important factors to be considered in designing composite components, and some sample design cases. Numerous illustrations are included; these illustrate design concepts, design procedures, or structural response. Due to volume space limitation, extensive design examples are not given. However, references are cited wherein design examples are described in detail.

Since the field is still in a fluid state, it is understandable that each chapter author will have a notation preference. To facilitate reading, a list of symbols is given for each chapter.

The editor of this volume expresses his gratitude to the National Aeronautics and Space Administration, Lewis Research Center, for granting him approval to participate in this treatise as both volume editor and chapter author, and also for providing him with secretarial assistance. The editor wishes to thank the authors for the generous contribution of their overtaxed free time and for their outstanding cooperation. The editor also wishes to thank the treatise editors and the publisher for their patience and valuable assistance. Finally, the editor wishes to acknowledge all the researchers of the fiber composite community who have contributed to the progress of this ever-changing fascinating field; to those of you whose work is not directly cited, you can be sure that your contributions influenced the organization of this volume and the technical content of each chapter; to those of you yet to join the ranks of the fiber composite community, the editor hopes that this volume will provide you with a launching pad for a successful and rewarding career.

C. C. CHAMIS

Contents of Other Volumes

Volume 4

Composite Materials

VOLUME 8

Structural Design and Analysis

Part II

7

Discrete Element Analysis of Composite Structures

DAVID M. PURDY

Douglas Aircraft Company
Long Beach, California

I. Introduction

Discrete element analysis methods, sometimes called finite element analysis methods or matrix analysis methods, have become increasingly popular with the advent of high-speed computers. The basic procedure is to consider the structure as made up of a series of discrete elements with basic

1

simplifying assumptions having been made over each element. The special case of discrete element analysis where the stretching and shearing capability of the structure are separated into bars and shear panels is often referred to as lumped parameter analysis, since a system of linear alegbraic equations results which can be solved for unknown variables. Methods and the resulting computer programs have developed rapidly in the past decade primarily to meet the analysis needs of the aerospace industry. Until recently most of the discrete element analysis capability that was developed applied only to structures fabricated from isotropic materials. With the increasing use of composite materials which exhibit nonisotropic behavior the discrete element methods and capabilities for analysis of composite structures are starting to come into being.

The objective of this chapter is to discuss the basic methods of discrete element analysis and to demonstrate how these methods may be applied to composite structures. The basic methods are discussed in general terms. For greater detail the reader is referred to any of the excellent books available on the subject. The basic methods can be subdivided into two basic categories: element theory and methods of analyzing the multielement representation of the structure normally called the idealization. The methods of analyzing the idealization remain unchanged between isotropic and nonisotropic structures, but the element properties must be modified to account for the nonisotropic behavior.

It should be noted that there is a significant difference between having the methods available to solve discrete element problems and having the capability to solve those problems. Utilization of the discrete element methods requires the development of sophisticated digital computer programs. As the problems become more complex the number of unknown variables which are found from an equal number of linear algebra equations becomes larger. With the limitation of digital computers on the number of significant digits and the number of variables which can be stored and directly operated on, it is an extremely difficult task to develop computer methods which can be used for solution of large and complex discrete element problems. A number of large computer systems have been developed for solution of discrete element problems. Three systems which have been developed under government sponsorship and are therefore generally available will be mentioned here. The FORMAT System (Pickard, 1968) was developed by the Douglas Aircraft Company under the sponsorship of the Air Force Flight Dynamics Laboratory; the MAGIC System (Batt and Jordan, 1972) was developed by Bell Aerospace under the sponsorship of the Air Force Flight Dynamics Laboratory; and the NASTRAN System (McCormick, 1970) was developed primarily by Computer Sciences Corporation under the sponsorship of NASA. Each of these systems contains elements which are appropriate for use in analyzing composite structures.

Matrix notation is normally used in presentation of the discrete element methods. In order, however, to permit the material to be studied without requiring prior study of matrix notation, index notation is used throughout this chapter. Expansion of the equations can be accomplished using the two rules of index notation.

1. An unrepeated index in a term represents a range over all values of that index.
2. A repeated index in a term represents a summation over all values of the index.

Italic indices have been used when the range is over the standard rectangular Cartesian coordinates and Greek indices have been used for all other cases.

II. Basic Equations

The fundamental equations of elasticity form the basic framework for discrete element analysis. By applying the basic elasticity equations to a composite structure it is observed that 9 of the basic 15 equations remain unchanged from an analysis of isotropic structures. That is, the 6 strain–displacement equations

$$\epsilon_{ij} = \frac{1}{2}\left(\frac{\partial u_i}{\partial x_j} + \frac{\partial u_j}{\partial x_i}\right) \tag{1}$$

and the three equations of equilibrium

$$\frac{\partial \sigma_{ij}}{\partial x_j} + f_i = 0 \tag{2}$$

where f_i are body forces, remain unchanged. The 6 stress–strain equations, however, may be significantly different for analysis of a composite structure. For the general anisotropic structure stress and strain are related by the generalized Hooke's law

$$\sigma_{ij} = C_{ijmn}\epsilon_{mn} \tag{3}$$

and

$$\epsilon_{ij} = S_{ijmn}\sigma_{mn} \tag{4}$$

where

$$C_{ijmn} = C_{jimn} = C_{ijnm} = C_{mnij}$$

and

$$S_{ijmn} = S_{jimn} = S_{ijnm} = S_{mnij}$$

For the completely general three-dimensional anisotropic problem all 21 of the independent C_{ijmn}'s would be required. This compares with two independent values for three-dimensional isotropic materials.

$$\sigma_{11} = \frac{E}{(1+\nu)(1-2\nu)} \left[(1-\nu)\epsilon_{11} + \nu\epsilon_{22} + \nu\epsilon_{33}\right] \tag{5}$$

$$\sigma_{22} = \frac{E}{(1+\nu)(1-2\nu)} \left[\nu\epsilon_{11} + (1-\nu)\epsilon_{22} + \nu\epsilon_{33}\right] \tag{6}$$

$$\sigma_{33} = \frac{E}{(1+\nu)(1-2\nu)} \left[\nu\epsilon_{11} + \nu\epsilon_{22} + (1-\nu)\epsilon_{33}\right] \tag{7}$$

$$\sigma_{12} = \frac{E}{1+\nu}\epsilon_{12} \tag{8}$$

$$\sigma_{13} = \frac{E}{1+\nu}\epsilon_{13} \tag{9}$$

$$\sigma_{23} = \frac{E}{1+\nu}\epsilon_{23} \tag{10}$$

where E is Young's modulus and ν is Poisson's ratio.

TABLE I

DIRECTION COSINES BETWEEN PRIMED
AND UNPRIMED AXES

	x_1	x_2	x_3
x_1'	a_{11}	a_{12}	a_{13}
x_2'	a_{21}	a_{22}	a_{23}
x_3'	a_{31}	a_{32}	a_{33}

Most composite structures, particularly those for which discrete element analysis would be appropriate, can be analyzed using two-dimensional analysis techniques. For example, in the plane stress problem

$$\sigma_{13} = \sigma_{23} = \sigma_{33} = 0 \tag{11}$$

and there are six independent C_{ijmn} which must be determined:

$$C_{1111} \quad C_{1112} \quad C_{1122}$$
$$C_{1212} \quad C_{1222}$$
$$C_{2222}$$

If all six pertinent C_{ijpq} have values, the problem is said to be anisotropic. This would indicate a coupling between shearing and stretching. If C_{1112} and C_{1222} are zero, the problem is called orthotropic and there is no coupling between shearing and stretching. For a composite composed of layered orthotropic sheets the appropriate stiffness of the entire laminate is found in terms of the stiffness of each layer in its orthotropic axes as

$$C_{ijpq} = \frac{1}{t} \sum_{t=1}^{N} t^{(i)} a_{ri}^{(i)} a_{sj}^{(i)} a_{mp}^{(i)} a_{nq}^{(i)} C_{rsmn}^{(i)} \tag{12}$$

where i indicates the layer, N is the total number of layers, $t^{(i)}$ is the thickness of the ith layer, t is the total laminate thickness, and a_{ij} are the direction cosines of the layer orientation angles.

The a_{ij}'s for a rotation from the lamina axis (primed) to the laminate axis (unprimed) are defined in Table I for the rotation in Fig. 1. It should be noted that four of the six independent C_{ijpq} can be given physical interpretation in terms of Young's modulus, Poisson's ratio, and the shear

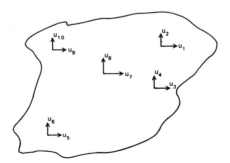

FIG. 1. Generalized displacement element.

modulus:

$$C_{1111} = \frac{E_{11}}{1 - \nu_{12}\nu_{21}} \tag{13}$$

$$C_{1122} = \frac{\nu_{12}E_{22}}{1 - \nu_{12}\nu_{21}} \tag{14}$$

$$C_{2222} = \frac{E_{22}}{1 - \nu_{12}\nu_{21}} \tag{15}$$

$$C_{1212} = 2G_{12} \tag{16}$$

and that the other two relate the coupling between shearing and stretching. This compares with the isotropic plane stress Hooke's law:

$$\sigma_{11} = \frac{E}{1 - \nu^2}\left[\epsilon_{11} + \nu\epsilon_{22}\right] \tag{17}$$

$$\sigma_{22} = \frac{E}{1 - \nu^2}\left[\nu\epsilon_{11} + \epsilon_{22}\right] \tag{18}$$

$$\sigma_{12} = \frac{E}{1 + \nu}\epsilon_{12} \tag{19}$$

Formulation of the composite constitutive equations must be generated considering not only the properties and orientation of each layer but also the stacking order of the laminate. Using the Kirchhoff–Love hypothesis of thin plate theory, where z is the coordinate normal to the plate,

$$\epsilon_{ij} = \epsilon_{ij}^0 + \kappa_{ij}z \tag{20}$$

and defining forces N_{ij} and moments M_{ij} as

$$N_{ij} = \int_{-t/2}^{+t/2} \sigma_{ij}\, dz \tag{21}$$

$$M_{ij} = \int_{-t/2}^{+t/2} \sigma_{ij}z\, dz \tag{22}$$

the constitutive relations are found as

$$N_{ij} = \epsilon_{mn}^0 \int_{-t/2}^{+t/2} C_{ijmn}\, dz + \kappa_{mn} \int_{-t/2}^{+t/2} C_{ijmn}z\, dz \tag{23}$$

$$M_{ij} = \epsilon_{mn}^0 \int_{-t/2}^{+t/2} C_{ijmn} z \, dz + \kappa_{mn} \int_{-t/2}^{+t/2} C_{ijmn} z^2 \, dz \tag{24}$$

Applying these equations to a laminate it is noted that if the laminate is symmetric about its midplane,

$$\int_{-t/2}^{+t/2} C_{ijmn} z \, dz = 0 \tag{25}$$

and the in-plane and bending effects may be treated separately. If, however, the laminate does not have midplane symmetry, the integral has a value and the coupling of bending and stretching must be considered.

If thermal effects are included, the total strain (e_{ij}) is the sum of the strain due to mechanical loads (ϵ_{ij}) and the strain due to thermal expansion $(\alpha_{ij}\Delta T)$:

$$e_{ij} = \epsilon_{ij} + \alpha_{ij}\Delta T \tag{26}$$

Equations (1) and (3) are therefore of the form:

$$e_{ij} = \frac{1}{2}\left(\frac{\partial u_i}{\partial x_j} + \frac{\partial u_j}{\partial x_i}\right) \tag{27}$$

and

$$\sigma_{ij} = C_{ijmn} e_{mn} - C_{ijmn} \alpha_{mn}\Delta T \tag{28}$$

III. Element Properties

The basic building block of discrete element analysis is the element. Following Fraeijs de Veubeke (1965), it is noted that three basic classes of models exist:

1. elements satisfying compatibility but not equilibrium;
2. elements satisfying equilibrium but not compatibility;
3. elements violating both equilibrium and compatibility.

In this chapter two classes of elements will be examined. These elements are normally referred to as displacement elements and equilibrium elements. Displacement elements are based on an assumed displacement field, thus ensuring compatibility within the element and across its boundaries. Equilibrium elements are based on an assumed stress field with equilibrium of the stress field being enforced.

A. Stiffness Element Theory

Assume that over an element the displacement may be found in terms of the displacements at certain selected node points:

$$u_i = \bar{a}_{i\alpha}\bar{u}_\alpha \tag{29}$$

where $i = 1, 2, 3$ for three-dimensional problems and $\alpha = 1, 2, 3, \ldots, 3 \cdot N$, where N = number of nodes. This basic assumption (Eq. (29)) forms the basis for the displacement method of analysis.

The strain can be found in terms of the discrete displacements using the strain displacement equations

$$e_{ij} = \frac{1}{2}\left(\frac{\partial u_i}{\partial x_j} + \frac{\partial u_j}{\partial x_i}\right)$$

$$= D_{ij\alpha}\bar{u}_\alpha \tag{30}$$

where

$$D_{ij\alpha} = \tfrac{1}{2}(\bar{a}_{i\alpha,j} + \bar{a}_{j\alpha,i})$$

and where the comma represents partial differentiation with the indexed coordinate following it.

The stresses in terms of the discrete displacements are found from the generalized Hooke's law

$$\sigma_{ij} = C_{ijmn}\epsilon_{mn}$$

$$= E_{ij\alpha}\bar{u}_\alpha \tag{31}$$

where

$$E_{ij\alpha} = \frac{C_{ijmn}}{2}(\bar{a}_{m\alpha,n} + \bar{a}_{n\alpha,m})$$

The discrete forces P_α corresponding to the discrete displacements $\bar{u}_\alpha$ are found using Castigliano's theorem:

$$P_\alpha = \partial U/\partial \bar{u}_\alpha \tag{32}$$

where U is the strain energy

$$U = \frac{1}{2}\int_v \sigma_{ij}e_{ij}\,dV$$

$$= \frac{1}{2}\int_v \frac{C_{ijmn}}{2}(\bar{a}_{m\alpha,n} + \bar{a}_{n\alpha,m})\bar{u}_\alpha \frac{\bar{u}_\beta}{2}(\bar{a}_{i\beta,j} + \bar{a}_{j\beta,i})\,dV \tag{33}$$

Using $C_{ijmn} = C_{jimn} = C_{ijnm} = C_{mnij}$, then

$$U = \frac{1}{2} \int_v C_{ijmn} \bar{a}_{i\alpha,j} \bar{a}_{m\beta,n} \bar{u}_\alpha \bar{u}_\beta \, dV \tag{34}$$

Therefore

$$P_\gamma = \frac{\partial U}{\partial \bar{u}_\gamma} = \bar{u}_\alpha \int_v C_{ijmn} \bar{a}_{i\alpha,j} \bar{a}_{m\gamma,n} \, dV \tag{35}$$

Rewriting,

$$P_\gamma = C_{\gamma\alpha} \bar{u}_\alpha \tag{36}$$

where

$$C_{\gamma\alpha} = \int_v C_{ijmn} \bar{a}_{i\alpha,j} \bar{a}_{m\alpha,n} \, dV$$

is the stiffness of the element in terms of the material properties and the assumed displacement distribution.

B. Stiffness Elements

A large number of stiffness elements have been developed and are available in the general literature. Only a small percentage of these elements have been developed using constitutive equations appropriate for composite structures, however. If the composite structure is composed of symmetric laminates so that the in-plane and bending effects may be separated, modification of existing elements to account for orthotropic or anisotropic behavior is generally straightforward. One-dimensional elements such as bars and beams may be used directly without modification if they are compatible with other elements being used.

For a plane stress triangular element (Fig. 2) Turner *et al.* (1956) as-

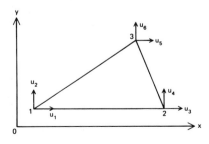

FIG. 2. Triangular plate element.

sumed displacements as

$$u_x = C_1 x + C_2 y + C_3 \tag{37}$$

$$u_y = C_4 x + C_5 y + C_6 \tag{38}$$

where the six coefficients $C_1, \ldots, C_6$ are found in terms of the displacements of the vertices of the triangle.

Therefore, in the basic assumption

$$u_i = \bar{a}_{i\alpha} \bar{u}_\alpha \tag{39}$$

$$\bar{a}_{11} = \frac{1}{2A_{123}} \left[y_{32}(x - x_2) - x_{32}(y - y_2) \right]$$

$$\bar{a}_{12} = 0$$

$$\bar{a}_{13} = \frac{1}{2A_{123}} \left[-y_{31}(x - x_3) + x_{31}(y - y_3) \right]$$

$$\bar{a}_{14} = 0$$

$$\bar{a}_{15} = \frac{1}{2A_{123}} \left[y_{21}(x - x_1) - x_{21}(y - y_1) \right]$$

$$\bar{a}_{16} = 0$$

$$\bar{a}_{21} = 0$$

$$\bar{a}_{22} = \frac{1}{2A_{123}} \left[y_{32}(x - x_2) - x_{32}(y - y_2) \right]$$

$$\bar{a}_{23} = 0$$

$$\bar{a}_{24} = \frac{1}{2A_{123}} \left[-y_{31}(x - x_3) + x_{31}(y - y_3) \right]$$

$$\bar{a}_{25} = 0$$

$$\bar{a}_{26} = \frac{1}{2A_{123}} \left[y_{21}(x - x_1) - x_{21}(y - y_1) \right]$$

where

$$A_{123} = \tfrac{1}{2}(x_{32}y_{21} - x_{21}y_{32}) = \text{area of triangle}$$

and

$$x_{ij} = x_i - x_j \qquad y_{ij} = y_i - y_j$$

A variation of this element, using the same basic assumptions, suitable for use with composite structures was developed by Mikkelson (1969). The element was developed in such a manner that the composite must have a set of orthotropic axes and these axes must be parallel to the local element axes.

The $D_{ij\alpha}$ relating the nodal displacements to the element strains are found as

$$D_{11\alpha} = \frac{1}{2A_{123}} \begin{bmatrix} y_{32} & 0 & -y_{32} & 0 & y_{21} & 0 \end{bmatrix}$$

$$D_{22\alpha} = \frac{1}{2A_{123}} \begin{bmatrix} 0 & -x_{32} & 0 & x_{31} & 0 & -x_{21} \end{bmatrix}$$

$$D_{12\alpha} = \frac{1}{2A_{123}} \begin{bmatrix} -x_{32} & y_{32} & x_{31} & -y_{31} & -x_{21} & y_{21} \end{bmatrix}$$

Using the orthotropic plane stress Hooke's law

$$\sigma_{11} = \frac{1}{1 - \nu_{xy}\nu_{yx}} \begin{bmatrix} E_x\epsilon_{11} + \nu_{xy}E_y\epsilon_{22} \end{bmatrix} \tag{40}$$

$$\sigma_{22} = \frac{1}{1 - \nu_{xy}\nu_{yx}} \begin{bmatrix} E_y\epsilon_{22} + \nu_{yx}E_x\epsilon_{11} \end{bmatrix} \tag{41}$$

$$\sigma_{12} = 2G_{xy}\epsilon_{12} \tag{42}$$

The $E_{ij\alpha}$ relating the nodal displacements to the element stresses are found as

$$E_{11\alpha} = \frac{1}{2A_{123}} \begin{bmatrix} E_x y_{32} & -\nu_{yx}E_x x_{32} & -E_x y_{31} & \nu_{yx}E_x x_{31} & E_x y_{21} & -\nu_{yx}E_x x_{21} \end{bmatrix}$$

$$E_{22\alpha} = \frac{1}{2A_{123}} \begin{bmatrix} \nu_{xy}E_y y_{32} & -E_y x_{32} & -\nu_{xy}E_y y_{31} & E_y x_{31} & \nu_{xy}E_y y_{21} & -E_y x_{21} \end{bmatrix}$$

$$E_{12\alpha} = \frac{1}{2A_{123}} \begin{bmatrix} -\lambda G_{xy} x_{32} & \lambda G_{xy} y_{32} & \lambda G_{xy} x_{31} & -\lambda G_{xy} y_{31} & -\lambda G_{xy} x_{21} & \lambda G_{xy} y_{21} \end{bmatrix}$$

where $\lambda = 1 - \nu_{xy}\nu_{yx}$. The element stiffness

$$C_{\gamma\alpha} = \int_v C_{ijmn}\bar{a}_{i\alpha,j}\bar{a}_{m\alpha,n}\, dV \tag{43}$$

is found as the sum

$$C_{\gamma\alpha} = C_{\gamma\alpha}^1 + C_{\gamma\alpha}^2 \tag{44}$$

where

$$C^1_{\gamma\alpha} = \frac{1}{4A_{123}\lambda}$$

$$\times \begin{bmatrix}
-E_x y^2_{32} & -\nu_{yx}E_x x_{32}y_{32} & -E_x y_{31}y_{32} & \nu_{yx}E_x x_{31}y_{32} & E_x y_{21}y_{32} & -\nu_{yx}E_x x_{21}y_{32} \\
-\nu_{xy}E_y x_{32}y_{32} & E_x x^2_{32} & \nu_{xy}E_y x_{32}y_{31} & -E_y x_{31}x_{32} & -\nu_{xy}E_y x_{32}y_{21} & E_y x_{21}x_{32} \\
-E_x y_{31}y_{32} & \nu_{yx}E_x x_{32}y_{31} & E_x y^2_{31} & -\nu_{yx}E_x x_{31}y_{31} & -E_x y_{21}y_{31} & \nu_{yx}E_x x_{21}y_{31} \\
\nu_{xy}E_y x_{31}y_{32} & -E_y x_{31}x_{32} & -\nu_{xy}E_y x_{31}y_{31} & E_y x^2_{31} & \nu_{xy}E_y x_{31}y_{21} & -E_y x_{21}x_{31} \\
E_x y_{21}y_{32} & -\nu_{yx}E_x x_{32}y_{21} & -E_x y_{21}y_{31} & \nu_{yx}E_x x_{31}y_{21} & E_x y^2_{21} & -\nu_{yx}E_x x_{21}y_{21} \\
-\nu_{xy}E_y x_{21}y_{32} & E_y x_{21}x_{32} & \nu_{xy}E_y x_{21}y_{31} & -E_y x_{21}x_{31} & -\nu_{xy}E_y x_{21}y_{21} & E_y x^2_{21}
\end{bmatrix}$$

and

$$C^2_{\alpha\gamma} = \frac{tG_{xy}}{4A_{123}} \begin{bmatrix}
x^2_{32} & & & & & \text{symmetric} \\
-x_{32}y_{32} & y^2_{32} & & & & \\
-x_{32}x_{31} & y_{32}x_{31} & x^2_{31} & & & \\
x_{32}y_{31} & -y_{32}y_{31} & -x_{31}y_{31} & y^2_{31} & & \\
x_{32}x_{21} & -\beta_{32}x_{21} & -x_{31}x_{32} & y_{31}x_{21} & x^2_{21} & \\
-x_{32}y_{21} & y_{32}y_{21} & x_{31}y_{21} & -y_{31}y_{21} & -x_{21}y_{21} & y^2_{21}
\end{bmatrix}$$

A plane stress rectangular element (Fig. 3) developed by Przemieniecki and Berke (1964) was also modified by Mikkelson (1969). The displacements were assumed in the following form:

$$u_x = C_1 x + C_2 xy + C_3 y + C_4 \tag{45}$$

$$u_y = C_5 x + C_6 xy + C_7 y + C_8 \tag{46}$$

Solving for the C_i's in terms of the nodal displacements, the $a_{i\alpha}$ in

$$u_i = a_{i\alpha}\bar{u}_\alpha \tag{47}$$

are found as

$$a_{i\alpha} = \begin{bmatrix}
(1-x)(1-y) & 0 & (1-x)y & 0 & xY & 0 & x(1-y) & 0 \\
0 & (1-x)(1-y) & 0 & (1-x)y & 0 & x & 0 & x(1-y)
\end{bmatrix}$$

The $D_{ij\alpha}$ relating the nodal displacements to the element strains are found as

$$D_{11\alpha} = \begin{bmatrix}
\dfrac{-(1-y)}{a} & 0 & \dfrac{-y}{a} & 0 & \dfrac{y}{a} & 0 & \dfrac{1-y}{a} & 0
\end{bmatrix}$$

$$D_{22\alpha} = \begin{bmatrix}
0 & \dfrac{-(1-x)}{b} & 0 & \dfrac{1-x}{b} & 0 & \dfrac{x}{b} & 0 & \dfrac{-x}{b}
\end{bmatrix}$$

$$D_{12\alpha} = \begin{bmatrix}
\dfrac{-(1-x)}{b} & \dfrac{-(1-y)}{a} & \dfrac{1-x}{b} & \dfrac{-y}{a} & \dfrac{x}{b} & \dfrac{y}{a} & \dfrac{-x}{b} & \dfrac{1-y}{a}
\end{bmatrix}$$

and the $E_{ij\alpha}$ relating the nodal displacements and the element stresses are found as

$$E_{11\alpha} = \frac{1}{\lambda} \left[\frac{-(1-y)}{a} E_x \quad \frac{-(1-x)}{b} \nu_{yx} E_x \quad \frac{-y}{a} E_x \quad \frac{1-x}{b} \nu_{yx} E_x \right.$$

$$\left. \frac{y}{a} E_x \quad \frac{x}{b} \nu_{yx} E_x \quad \frac{1-y}{a} E_x \quad \frac{-x}{b} \nu_{yx} E_x \right]$$

$$E_{22\alpha} = \frac{1}{\lambda} \left[\frac{-(1-y)}{a} \nu_{xy} E_y \quad \frac{-(1-x)}{b} E_y \quad \frac{-y}{a} \nu_{xy} E_y \quad \frac{(1-x)}{b} E_y \right.$$

$$\left. \frac{y}{a} \nu_{xy} E_y \quad \frac{x}{b} E_y \quad \frac{1-y}{a} \nu_{xy} E_y \quad \frac{-x}{b} E_y \right]$$

$$E_{12\alpha} = \left[\frac{-(1-x)}{b} G_{xy} \quad \frac{-(1-y)}{a} G_{xy} \quad \frac{(1-x)}{B} G_{xy} \quad \frac{-y}{a} G_{xy} \right.$$

$$\left. \frac{x}{b} G_{xy} \quad \frac{y}{a} G_{xy} \quad \frac{-x}{b} G_{xy} \quad \frac{1-y}{a} G_{xy} \right]$$

The element stiffness is found as the sum

$$C_{\gamma\alpha} = C_{\gamma\alpha}^1 + C_{\gamma\alpha}^2 \tag{48}$$

where

$$C_{\gamma\alpha}^1 = \frac{t}{\lambda} \begin{bmatrix} \dfrac{bE_x}{3a} & \dfrac{\nu_{yx}E_x}{4} & \dfrac{bE_x}{6a} & \dfrac{-\nu_{yx}E_x}{4} & \dfrac{-bE_x}{6a} & \dfrac{-\nu_{yx}E_x}{4} & \dfrac{-bE_x}{3a} & \dfrac{-\nu_{yx}E_x}{4} \\[2mm] \dfrac{\nu_{xy}E_y}{4} & \dfrac{aE_y}{3b} & \dfrac{\nu_{xy}E_y}{4} & \dfrac{-aE_y}{3} & \dfrac{-\nu_{xy}E_y}{4} & \dfrac{-aE_y}{6b} & \dfrac{-\nu_{xy}E_y}{4} & \dfrac{aE_y}{6b} \\[2mm] \dfrac{bE_x}{6a} & \dfrac{\nu_{yx}E_x}{4} & \dfrac{bE_x}{3a} & \dfrac{-\nu_{yx}E_x}{4} & \dfrac{-bE_x}{3a} & \dfrac{-\nu_{yx}E_x}{4} & \dfrac{-bE_x}{6a} & \dfrac{\nu_{yx}E_x}{4} \\[2mm] \dfrac{-\nu_{xy}E_y}{4} & \dfrac{-aE_y}{3b} & \dfrac{-\nu_{xy}E_y}{4} & \dfrac{aE_y}{3b} & \dfrac{\nu_{xy}E_y}{4} & \dfrac{aE_y}{6b} & \dfrac{\nu_{xy}E_y}{4} & \dfrac{-aE_y}{6b} \\[2mm] \dfrac{-bE_x}{6a} & \dfrac{-\nu_{yx}E_x}{4} & \dfrac{-bE_x}{3a} & \dfrac{\nu_{yx}E_x}{4} & \dfrac{bE_x}{3a} & \dfrac{\nu_{yx}E_x}{4} & \dfrac{bE_x}{6a} & \dfrac{-\nu_{yx}E_x}{4} \\[2mm] -\nu_{xy}E_y & \dfrac{-aE_y}{6b} & \dfrac{-\nu_{xy}E_y}{4} & \dfrac{aE_y}{6b} & \dfrac{\nu_{xy}E_y}{4} & \dfrac{aE_y}{3b} & \dfrac{\nu_{xy}E_y}{4} & \dfrac{-aE_y}{3b} \\[2mm] \dfrac{-bE_x}{3a} & \dfrac{-\nu_{yx}E_x}{4} & \dfrac{-bE_x}{6a} & \dfrac{\nu_{yx}E_x}{4} & \dfrac{bE_x}{6a} & \dfrac{\nu_{yx}E_x}{4} & \dfrac{bE_x}{3a} & \dfrac{-\nu_{yx}E_x}{4} \\[2mm] \dfrac{\nu_{xy}E_y}{4} & \dfrac{aE_y}{6b} & \dfrac{\nu_{xy}E_y}{4} & \dfrac{-aE_y}{6b} & \dfrac{-\nu_{xy}E_y}{4} & \dfrac{-aE_y}{3b} & \dfrac{-\nu_{xy}E_y}{4} & \dfrac{aE_y}{3b} \end{bmatrix}$$

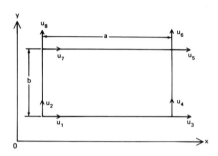

Fig. 3. Rectangular plate element.

$$C^2_{\gamma\alpha} = tG_{xy} \begin{bmatrix} \dfrac{a}{3b} & \dfrac{1}{4} & \dfrac{-a}{.3b} & \dfrac{1}{4} & \dfrac{-a}{6b} & \dfrac{-1}{4} & \dfrac{a}{6b} & \dfrac{-1}{4} \\[2ex] & \dfrac{b}{3a} & \dfrac{-1}{4} & \dfrac{b}{6a} & \dfrac{1}{4} & \dfrac{b}{6a} & \dfrac{1}{4} & \dfrac{b}{3a} \\[2ex] & & \dfrac{a}{3b} & \dfrac{-1}{4} & \dfrac{a}{6b} & \dfrac{1}{4} & \dfrac{-a}{6b} & \dfrac{1}{4} \\[2ex] & & & \dfrac{b}{3a} & \dfrac{-1}{4} & \dfrac{-b}{3a} & \dfrac{1}{4} & \dfrac{-b}{6a} \\[2ex] & & & & \dfrac{a}{3b} & \dfrac{1}{4} & \dfrac{-a}{3b} & \dfrac{1}{4} \\[2ex] & \text{symmetric} & & & & \dfrac{b}{3a} & \dfrac{-1}{4} & \dfrac{b}{6a} \\[2ex] & & & & & & \dfrac{a}{3b} & \dfrac{-1}{4} \\[2ex] & & & & & & & \dfrac{b}{3a} \end{bmatrix}$$

C. Equilibrium Element Theory

For an equilibrium element it is assumed that the stresses are found from a set of force parameters

$$\sigma_{ij} = \bar{b}_{ij\alpha}\bar{F}_\alpha \tag{49}$$

The forces $\bar{F}_\alpha$ are in general not independent if equilibrium is to be satisfied. Therefore, the equations of equilibrium

$$\partial\sigma_{ij}/\partial x_j = 0 \tag{50}$$

are used to find a reduced set of independent forces F_α called the element forces:

$$\bar{F}_\alpha = d_{\alpha\beta}F_\beta \tag{51}$$

The stresses are found in terms of the element forces as

$$\sigma_{ij} = \bar{b}_{ij\alpha}d_{\alpha\beta}F_\beta = b_{ij\beta}F_\beta \tag{52}$$

The element deformations $\bar{e}_\alpha$ corresponding to the element force are found from Castigliano's theorem:

$$\bar{e}_\beta = \partial U/\partial F_\beta \tag{53}$$

where U is the strain energy

$$U = \frac{1}{2}\int_v \sigma_{ij}\epsilon_{ij}\,dV$$

$$= \frac{1}{2}\int_v \sigma_{ij}\sigma_{\kappa l}S_{ijkl}\,dV$$

$$= \frac{1}{2}\int_v b_{ij\beta}F_\beta b_{\kappa l\gamma}F_\gamma S_{ijkl}\,dV \tag{54}$$

Therefore, Eq. (53) becomes

$$e_\beta = \int_v S_{ijkl}b_{ij\gamma}b_{\kappa l\beta}F_\gamma\,dV \tag{55}$$

This is the element flexibility and can be rewritten as

$$e_\beta = f_{\beta\gamma}F_\gamma \tag{56}$$

where

$$f_{\beta\gamma} = \int_v S_{ijkl}b_{ij\gamma}b_{\kappa l\beta}\,dV$$

D. Equilibrium Elements

As an example of an equilibrium element, a plate bending triangular element (Fig. 4) developed by Fraeijs de Veubeke and Sander (1968) and modified by Teodosiadis (1970) to enable it to be used in the analysis of

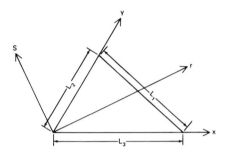

FIG. 4. Triangular plate element.

composite structures is discussed. The variations of the stress field, in this case moments per unit length, have been assumed in the following form:

$$M_x = F_1 + \left(\frac{x}{L_3}\right)F_2 + \left(\frac{y}{L_2}\right)F_3 + \frac{1}{3}\frac{L_3}{L_2}\left(1 - \frac{x}{L_3}\right)\frac{x}{L_3}q \qquad (57)$$

$$M_y = F_4 + \left(\frac{x}{L_3}\right)F_5 + \left(\frac{y}{L_2}\right)F_6 + \frac{1}{3}\frac{L_2}{L_3}\left(1 - \frac{y}{L_2}\right)\frac{y}{L_2}q \qquad (58)$$

$$M_{xy} = F_7 + \left(\frac{x}{L_3}\right)F_8 + \left(\frac{y}{L_2}\right)F_9 - \frac{1}{3}\frac{x}{L_3}\frac{y}{L_2}q \qquad (59)$$

where q is the load on the element in the Z direction. The nine force parameters are an independent set which satisfy the condition of equilibrium

$$\frac{\partial^2 M_x}{2x^2} + 2\frac{\partial^2 M_{xy}}{\partial x \partial y} + \frac{\partial^2 M_y}{\partial y^2} + \frac{q}{A}\sin\alpha = 0 \qquad (60)$$

where A is the area of the element.

Assume that the material properties are known in an r, s coordinate system and that the material is orthotropic. Therefore, the independent values of S_{ijkl} are found in terms of Young's modulus, Poisson's ratio, and the shear stiffness as

$$S_{1111} = 1/E_r, \qquad (61)$$

$$S_{1122} = \nu_{sr}/E_{ss} \qquad (62)$$

$$S_{2222} = 1/E_s \qquad (63)$$

$$S_{1212} = 1/(2G_{rs}) \qquad (64)$$

The strain energy becomes

$$v = \frac{1}{2} \int_v \sigma_{ij}^{(r,s)} t_{ij}^{(r,s)} \, dV = \frac{1}{2} \int_v M_{ij}^{(r,s)} Z K_{\kappa l}^{(r,s)} \, dV$$

$$= \frac{t^3}{24} \int_A M_{ij}^{(r,s)} S_{ij\kappa l} M_{\kappa l}^{(r,s)} \, dA \tag{65}$$

The moments in the r, s system are found from the moments in the x, y system as

$$M_r = \frac{\cos^2 \zeta}{\sin \alpha} M_x + \frac{\cos^2(\alpha - \zeta)}{\sin \alpha} M_y + \frac{2 \sin \zeta \cos(\alpha - \zeta)}{\sin \alpha} M_{xy} \tag{66}$$

$$M_s = \frac{\sin^2 \zeta}{\sin \alpha} M_x + \frac{\sin^2(\alpha - \zeta)}{\sin \alpha} M_y - \frac{2 \sin \zeta \sin(\alpha - \zeta)}{\sin \alpha} M_{xy} \tag{67}$$

$$M_{rs} = \frac{\sin \zeta \cos \zeta}{\sin \alpha} M_x \frac{\cos(\alpha - \zeta) \sin(\alpha - \zeta}{\sin \alpha} M_y \tag{68}$$

$$+ \frac{[\cos \zeta \sin(\alpha - \zeta) - \sin \zeta \cos(\alpha - \zeta)]}{\sin \alpha} M_{xy}$$

which can be written in index notation as

$$M_{ij}^{(r,s)} = T_{ij\kappa l} M_{\kappa l}^{(x,y)} \tag{69}$$

Therefore, the strain energy is found as

$$U = \frac{t^3}{24} \int_A T_{ijrs} M_{rs}^{(x,y)} S_{ij\kappa l} T_{\kappa lmn} M_{mn}^{(x,y)} \, dA \tag{70}$$

The assumed stress state was of the following form:

$$M_{ij}^{(x,y)} = b_{ij\alpha} F_\alpha \tag{71}$$

where q is taken as F_{10}.
Therefore, the element flexibility is found as

$$f_{\beta\gamma} = \frac{t^3}{24} \int_A T_{ijrs} S_{ij\kappa l} T_{\kappa lmn} b_{rs\gamma} b_{mn\beta} \, dA \tag{72}$$

IV. Methods of Analysis

In order to perform an analysis the basic elements, either stiffness or flexibility, are used in an idealization of the actual structure. The idealization is developed in a manner that represents the structure and emphasizes those critical areas where high stresses and high stress gradients are expected. Also, the idealization may depend upon the method of solution used. In this section three methods of solution are discussed: the displacement method, the force method, and the unified method. Although in general either type of element may be used with any of the three methods, normally displacement elements are used in the displacement method and flexibility elements in the force and unified methods.

A. Displacement Method

The displacement method uses the stiffnesses of the individual elements and forms the stiffness of the total structure. The stiffness of the total structure is in the form of linear algebraic equations relating the nodal displacements and the applied loads. This system of equations is solved for the nodal displacements from which the stresses, strains, and displacements of the structure are found consistent with the basic element assumptions.

Starting from the stiffness relationship of the ith element in a global coordinate system:

$$P_\gamma{}^i = C_\gamma{}^i \bar{u}_\alpha{}^i \tag{73}$$

the stiffness relationship (Eq. (73)) in the global coordinate system is obtained by transforming the element stiffness (Eq. (36)). With the use of appropriate direction cosines the displacements will transform according to the following rule:

$$\bar{u}_\alpha^{(L)} = \lambda_{\alpha\beta} \bar{u}_\beta^{(G)} \tag{74}$$

where L and G indicate local and global coordinates, respectively. Since the work must be the same in both coordinate systems,

$$\bar{u}_\alpha^{(L)} P_\alpha^{(L)} = \bar{u}_\alpha^{(G)} P_\alpha^{(G)} \tag{75}$$

Using Eq. (74),

$$\lambda_{\alpha\beta} \bar{u}_\beta^{(G)} P_\alpha^{(L)} = \bar{u}_\alpha^{(G)} P_\alpha^{(G)} \tag{76}$$

Therefore

$$[\lambda_{\beta\alpha} P_\alpha^{(L)} - P_\alpha^{(G)}] \bar{u}_\alpha^{(G)} = 0 \tag{77}$$

Since this must apply for any set of displacements, the transformation between the forces in the local and global coordinates is as follows:

$$P_\alpha^{(G)} = \lambda_{\beta\alpha} P_\beta^{(L)} \tag{78}$$

The element stiffness Eq. (36) was found in the local coordinate system

$$P_\gamma^{(L)} = C_{\gamma\alpha}^{(L)} \bar{u}_\alpha^{(L)} \tag{79}$$

Using Eq. (74) and multiplying both sides by $\lambda_{\gamma\beta}$ gives

$$\lambda_{\gamma\beta}P_\gamma^{(L)} = \lambda_{\gamma\beta}C_{\gamma\alpha}^{(L)}\lambda_{\alpha\delta}u_\delta^{(G)} \tag{80}$$

Therefore

$$P_\beta^{(G)} = \lambda_{\gamma\beta}C_{\gamma\alpha}^{(L)}\lambda_{\alpha\delta}u_\delta^{(G)} \tag{81}$$

This may be rewritten as

$$P_\beta^{(G)} = C_{\beta\delta}^{(G)}u_\delta^{(G)} \tag{82}$$

where

$$C_{\beta\delta}^{(G)} = \lambda_{\gamma\beta}C_{\gamma\alpha}^{(L)}\lambda_{\alpha\delta} \tag{83}$$

Equation (83) is the element stiffness in the global coordinate system.

The total structure stiffness relationship is found by observing that when node A of element X is connected to node B of element Y,

$$P_\gamma = P_{\gamma'}^X(A) + P_{\gamma''}^Y(B) \tag{84}$$

and

$$\bar{u}_\gamma = \bar{u}_{\gamma'}^X(A) = \bar{u}_{\gamma''}^Y(B) \tag{85}$$

where γ refers to the global forces and displacements on the entire idealization and γ' and γ'' refer to the corresponding forces and displacements on elements A and B, respectively.

Equations (84) and (85) form the basis for the development of the total structure stiffness

$$P_\gamma = C_{\delta\alpha}u_\alpha \tag{86}$$

At this point the structural stiffness (86) still contains the reaction forces and displacements which must be removed for solution. By accounting for the reactions by removing the appropriate displacements and forces, a reduced structural stiffness is obtained:

$$P_\gamma^{(R)} = C_{\gamma\alpha}^{(R)}u_\alpha^{(R)} \tag{87}$$

This system of equations can be solved using techniques for solution of simultaneous linear algebraic equations. For all but the very small problems a digital computer will be required. Przemieniecki (1968) discusses many of the techniques for which computer coding has been developed. In selecting the solution technique one should consider not only the problem being solved, but the computer and the computer routines being used. Because the computer can only use a certain number of significant digits some problems and solution methods are susceptible to roundoff errors which can seriously affect the results.

A displacement method analysis of a graphite–epoxy horizontal stabilizer for an A-4 aircraft (Fig. 5) was reported by Purdy and Schaeffer (1971).

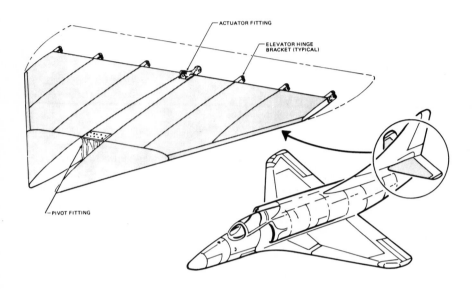

FIG. 5. Graphite composite horizontal stabilizer.

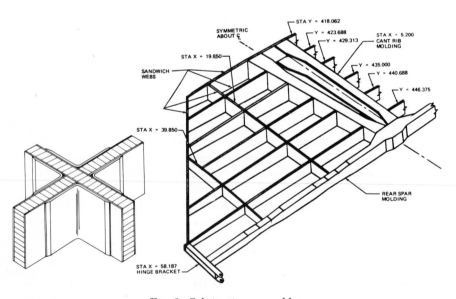

FIG. 6. Substructure assembly.

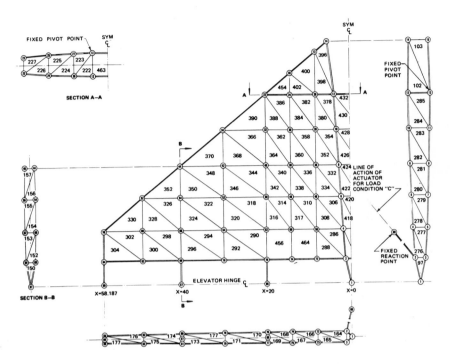

Fɪɢ. 7. Idealized structural model of A-4 horizontal stabilizer. Section A-A—idealization of spar structure at forward pivot; Section B-B—typical idealization of bulkhead.

The stabilizer was developed under Navy Contract N00156-70-C-1321 with the Naval Air Development Center, Warminister, Pennsylvania. A multispar design (Fig. 6) with solid graphite skins was analyzed using the idealization shown in Fig. 7. The analysis was used to determine the internal load distribution from which a strength analysis could be conducted.

B. Force Method

The force method is based on the equations of equilibrium in terms of the element forces, F_β. If the number of equilibrium equations which can be written is equal to the number of unknown element forces, the problem is said to be statically determinate and the solution is obtained directly. In general, however, the number of element forces exceeds the number of equilibrium equations. For these cases redundant forces are selected so that there exists a set of statically determinate forces and a set of redundant forces. The statically determinate forces are found directly and the redundant forces are found using the element flexibilities.

After an idealization has been prepared equilibrium equations may be written in terms of the element forces, F_β, and the applied forces, P_α:

$$n_{\alpha\beta}F_\beta = S_\alpha \qquad (88)$$

If the ranges of α and β are equal, Eq. (88) is a complete set of linear algebraic equations which can be solved directly. In general, however,

$$\alpha = 1, \ldots, N$$

$$\beta = 1, \ldots, M \qquad M > N$$

In this case the element forces may be subdivided:

$$F_\beta = G_{\beta\alpha}F_\alpha{}^0 + H_{\beta\delta}F_\delta{}^R$$

$$\beta = 1, \ldots, M \qquad \alpha = 1, \ldots, N \qquad \delta = 1, \ldots, M - N \qquad (89)$$

The redundant forces $F_\delta{}^R$ may be selected by observation or by automated techniques. The automated techniques were first developed by Denke (1954, 1962, 1965), who used the Jordanian elimination technique to develop the so-called Douglas structure cutter. If the redundant forces are selected by observation, care must be taken to ensure that the remaining forces constitute a stable structure.

Rewriting Eq. (89) gives

$$G_{\beta\alpha}F_\alpha{}^0 = F_\beta - H_{\beta\delta}F_\delta{}^R \qquad (90)$$

Multiplying both sides by $n_{\gamma\beta}$ gives

$$n_{\gamma\beta}G_{\beta\alpha}F_\alpha{}^0 = n_{\gamma\beta}F_{\beta\delta} - n_{\gamma\beta}H_{\beta\delta}F_\delta{}^R \qquad (91)$$

$$\alpha = 1, \ldots, N \qquad \beta = 1, \ldots, M \qquad \gamma = 1, \ldots, N \qquad \delta = 1, \ldots, M - N$$

Since the range of γ and α are equal, an array $B_{\eta\gamma}$ may be found such that

$$B_{\eta\gamma}n_{\gamma\beta}G_{\beta\alpha} = \delta_{\eta\alpha} \qquad n = 1, \ldots, N \qquad (92)$$

Therefore

$$F_\eta{}^0 = B_{\eta\gamma}n_{\gamma\beta}F_\beta - B_{\eta\gamma}n_{\gamma\beta}H_{\beta\delta}F_\delta{}^R$$

$$= B_{\eta\gamma}P_\gamma - B_{\eta\gamma}n_{\gamma\beta}F_\delta{}^R \qquad (93)$$

By using this expression in Eq. (89) the element forces are found in terms of the applied loads and the redundant forces:

$$F_\xi = G_{\xi\eta}B_{\eta\gamma}P_\gamma + R_{\xi\delta}F_\delta{}^R \qquad (94)$$

where

$$R_{\xi\delta} = H_{\xi\delta} - G'_{\xi\eta}B_{\eta\gamma}n_{\gamma\beta}H_{\beta\delta}$$

The redundant forces are found from the flexibility relationship of the entire idealization:

$$e_\gamma = f_{\gamma\beta}F_\beta \qquad (95)$$

Corresponding to the applied loads, P_α, there exists a set of displacements, u_α. Since the internal work must equal the external work,

$$e_\beta F_\beta = u_\alpha P_\alpha \qquad (96)$$

but

$$P_\alpha = n_{\alpha\beta}F_\beta \qquad (97)$$

Therefore

$$(e_\beta - n_{\alpha\beta}u_\alpha)F_\beta = 0 \qquad (98)$$

Since this must be true for any set of element forces, the transformation between the element formations and the displacements of the idealization is

$$e_\beta = n_{\alpha\beta}u_\alpha \qquad (99)$$

Multiplying this expression by

$$R_{\xi\delta}$$

the following expression for the right-hand side is obtained:

$$R_{\xi\delta}n_{\alpha\xi}u_\alpha = (n_{\alpha\xi}H_{\xi\delta} - B_{\eta\gamma}n_{\alpha\xi}G'_{\delta\eta}n_{\gamma\beta}H_{\beta\delta})u_\alpha$$
$$= (n_{\alpha\xi}H_{\xi\delta} - n_{\alpha\xi}H_{\xi\delta})u_\alpha = 0 \qquad (100)$$

Therefore, using the flexibility relationship (Eq. (95)),

$$(H_{\xi\delta} - G'_{\xi\eta}B_{\eta\gamma}n_{\gamma\beta}H_{\beta\delta})f_{\xi\theta}F_\theta = 0 \qquad \theta = 1, \ldots, M \qquad (101)$$

Using Eq. (94) to substitute in for F_θ,

$$(H_{\xi\delta} - G'_{\xi\eta}B_{\eta\gamma}n_{\gamma\beta})f_{\xi\theta}G'_{\theta\rho}B_{\rho\sigma}P_\sigma$$
$$+ (H_{\xi\delta} - G'_{\xi\eta}B_{\eta\gamma}n_{\gamma\beta}H_{\beta\delta})f_{\xi\theta}(H_{\theta\phi} - G'_{\phi\rho}B_{\rho\sigma}n_{\sigma\psi}H_{\psi\phi})F_\phi^R = 0 \qquad (102)$$

This is a system of $M - N$ linear algebra equations in terms of $M - N$ unknown redundant forces, F_ϕ^R. After obtaining the redundant forces the element forces are obtained from Eq. (94).

An analysis of an STOL transport composite wing (Fig. 8) was reported by Purdy *et al.* (1971). The internal stresses were computed using a force method analysis using the idealization shown in Fig. 9. Membrane stresses and strains only were accounted for, while plate bending stresses and strains were assumed to be insignificant, and were ignored. The triangular mem-

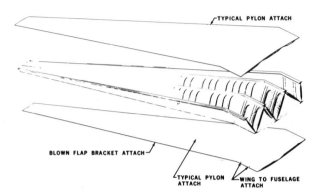

FIG. 8. MST truss web wing box concept. Upper cover: boron–epoxy, bolted; lower cover: graphite–epoxy, bonded; truss web: graphite–epoxy.

brane elements are of the equilibrium type and based on an assumed linear membrane stress state. Nine element forces are associated with each element, four degrees of freedom with each connecting edge in two-dimensional space, and six degrees of freedom with each connecting edge in three-dimensional space. The inner webs were modeled with chordwise modulus of elasticity modified to simulate the intermittent posts, and zero spanwise and shear moduli.

The idealization used 132 triangular membrane elements and 143 bar elements. The bar elements were used to carry the kick loads which occurred when connected membrane elements were not coplanar. The problem had 1903 unknown forces and 676 redundants. In Eq. (89) the ranges of the subscripts are

$$\beta = 1, \ldots, 1903 \qquad \alpha = 1, \ldots, 1227 \qquad \delta = 1, \ldots, 676$$

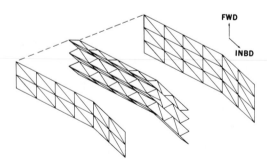

FIG. 9. Composite wing finite element model.

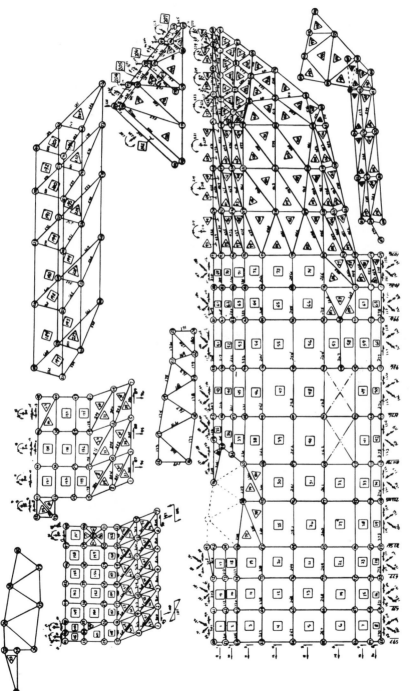

FIG. 10. Composite fuselage idealization.

C. Unified Method

Equations (88), (95), and (99) are used to form the unified equations

$$f_{\alpha\beta}F_\beta - n_{\beta\alpha}u_\beta = 0 \tag{103}$$

$$n_{\alpha\beta}F_\beta - P_\alpha = 0 \tag{104}$$

This is a complete system of equations which could be solved directly and simultaneously for the unknown forces and displacements. A unified approach to discrete element analysis was first developed by Klein (1957).

One solution method which is becoming increasingly popular uses the unified equations to solve directly for the displacements. From Eq. (103),

$$F_\delta = g_{\delta\alpha}n_{\beta\alpha}u_\beta \tag{105}$$

where $g_{\delta\alpha}$ is found such that

$$g_{\delta\alpha}f_{\alpha\beta} = \delta_{\alpha\beta} \tag{106}$$

Substitution into Eq. (104) gives

$$n_{\alpha\delta}g_{\delta\eta}n_{\beta\eta}u_\beta = P_\alpha \tag{107}$$

This equation corresponds to the structural stiffness relationship (86) of the displacement method. It has the advantage, however, that it is developed from equilibrium elements rather than displacement elements.

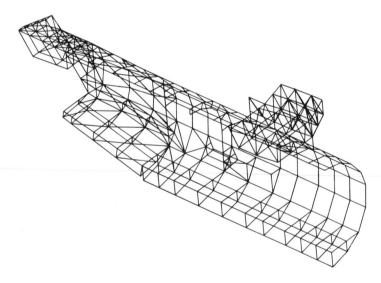

Fig. 11. Composite STOL transport fuselage idealization.

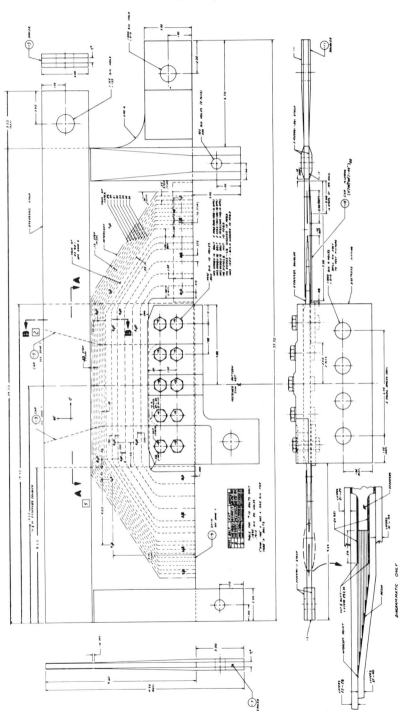

Fig. 12. Composite fitting subcomponent.

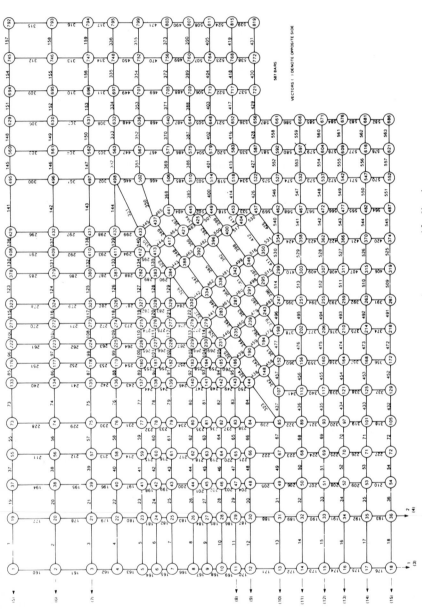

Fig. 13. Composite fitting subcomponent idealization.

As an example of a problem solved using equilibrium elements and the unified equations the idealization shown in Figs. 10 and 11 was analyzed. The structure is a fuselage of an STOL transport fabricated from graphite–epoxy. The idealization contains 597 bar elements to simulate the fuselage frames and floor beams and 209 parallelogram panels and 230 triangular panels to simulate the fuselage skin and floor panels. The panel elements, which represent the membrane action of the skin, are based upon an assumed linear variation of stresses. The problem has 6890 unknown forces, 4247 equations, and 2643 redundant forces. Equation (107) therefore represents 4247 linear simultaneous equations which were solved for the displacements.

An example of local or detail stress analysis is shown in the analysis of the major fitting subcomponent specimen (Fig. 12). The specimen repre-

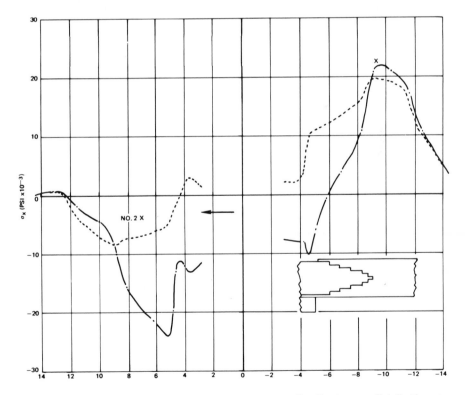

FIG. 14. Impact of thermal effects on internal stress distribution. σ_x distribution at $Y = 0.265$; ·——· room temperature analysis (mechanical + thermal stresses) (ultimate load); – – – – mechanical stresses only (ultimate load).

sents a portion of the graphite–epoxy A-4 stabilizer described in Section IV,A. The major design feature of the specimen was the graphite–epoxy to titanium step lap joint. In order to capture the thermal stresses developed, the graphite–epoxy (Fig. 13) and the titanium were idealized separately and connected by a series of bar elements representing the adhesive behavior. The significant impact of the thermal stresses can be seen in Fig. 14.

V. Conclusions

Discrete element analysis techniques are a powerful tool for determining internal loads and stresses. When the techniques are used on composite structures it is necessary to use elements which have been developed for use on nonisotropic structures. Further problems arise in that a finer idealization is often required for a composite structure since the brittle nature of the materials requires a better definition of the state of stress. Discrete element analysis is generally an integral part of the development of a composite structure. As computer and numerical methods continue to be refined and developed, more widespread and detailed usage is anticipated.

List of Symbols

$B_{\alpha\beta}$	Inverse of $n_{\gamma\alpha}G_{\alpha\beta}$	M_{ij}	Moments
$C_{\gamma\alpha}$	Idealization stiffness	N_{ij}	Forces
$C_{\gamma\alpha}^{i}$	Element stiffness	P_{α}	Discrete forces
C_{ijmn}	Elastic constants	S_{ijmn}	Elastic constants
E	Isotropic Young's modulus	U	Strain energy
$D_{ij\alpha}$	Coefficients relating strains and discrete displacements	a_{ij}	Direction cosines
		$\bar{a}_{i\alpha}$	Assumption relating general and discrete displacements
E_{ij}	Orthotropic elastic constants		
$E_{ij\alpha}$	Coefficients relating stresses and discrete displacements	$b_{ij\alpha}$	Coefficients relating independent force parameters and stresses
F_{α}	Independent force parameters	$\bar{b}_{ij\alpha}$	Coefficients relating dependent force parameters and stresses
$\bar{F}_{\alpha}$	Dependent force parameters		
F_{α}^{0}	Statically determinate force parameters	e_{ij}	Total strains
		e_{α}	Idealization deformations
F_{α}^{R}	Redundant force parameters	$\bar{e}_{a}$	Element deformations
$G_{\alpha\beta}$	Coefficients relating statically determinate forces to the independent forces	$d_{\alpha\beta}$	Coefficients relating independent and dependent force parameters
$H_{\alpha\beta}$	Coefficients relating the redundant forces to the total forces	f_{i}	Body forces
		$n_{\alpha\beta}$	Equilibrium coefficients relating element and applied forces

q	Normal load	ΔT	Temperature change
u_i	Displacements	κ_{ij}	Curvatures
$\bar{u}_\alpha$	Discrete displacements	σ_{ij}	Stresses
α_{ij}	Thermal coefficient of expansion	ν	Isotropic Poisson's ratio
e_{ij}	Mechanical strains	ν_{ij}	Orthotropic Poisson's ratio
e_{ij}^0	Midplane strains		

References

Batt, J. R., and Jordan, S. (1972). AFFDL-TR-66-203.

Denke, P. H. (1954). *Proc. U. S. Nat. Congr. Appl. Mech., 2nd* pp. 445–451.

Denke, P. H. (1962) *NASA Tech. Note D-1666*

Denke, P. H. (1965). *Soc. Automotive Congr. Int. Congr. Exposition, Detroit.*

Fraeijs de Veubeke, B. M. (1965). *In* "Stress Analysis," Chapter 9, pp. 145–197. Wiley, New York.

Fraeijs de Veubeke, B. M., and Sanders, G. (1968). *Int. J. Solids Struct.* **4**, 447–468.

Klein, B. (1957). *J. Aeronaut. Sci.* 39–46.

McCormick, C. W. (1970). NASA SP-222.

Mikkelson, P. T. (1969). Amer. Soc. Civil Eng., Nashville, Tennessee.

Pickard, J. (1968). AFFDL-TR-66-203.

Przemieniecki, J. S. (1968). "Theory of Matrix Structural Analysis." McGraw-Hill, New York.

Przemieniecki, J. S., and Berke, L. (1964). AFFDL-TR-64-18.

Purdy, D. M., and Schaeffer, H. G. (1971). *Amer. Soc. Mech. Eng., Design Eng. Conf., New York.*

Purdy, D. M., Dietz, C. G., and McGrew, J. A. (1971). *A. F. Conf. Fibrous Compos. Flight Vehicle Design, Dayton, Ohio.*

Teodosiadis, R. (1970). McDonnell Douglas Corp. Rep. No. MDC-J0357.

Turner, M. J., Clough, R. W., Martin, H. C., and Topp, L. J. (1956). *J. Aeronaut. Sci.* 805–823.

8

Probabilistic Design and Reliability

BRIAN H. JONES

Goldsworthy Engineering, Inc.
Torrance, California

I. Introduction

Probabilistic design criteria that apply to conventional materials and
structures generally have equal applicability to composites. If differences
arise, they are mainly of degree. This is particularly evident during the
present accelerated period of composite materials technology development,
when standardization of material systems, processes, and testing has not
yet been attained. The problem is compounded by some of the inherent
characteristics of composite materials; in particular, generally different
failure mechanisms in each principal direction of the material and lack of
yielding characteristics similar to those exhibited by metals. In a sense, it
is the latter fact that has brought about the general need to define structural integrity from a probabilistic standpoint. This is not to say that there
is any *intrinsic* characteristic of composites that demands that this should
be so; the use of homogeneous, isotropic metals exhibiting generally brittle
characteristics would have led ultimately to the same situation. Apart
from this, a probabilistic approach, irrespective of the nature of the materials involved, is the only one that is really rational and universal for any
application. As is pointed out by Haughen (1968) statistical methods of
design lead to a new order of realism in engineering science—wherever it is
applied.

In this chapter, the relationship between structural reliability and various
design factors will be brought out, if possible. The purpose of this is two-
fold: one, it will emphasize that the unqualified use of factors of safety will
not *necessarily* provide any consistent level of reliability; two, it will
enable past experience, with more conventional structures, to be related to
a composite design in a manner that enhances both designer and user confidence. If the use of composites and the techniques of reliability analysis
are to be integrated efficiently into the mainstream of industrial design, this
final point should not be underrated. Additionally, it is also essential to
prevent the considerable potential for highly efficient structures presented

by composites from being negated by the use of *ad hoc* factors of safety which create either an over- or underdesigned situation.

A. Structural Reliability

A physical law may be considered as describing the deterministic evolution of nature. A probabilistic interpretation of a physical law becomes necessary only when insufficient data or knowledge exist to account completely for all variables which affect the outcome of a phenomenon.

Thus a *probabilistic design* denotes that the values used to evaluate design integrity are random, not discrete. Probabilistic parameters are chosen on the basis of statistical inference. This is in contrast to a *deterministic design* denoting that the values used to evaluate design integrity are discrete, not random. Deterministic values are derived on the basis of available information and experience.

For many engineering situations, there is an implied overlapping of the two concepts. This arises from the difficulty in totally accounting for limitations in analysis, inaccuracies in design, and restricted control over processes, construction, and use—to say nothing of the ever present possibility of inadequate definition of material strength and applied loads. If the reliability of the structure is to be based on a "no failure ever" requirement, then it is obvious that the result is an infinitely strong, and thereby infinitely heavy, structure. Thus something less must be accepted. The "no failure ever" situation is of course generally relaxed to a "no failure unless" requirement. As a rule, the structure is only permitted to fail provided it is operated outside the defined and expected boundaries of some prescribed load profile by a significant increment. More concisely, an acceptable design demands that no failure be tolerated while the structure is being operated normally, but failure during abnormal operation will be tolerated (Bouton *et al.*, 1968).

With this inherent assumption, structural reliability is the probability that intrinsic load-carrying capacity, in a specific environment and at a particular time, exceeds the applied loads. If the structural reliability is defined by a number between 0 (totally unreliable) and 1 (totally reliable), then the possibility that it is a specific value between these two limits may be expressed as a probability. If all possible reliability values are assigned relative probabilities, the result is a reliability distribution. The degree of confidence in stating a particular reliability R is obviously the area under the distribution curve between R and unity. The total area under the distribution curve equals 1, since it represents all possible outcomes for a particular situation.

B. *Structural Design Criteria and Concepts*

To place the reliability concepts applicable to composite structures in broad perspective, it seems appropriate to mention briefly general design criteria that are in current use. Establishing design criteria and stresses for composites has produced considerable disparity of application, not only between conventional metallic practice but also between users. In general, the design limit load stresses are chosen so that no lamina within the laminated structure is subjected to a stress exceeding certain limits, frequently defined with implicit reference to the basic lamina properties. Typically, the requirement is to use initial failure in some critical lamina as the basis for either design limit or design ultimate, depending upon the degree of conservatism required. A complete review of some of the most prevalent criteria may be found in Structural Design Guide for Advanced Composite Applications (1971).

Some fundamental concepts in design philosophy are now considered.

A *fail-safe design* is a design philosophy in which failure propogation is so limited that the failure of any single structural component will not degrade the strength or stiffness of the remainder of the structure to the extent that it cannot function in the manner in which it was intended at a specified percentage of limit load.

A *safe-life design* is a design philosophy under which failure will not occur because of undetected flaws or damage during the specified service life of the component or structure; also the period of time for which the integrity of the structure can be guaranteed in the anticipated operating environment.

It is generally understood that safe-life design should be applied to all structures that are vital to the integrity of the vehicle or the safety of personnel. Safe-life is determined by analysis and testing. It accounts for such items as material property and failure mechanisms, load spectra, cyclic effects, sustained loads, and cumulative damage. If safe-life cannot be guaranteed to an acceptable level of confidence, then fail-safe concepts should be implemented which take account of critical structural elements, extent of damage the structure can withstand, failure modes, etc.

C. *Design Loads and Stresses*

The following terms are frequently used in design analysis. While they are normally used in the deterministic sense, they should be more accurately qualified in terms of statistical parameters.

Limit Load

The limit load for a given design condition is the maximum load likely to be encountered in service. Of all the limit loads which may be considered to act under various conditions, the most critical for design is referred to as *design limit load*. *Design limit stress* is, of course, the stress associated with design limit load.

Ultimate Load

In general, the ultimate loads are merely the limit loads multiplied by an ultimate factor of safety. *Design ultimate load* on a component is that particular ultimate load which is the most critical for design. *Design ultimate stress* results from the design ultimate load. It is the maximum load the structure must sustain without rupture or collapse in the anticipated operating environment.

Proof Load

The product of the limit load and the proof factor is the proof load. It is the load applied to the structural components or assemblies as the basis for evaluating quality prior to acceptance.

Allowable Stress

The maximum stress that can be permitted in a material system for a given design condition to prevent rupture, collapse, or detrimental deformation is the allowable stress.

Material Strength

The stress level that the material is capable of withstanding in the local structural configurations in the expected operating environment is called the material strength.

"A" Allowable

The value above which at least 99% of the population is expected to fall with a confidence of 95% is called "A" allowable. This means that there is a 95% certainty that at least 99% of the individual property values are higher than the "A" values.

"B" Allowable

The value above which at least 90% of the population is expected to fall with a confidence of 95% is called "B" allowable. This in turn means that there is a 95% certainty that at least 90% of the individual property values are higher than the "B" value.

As a rule, "A" allowables are used in all applications where failure of a single load path would result in a loss of structural integrity, and "B" allowables are used where failure would result in a safe redistribution of applied load to other load-carrying members.

II. Statistical Aspects of Strength and Load

The reliability of a structural element may be viewed as being the probability that structural load-bearing capability exceeds the applied load. In the simplest sense, this definition may be reduced to the statement that structural reliability is the probability that the intrinsic material strength exceeds the applied stress. The underlying statistical characterization of strength and stress will now be reviewed from a phenomenological and analytical standpoint.

A. Strength Models and Probability Distributions

The statistical models used in the study of failure of composite materials almost always take as a starting point Griffith's theory, which states that strength-reducing flaws reside within the material, weakening it. Accepting this concept, then the strength of a given specimen is determined by the smallest value to be found in a sample of size n, where n is the number of flaws. The problem of finding how the strength depends on the volume is equivalent to studying the distribution of the smallest value as a function of n, the sample size.

During the last fifty years, considerable effort has been devoted to studying the distribution of extreme values (smallest or largest) in samples of size n drawn from a population possessing a probability density function $f(x)$. Generally, the literature treats the distribution of the nth values from top to bottom when the n sample values are arranged in order of magnitude.

Insofar as application of the statistical theory to fracture problems is concerned, the primary interest is the distribution of smallest value in samples of size n (for large n). The statistical theory underlying the distribution of smallest values is contained in Eqs. (1)–(4) (Epstein, 1948).

If the continuous probability density function $f(x)$ has an associated cumulative distribution function

$$F(x) = \int_{-\infty}^{x} f(x) \, dx \tag{1}$$

then the distribution of the smallest value in samples of size n drawn from the population is given by the probability density function

$$g_n(x) = nf(x)(1 - F(x))^{n-1} \qquad (2)$$

having a cumulative distribution function

$$G_n(x) = \int_{-\infty}^{x} g_n(x) \, dx$$

$$= 1 - (1 - F(x))^n \qquad (3)$$

The mode of $g_n(x)$ (the most probable value) of the smallest value of samples of size n is found by finding the maximum of $g_n(x)$. If a solution exists, it may be written as

$$f^2(x_n{}^*)(n - 1) = [f^1(x_n{}^*)][1 - F(x_n{}^*)] \qquad (4)$$

Equation (4) is the form used implicitly or explicitly by all writers dealing with the weakest link phenomenon.

The general features of some commonly used distribution functions $f(x)$ are summarized in Table I in terms of smallest values in samples of size n, the distribution of smallest values in samples of size n (n large), and the characteristics of the distribution of the smallest value. From this table the following deductions can be made (Epstein, 1948):

(1) The rectangular distribution implies that strength does not depend on volume; this is at variance with observed behavior.

(2) The Cauchy distribution also leads to results that do not agree with observed behavior.

(3) The Laplace, Gauss (or normal), and Weibull distributions all imply that strength does decrease with increasing volume.

(4) The Laplace and Gauss distributions both lead to relationships that are semilogarithmic in character ($\log V$ and $\overline{\log V}^{1/2}$, respectively), the important difference being that in the Laplace case, the distribution does not become narrower with increasing V, whereas it does for the Gaussian case.

Epstein (1948) concluded that the distribution of strengths due to flaws could be written in the general form

$$f(x) = A \exp(-B \mid x - \mu \mid^p) \qquad (5)$$

for large values of $\mid x - \mu \mid$, where A, B, μ, and p are positive constants. On the basis of this, the most probable value of the smallest value in samples of size m must decrease as $(\log m)^{1/p}$ and the distribution of small-

TABLE I Summary of Essential Features of Commonly Used Distribution Functions[a]

Distribution	Mode of smallest value in sample of size m	Distribution of smallest values in samples of size large m	General characteristics of distribution of x (n large)
Rectangular $f(x) = 1/b - a,\ a \leq x \leq b$ $f(x) = 0$ elsewhere	a	$x = a + (b-a)\xi/m$	x is nearly independent of m
Cauchy $f(x) = \dfrac{1}{\pi}\dfrac{\lambda}{\lambda^2 + (x - \mu)^2}$	$\mu - \dfrac{\lambda m}{2\pi}$	$x = \mu - \dfrac{\lambda m}{\pi \xi}$	Most probable value of x decreases linearly with m. Both mean value and variance are infinite.
Laplace $f(x) = \dfrac{1}{2\lambda}\exp\left[-\dfrac{(x-\mu)}{\lambda}\right]$	$\mu - \lambda \log \dfrac{m}{2}$	$x = \mu - \lambda \log \dfrac{m}{2} + \lambda \log \xi$	Most probable value decreases as a multiple of $\log m$. Variance remains equal to $\lambda^2 \pi^2/6$, independently of m.
Gauss $f(x) = \dfrac{1}{(2\pi)^{1/2}\sigma}\exp\left[-\dfrac{(x-u)^2}{2\sigma^2}\right]$	$\mu - \sigma(2\log m)^{1/2}$ $+ \sigma\left(\dfrac{\log\log m + \log 4\pi}{2(2\log m)^{1/2}}\right)$	$x = \mu - \sigma(2\log m)^{1/2}$ $+ \sigma\dfrac{\log\log m + \log 4\pi}{2(2\log m)^{1/2}}$ $+ \dfrac{\sigma}{(2\log m)^{1/2}}\log \xi$	Most probable value decreases as a multiple of $(\log m)^{1/2}$. Variance decreases as m increases and is given by $\pi^2\sigma^2/12 \log m$.
Weibull $f(x) = \alpha\beta x^{\beta-1}\exp(-\alpha x^\beta)$ $x \geq 0$ $\alpha > 0, \beta > 1$	$\dfrac{1}{[\alpha m]^{1/\beta}}\left(1 - \dfrac{1}{\beta}\right)^{1/\beta}$	$x = (\xi/m\alpha)^{1/\beta}$	Most probable value decreases as $m^{1/\beta}$. Mean value decreases as $m^{-1/\beta}$ and variance as $m^{-2/\beta}$.

[a] ξ is distributed with probability density function $h(\xi) = e^{-\xi}, \xi \geq 0$.

est values must be negatively skewed. This implies that given a physical phenomenon in which the weakest link hypothesis represents the true state, there is a statistical compulsion for skewed distribution of strengths of samples of the same size and an approximately semilogarithmic dependence of the most probable value of the strength (or whatever is equivalent to strength) on the size of the specimen or number of places at which a break may occur. This appears to account for the skewed distribution and semilogarithmic relationship in studies of strength of materials.

B. Strength Distribution Functions for Composites

Two basic distribution forms are commonly used to reduce strength data for composite materials. They are the normal and Weibull distributions; the log-normal form is frequently used to represent fatigue life scatter. (This will be referred to subsequently.) A comparison of the essential differences between the two distributions and the relationship between the essential parameters of each are given in Table II.

The first person attributed with the realization that the strength of a specimen was mathematically related to the distribution of smallest values was Pierce (1926) and he assumed a Gaussian distribution of strengths. This distribution was also assumed by Kontorova (1940) and Frenkel and Kontorova (1943). Since that time, a considerable body of literature has developed around the exact distribution of extreme values for both large and small values of m for the normal distribution.

Weibull (1939) suggested that the probability of failure of a unit volume

TABLE II

Comparison of Weibull and Normal Distributions[a]

Distribution	Function	Range (X)	Mode location	Shape parameter
Normal	$\exp\left[-\dfrac{1}{2}\left(\dfrac{x}{\sigma}\right)^{2}\right]$	$-\infty$ to ∞	$\bar{X}$	$\dfrac{\sigma}{X}$
Weibull	$\exp\left[-\left(\dfrac{x}{\beta}\right)^{a}\right]$	0 to ∞	β	α

[a] $\bar{X} = \beta\Gamma\left(\dfrac{1+\alpha}{\alpha}\right), \quad \sigma^{2} = \beta^{2}\left\{\Gamma\left(\dfrac{2+\alpha}{\alpha}\right) - \Gamma^{2}\left(\dfrac{1+\alpha}{\alpha}\right)\right\}$

as a function of the stress σ is given by

$$F_0(\sigma) = 1 - \exp[-(\sigma/\sigma_0)^m]$$

where σ_0 and m are unknown parameters characteristic of the material under test. This distribution has found considerable application in describing the strength behavior of composites, and will be described in more detail subsequently.

A frequent criticism of the Weibull distribution is that it is devoid of physical meaning, the normal distribution being viewed as Nature's own. At the moment, there is insufficient knowledge to say whether the Weibull distribution is less suitable as an *a priori* distribution than one that is purely normal. Both involve two free undetermined parameters. The Weibull does implicitly involve the principle that it is the weakest link that determines fracture strength. It is easy to calculate the maximum (mode or most probable value) of the distribution of strengths of size m in each distribution.

C. Load-Time Histories for Structures

The discussion so far has been directed toward statistical concepts associated with defining strength and failure in the material. It is apparent, however, that the reliability of the overall structural system can only be adequately established provided the applied loads acting on the structure are also capable of definition, since it is the loads that create "stress." It is not appropriate in this treatise to consider at length the means available for defining load-time history. This has been carried out elsewhere and

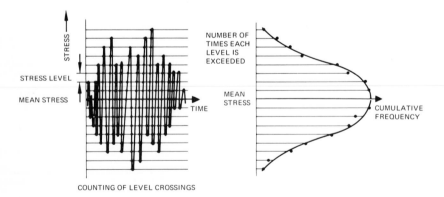

FIG. 1. Cumulative stress spectrum from a random loading record.

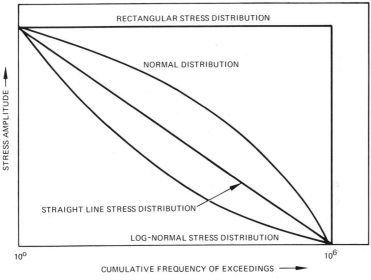

FIG. 2. Basic load spectra.

is a technology independent of the material system being evaluated. Sufficient be it to say that several techniques for reducing a random load-time history have been proposed and these may be divided into (Jacoby, 1967)

(a) counting methods,
(b) power spectral methods.

An example of how a cumulative stress function may be derived by counting level crossings from a random loading record is shown in Fig. 1. Normalized load spectra are shown in Fig. 2 for a

(a) rectangular stress distribution,
(b) normal stress distribution,
(c) log-normal stress distribution,
(d) straight-line stress distribution,

the last three being of greatest value in design engineering. The following indicates where each load distribution finds greatest application.

The *normal distribution* is used with many engineering components (particularly those under relatively stationary loads) such as maneuver loads of aircraft and loads in automobiles.

The *log-normal distribution* applies to gust loads and ground–air–ground cyclic loading in aircraft.

The *straight-line distribution* is used with automobile components subject to a stationary random process. (It should be noted that the straight-line distribution is in fact made up of several normal distributions with different frequencies and peak values.)

III. Macro- and Micromechanical Aspects of Strength

As a rule, the composite material structural designer will not be too concerned by the micromechanical (mechanics applied at the matrix–filament level) aspects of failure—but rather those that manifest themselves at a macromechanical level. Nevertheless, a brief consideration of failure modes as they occur in tension, compression, and shear in a single, unidirectional lamina is useful in providing insight into the overall behavior of a multioriented laminate.

It is obvious that it is highly desirable to be able to predict the strength and stiffness of an arbitrary lamina from fundamental properties of the constituents, thence to predict similar properties of a laminate composed of the same lamina oriented in some chosen manner. Calculations on stiffnesses have generally proved successful; predictions of strengths have not met with the same degree of wide success. Fundamental research in these areas is continuing.

As far as is known, the only lamina failure mode that has been explained in terms of a statistical model is longitudinal tension. The nature of composite materials would, however, make all characteristic failure modes, i.e., longitudinal and transverse tension and compression and in-plane and interlaminar shear, amenable to a probabilistic analysis.

A. Longitudinal Tension

The longitudinal tensile strength of a composite lamina has been summarized by Rosen and Zweben (1972) in terms of two micromechanical failure modes:

(a) cumulative weakening failure,
(b) weakest link failure.

In the former, failure is considered to occur by progressive random fracturing of filaments in the material under gradually increasing composite stress. From a knowledge of matrix elastic properties, constituent volume fractions, and filament strength statistics, it is shown (Rosen, 1964) that the statistical mode of the composite tensile strength (σ_c), based on fiber area, is given by

$$\sigma_c = (\alpha\beta\delta e)^{-1/\beta} \tag{6}$$

where α and β are Weibull parameters and δ is an ineffective length parameter.

The weakest link failure mode, as postulated by Zweben (1968), assumes that catastrophic failure is induced by the occurrence of one or a small number of filament failures. The redistribution of internal stresses caused by initial filament failure creates a rapid instability manifesting itself as a crack or stress wave, which leads to virtually instantaneous failure. Again assuming a fiber strength relationship based upon the Weibull distribution, an estimate of the failure stress is given by

$$\sigma_w = \frac{\beta - 1}{NL\alpha\beta}$$

where α and β have the same significance as in Eq. (6), L is the fiber length, and N is the number of fibers in the material.

B. Longitudinal Compression

The problem of predicting the longitudinal compressive strength of a unidirectional lamina has been considered by a number of authors, the basic approach being one of individual filament stability when supported by the matrix (for a review see, for instance, Noyes and Jones, 1968). In such cases, the results are stated in terms of deterministic elastic and volume properties of the constituents. One approach to the problem taken by Herrmann *et al.* (1967), which treated the foundation as a three-dimensional continuous body supporting an initially nonstraight filament, might lend itself to a probabilistic treatment, provided a distribution of nonstraightness could be realistically established.

C. Transverse Tension, Compression; Interlaminar and In-Plane Shear

In contrast to the foregoing filament controlled failure modes, fractures under transverse (at right angles to the filaments) tension and compression are dominated by the matrix. The same comment applies to shear failures. Analysis of these cases is extremely difficult, mainly because of the complex stress field which exists around the filament and the difficulty of defining such characteristics as matrix–filament adhesion, effect of voids, etc.

Limit analysis methods of plasticity have nevertheless been used by Shu and Rosen (1967) and finite-element techniques by Chen and Lin (1969) with a certain degree of success. While such approaches were deterministically defined, an appropriate statistical approach could be incorporated to describe matrix strength behavior, distribution of voids, interfilament spacing, etc. For more extensive discussion on micromechanics strength theories, see Chapter 2, Volume 5.

D. Laminate Strength Predictions

For the sake of completeness, a very brief review of the most frequently used approaches to predicting the strength of multioriented laminated composites will be presented, mainly as an aid to perspective in the statistical evaluation of general laminate data.

The main objective in most of the failure theories which have been advanced is to predict the strength of a laminate made up of arbitrarily oriented laminae, under general conditions of combined load, from data established on single lamina tests, Chapter 2, Volume 7. The laminate is assumed to consist of homogeneous orthotropic laminae which are systematically evaluated in terms of an appropriate failure criterion. The majority of failure criteria are quadratic in form (Tsai, 1964; Hoffman, 1967) and indicate the onset, rather than the mode, of failure.† Puppo and Evensen (1971) advocate a so-called hybrid approach using the concepts of an interaction factor and principal strength axes. In explicit deterministic form, the failure criterion is typically given as:

$$\left(\frac{\sigma_{x1}}{T_{x1}}\right)^2 - \gamma_1\left(\frac{T_{x1}}{T_{yi}}\right)\left(\frac{\sigma_{x1}}{T_{x1}}\right)\left(\frac{\sigma_{y1}}{T_{y1}}\right) + \gamma_1\left(\frac{\sigma_{y1}}{T_{y1}}\right)^2 + \left(\frac{\tau_{x1y1}}{T_{x1y1}}\right)^2 = 1$$

$$\gamma_1\left(\frac{\sigma_{x1}}{T_{x1}}\right)^2 - \gamma_1\left(\frac{T_{y1}}{T_{x1}}\right)\left(\frac{\sigma_{x1}}{T_{x1}}\right)\left(\frac{\sigma_{y1}}{T_{y1}}\right) + \left(\frac{\sigma_{y1}}{T_{y1}}\right)^2 + \left(\frac{\tau_{x1y1}}{T_{x1y1}}\right)^2 = 1$$

where γ is an interaction factor; σ_{x1}, σ_{y1}, τ_{xiyi} are stresses referred to the principal strength axes; and T_{x1}, T_{y1}, T_{x1y1} are principal strengths.

Another criterion, based upon the concept of maximum strain applied to the lamina principal axes, was proposed by Petit (1967). Here the failure (or yield) surface for the laminate was obtained by the superposition of failure surfaces for all plies on a set of laminate stress coordinates.

In all the foregoing cases, the strength parameters were defined deter-

---

† Noyes and Jones (1968) postulated an approach for defining failure mode for criteria based upon quadratic formulations; this concept was subsequently developed by Chiu (1969).

TABLE III

LAMINATE EXPERIMENTAL AND THEORETICAL STRENGTHS

No. of laminae	No. of samples	Mean strength (KSI)		Standard deviation (KSI)	
		Exp.	Theory	Exp.	Theory
1	28	26.9	26.9	7.0	7.0
5	7	27.8	29.7	2.6	2.2
10	6	32.7	33.1	2.2	2.1

ministically although, in principle, probabilistic interpretations could be applied.

An interesting statistical analysis of the tensile properties of planar unidirectional laminates constructed of N brittle laminae bonded together was made by Scop and Argon (1967). This analysis demonstrated, experimentally and theoretically, that the tensile strength of a laminate is closer to the ideal strength of the lamina material than individual sheets. This is because the effects of flaws, which drastically lower the strength of simple laminae, are substantially reduced in a laminate.

Typical experimental and theoretical results obtained from filamentary glass ribbon are given in Table III. It should be noted that the model analyzed was similar in many respects to that developed by Rosen (1964).

A later paper by Scop and Argon (1969) was extended to take account of the effects of stress enhancement in the regions of primary fracture. In addition, the calculations were extended to evaluate the effects of more than 10 elements. The results on boron sheet and glass fiber tape composite showed that:

(a) the effective stress enhancement is less for an elastic matrix than for a rigid plastic matrix;

(b) for constant length, the strength of the composite rises with increasing numbers of parallel reinforcing elements for all flaw distributions and for both plastic and elastic matrices;

(c) for the same flaw distribution function, the composite with an elastic matrix is stronger than one with a plastic matrix.

IV. Design Applications of the Weibull Distribution

The Weibull distribution has a location, a scale, and a shape parameter, although the location parameter is generally known to be zero or set to zero by a suitable transformation of the data. In a failure analysis situation, this is equivalent to assuming that a failure can occur with some positive probability at any time or stress after time or stress zero. Thus if a random variable $X > 0$ represents failure time or stress, then

$$p[X \leq x] \equiv F(x) = \begin{cases} 1 - \exp[-(x/\beta)^\alpha] & x \geq 0 \\ 0 & \text{otherwise} \end{cases} \tag{7}$$

The scale parameter β in Eq. (7), referred to as the characteristic life or stress, is positive and is the $100(1 - e^{-1})$ percent point of the distribution of X. The parameter α, which is also positive, defines the shape of the distribution. As α increases, the mode of the distribution approaches β and for $1/\alpha \rightarrow 0$, the distribution degenerates at β. In practical terms, the wider is the amount of scatter, the lower is the value of α used to define the distribution. It was observed by Mann (1968) that in many lifetesting situations α is independent of stress level. This same characteristic has been observed in the failure behavior of many engineering materials—including composites.

In life or strength definition, the concern is generally the value of the reliability function $R(x)$, the proportion of the population of specimens sampled which will have survived at time or stress x. $R(x)$ is therefore equal to $p[X > x] = 1 - F(x)$ or

$$R(x) = \exp[-(x/\beta)^\alpha] \tag{8}$$

In some cases a required life or stress capability, x_0, is specified and a point or interval estimate is to be made of $R(x_0)$, the reliability at x_0. In other situations a reliability (or probability of survivability) is specified and x_R, the time at which $R\%$ of the population will have survived, is to be estimated. The value of x_R may be found from

$$x_R = \beta[\ln(1/R)]^{1/\alpha}$$

A. Weibull Distribution in Composites

Halpin *et al.* (1970) showed that the fracture properties of laminated composites under uniaxial tension could indeed be accurately described by a Weibull distribution which he stated in the form

$$P(f) = \exp[-(f/\hat{f})^\alpha] \tag{9}$$

where f is the fracture stress, $\hat{f}$ is a characteristic fracture stress, α is a shape parameter, and $P(f)$ is the probability of survivability [see Eq. (8)].

Significantly and in accordance with general expectations, the shape parameter in Eq. (9) was shown to remain nearly constant under varying loading conditions, temperatures, and strength degradations. This means that if a component suffers degradation of strength due to damage, corrosion processing, fatigue, etc., then the shape parameter of these distributions is the same as for undamaged material. This is illustrated in Fig. 3 which shows the cumulative survival functions for combinations of time, temperature, and stress concentration in a glass–epoxy $\pi/4$ laminate under tension. Essentially similar results were reported also by Halpin (1972) for graphite–epoxy laminates; Table IV shows the shape and location parameters observed for a number of orientation patterns, the values quoted being typical of early commercial prepreg materials. A more characteristic value of α for specimens utilizing close quality control of material and processing would be in the range 16–26.

It may be noted from the data of Table IV that the effect of a notch is to reduce the static strength without significantly changing the shape of the distribution. This is an important result which can generally be translated to other loading situations and material systems.

The same typical trends in boron–epoxy were observed by Kaminski

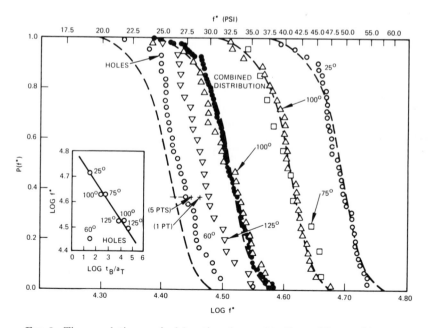

FIG. 3. The cumulative survival functions for combinations of time and temperature. Insert is relationship between lifetime and characteristic strength (Halpin *et al.*, 1970).

TABLE IV

COMPARISON OF WEIBULL PARAMETERS FOR GRAPHITE–EPOXY
LAMINATES IN TENSION

Orientation pattern	Shape parameter (α)	Location parameter (β)	Prime failure	Temp.
0	10.11	151.8	filaments	*RT*
0/90	10.91	76.5	filaments	*RT*
0/±45	10.8	66.9	filaments	*RT*
0/±45/90	11.46	49.4	filaments	*RT*
0/±45/90			—	
with round hole	11.5	39.2	—	*RT*
with a slit	10.8	39.8	—	*RT*
90	7.54	5.3	matrix	*RT*

(1972) for unnotched tension specimens, the essential results being summarized in Table V. Some significant facts emerge from a study of the data in Table V and should be noted carefully for extension to other cases.

(1) The statistics of strength data may well reflect the geometry of the test specimen used. For the 0° data, although the mode parameter β is different for each of the three specimens, the shape parameter is virtually identical for the coupon and flexure specimens. The same behavior is evident in the 90° data. The lower α in both these situations indicates greater scatter.

(2) Referring to the flexure data obtained at differing temperatures on the 0° specimen, it may be observed that α differs widely over the temperature range −65°F to 350°F. The same comment can be made for the 90° laminate shape parameters.

(3) Failure of laminates controlled by filament fracture is described by shape parameters which are essentially the same as for the 0° laminate. A similar observation can be made for failure of laminates controlled by matrix fracture in relation to 90° laminate data.

(4) From knowledge of α obtained over an applicable temperature range, by tests on 0° and 90° specimens, strength distributions for arbitrarily oriented laminates can be made to a high degree of accuracy—provided meaningful estimates of β can be made.

B. *Influence of α and β*

While the engineering variables that influence the representative values of α and β tend to overlap and interact, as a guide the following can be used.

TABLE V

COMPARISON OF WEIBULL PARAMETERS FOR BORON–EPOXY

Orientation pattern	Shape parameter (α)	Location parameter (β)	Test specimen[a]	Prime failure	Temp. °F
0	24.3	192.2	A	filament	RT
0	10.8	213.6	B	filament	RT
0	26.1	241.1	C	filament	RT
90	15.2	9.62	A	matrix	RT
90	9.2	13.66	B	matrix	RT
90	13.6	15.97	C	matrix	RT
0	27.9	247.5	C	filament	−65
0	19.5	203.8	C	filament	350
0	8.6	176.4	C	filament	420
90	21.1	17.59	C	matrix	65
90	16.0	11.19	C	matrix	350
90	17.4	8.26	C	matrix	420
0/±45/90	19.8	60.9	A	filament	RT
0/±45	18.7	106.6	A	filament	RT
90_2/±45	19.8	16.1	A	matrix	RT

[a] A—flat tension coupon, B—sandwich beam, C—flexure coupon.

(1) α is *strongly* influenced by process and manufacturing control, prime failure mode, test specimen size, and method and *less strongly* by ply orientation (provided the prime failure mode does not change), environment, and notches.

(2) β is *strongly* dependent upon constituents (matrix and filament), ply orientation, and environment (over a wide range) and *less strongly* by process and manufacturing method, and test method.

The above comments are generalizations only and there will always be exceptions to the situations mentioned. Additionally, other influences may have marked effects on α and β and in any design analysis, care should be exercised in identifying the likelihood and significance of any such influences.

C. The Statistics of Damage Accumulation

Halpin (1972) suggested an analytical approach to predicting the accumulation of damage in laminated composites. The rate of damage is given by

$$\frac{dc}{dt} \simeq MC^r \qquad r \geq 1.0 \tag{10}$$

where M is a quantity dependent upon the loading history and r is a material constant. It is further assumed that laminate failure occurs when

$$\sigma(c)^{1/2} = K \tag{11}$$

K being an apparent toughness parameter. A continuous change in static strength of the ith specimen can be expressed as

$$t = \frac{1}{(r-1)M} \cdot \frac{1}{K^{2(r-1)}} \left[\sigma_i(0)^{2(r-1)} - \sigma_i(t)^{2(r-1)} \right]$$

If the initial static strength distribution

$$P(\sigma) = \exp\{-[\sigma/\bar{\sigma}]^\alpha\}$$

is assumed to represent a distribution in the damage parameter C and if each damage site develops according to Eq. (10), then the fatigue lifetime distribution is

$$P(t) = \exp\{-[t/\bar{t}]^{\alpha/2(r-1)}\}$$

The term r is obtained from Eq. (11) or from

$$\frac{d\sigma_i(t)}{dt} = [\tfrac{1}{2}MK^{2(r-1)}]\sigma_i(t)^{-(2r-3)} \tag{12}$$

which is an indirect measure of Eq. (10). Preliminary material constants α and r are presented in Table VI.

TABLE VI

COMPARISON OF DAMAGE RATE PARAMETERS

	r	α (static)	$\alpha/2\,(r-1)$ (fatigue)
E-Glass–Epoxy	5.64	12.3	~1.32
Boron–Epoxy	9–11	18–23	0.9–1.1
Graphite–Epoxy	8.5–10	17–19[a]	0.9–1.1
Aluminum	4–6	30–45	4–5

[a] High quality prepreg.

TABLE VII

BONDED JOINT WEIBULL PARAMETERS

Test	Scale	Number of specimens	Weibull parameters[b]		
			α	β^c	γ_s (%)
Static	⅕	16	11.58	108.0	11
10% Lifetime	⅕	6	7.38	108.9	16
50% Lifetime	⅕	20	4.94	105.8	23
Fatigue-to-lifetime	⅕	20	1.44	1.99	68
10% Lifetime	½	5	7.05	227.6	17
Fatigue-to-failure	½	5	1.95	0.67	53

D. Statistics of Damage Accumulation in Bonded Joints

In the area of composite material structural design, a major effort has been directed toward a detailed evaluation of the characteristics of bonded joints.

It has been observed that Miner's rule does not predict the life of bonded joints, and experimental and theoretical investigations are being conducted to enable joint life estimates to be performed. Compounding the problem are the pronounced scale (volume) effects which have been noted in comparing data obtained on large substructures with that observed from apparently similar scaled test specimens. Both static ultimate and fatigue life have been observed to be reduced by a factor of two in scaling up by a factor of three in the case of a lap joint (Davis *et al.*, 1973). The Weibull parameters which characterize $\frac{1}{5}$ and $\frac{1}{2}$ scale similar bonded joints are shown in Table VII and cover a life spectrum from static ultimate to fatigue failure. The significant increase in scatter with life (indicated by a reduction in α and the coefficient of variation of the sample γ_s) should be noted, together with the change in the scale parameters β.

E. Proof Testing

Proof testing may be viewed as removing weak members of the population; if these members are removed, safety factors can be reduced. Proof testing, when referred to the Weibull distribution, changes the shape of the distribution by truncating it (see Fig. 4).

If the components that survive are unaffected by the proof test (implying there is no significant cumulative damage), the new (truncated) distribution $P(f)$ can be related to the original distribution function $P_p(\beta)$ by (Halpin *et al.*, 1970)

$$P_p(\beta) = P(\beta)/P(\beta_p)$$

The drawbacks to the proof test method are seen as:

(a) possible effect of cumulative damage on surviving specimens;

(b) truncated distribution creates a large number of components at or just above the proof stress; if components are weakened by aging or by slight changes in operational loads, numerous failures could occur almost simultaneously;

(c) the cost of the tests and the losses associated with rejected components.

All these effects must be weighed against the advantages of the reduced factors of safety.

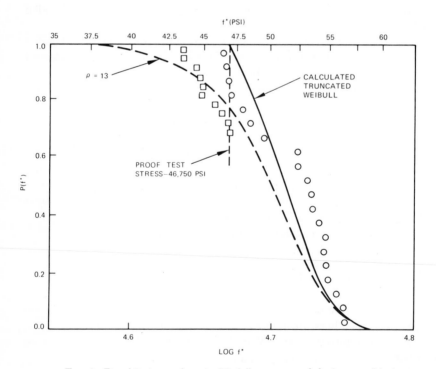

FIG. 4. Proof test experiment. □; failure occurred during proof test.

F. Probability of Failure under Multiaxial Stress

A rational approach to the problem of defining probability of failure of anisotropic materials under multiaxial stress assuming a Weibull distribution and a maximum stress criterion was suggested by Ho (1966). Under combined tension, compression, and shear it is suggested that the total risk of rupture is:

$$B = B_x + B_y' + B_{xy}$$

$$= \int_V K \left[\frac{\sigma_x - \sigma_u}{\sigma_0'} \right]^m dV + \int_V K' \left[\frac{\sigma_y' - \sigma_u'}{\sigma_0'} \right]^{m'} dV + \int_V K'' \left[\frac{\sigma_{xy} - \sigma_u''}{\sigma_0''} \right]^{m''} dV$$

(13)

$$\sigma_x \geq \sigma_u \geq 0, \qquad \sigma_y' \leq \sigma_u' \leq 0 \text{ (compression)}, \qquad |\sigma_{xy}| \geq |\sigma_u''| \geq 0$$

where B is the total risk of rupture, B_x is the risk of rupture due to uniaxial tension, B_y' is the risk of rupture due to uniaxial compression, B_{xy} is the risk of rupture due to shear, σ_x, σ_y', σ_{xy} are the stresses in tension ,compression, shear, σ_u, σ_u', σ_u'' are the threshold stresses, σ_0, σ_0', σ_0'' are the characteristic stresses, m is the material flaw intensity, K is the coefficient, and V is the volume. The types of failure surfaces that would be obtained are shown diagrammatically in Fig. 5 for various probabilities of failure, P.

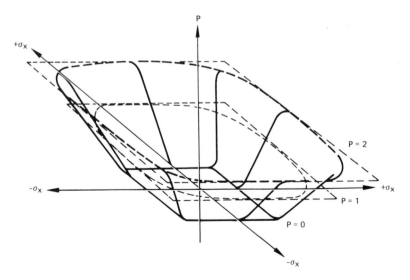

FIG. 5. Probability-of-failure surface (maximum stress criteria).

The only objection to this approach is that interaction effects are neglected; if, however, the maximum stress or strain criteria for failure in composite laminates are accepted, then the technique would prove valuable.

V. Design Applications of Normal Distribution

An early application of probability to relate "strength" and "design allowables," based in principle upon the normal distribution, involved taking the results of test data and computing a value equal to the mean minus three standard deviations. The minimum value so established was incorrectly assumed to represent a 99.87% probability of being exceeded. This approach is not strictly valid, as is pointed out by Moon *et al.* (1966), since the sample statistics derived were only estimates of the population. To place design allowables determination on a more rational basis, uncertainty in deriving population statistics is accounted for through confidence levels being applied to the estimates. This concept will be developed further in what follows.

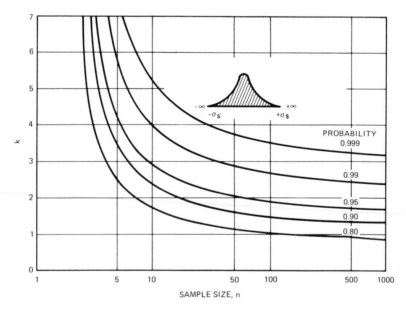

Fig. 6. One-sided tolerance limits and sample size for the normal distribution at 95% confidence level. $\bar{x}$ = sample mean; σ_s = sample standard deviation.

A. Design Allowables Definitions

Assume that n structural elements are tested for some particular property (such as strength, modulus, etc.) and it is required to determine design allowable to conform to a particular probability and confidence level. The procedure is as follows. From an analysis of the data are determined the mean $(\bar{X}_s)$ and standard deviation (σ_s) for the sample. To ascertain whether or not the sample distribution is approximated by the normal distribution chi-squared tests should be carried out. If the sample is near normal, then a design allowable X_q can be determined using the following expression:

$$X_q = \bar{X}_s - k\sigma_s \tag{14}$$

where k is the one-sided tolerance factor for the normal distribution at some specified confidence level and probability. Values of k at the 95% confidence level used to determine "A" and "B" allowables are indicated in Fig. 6; more general data is to be found in Bombara (1961).

B. Inadequate Data for Direct Definition

It is possible to determine design allowables from inadequate data if it is justifiable to assume that a proportional relationship exists between the

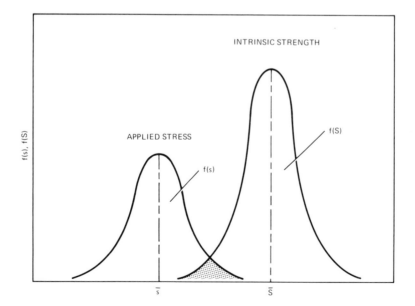

Fig. 7. Determination of design allowables by ratioing.

property in question and some other property for which design allowables have been previously determined. If a pair of related test values is available (e.g., tension data at $0° \pm 45°$ and $0° \pm 60°$, Fig. 7), then a ratio between these two properties may be established. Thus it is necessary only to obtain several such ratios, average them, and determine the lower confidence level for the average ratio. If the number of ratios of two property observations is represented by n, the average ratio by $\bar{R}$, and the standard deviation of the ratio by s, the lower confidence limit R on the average ratio is found to be (Moon *et al.*, 1966)

$$R = \bar{R} - ts/\sqrt{n}$$

where t is the fraction of the t distribution for the desired confidence level and $n - 1$ degrees of freedom. The reduced ratio is then used as the ratio between the two design allowables, one known, one to be derived.

It should be noted that allowables determined in this manner are presumed to have the same data basis as the allowables to which they were referred.

C. Effect of Using Sample Data on Design Allowables

It is of interest to consider the influence of using sample statistics rather than those which define the population, since in many composite material evaluation programs, the sample size is small. The consequence is that overly conservative design allowables result which may impose an unreasonable penalty on the design. Jones (1969) discusses the relationship between X_q and $\bar{X}_s$ on the assumption that the population (rather than the sample) coefficient of variations (γ) was known. The following expression was quoted:

$$\frac{X_q}{\bar{X}_s} = \frac{1 + \gamma K_{1-q}}{1 + \gamma K_{1-c} n^{1/2}} = b \tag{15}$$

where K_{1-q} and K_{1-c} are the values of standard normally distributed variates exceeded by $(1 - q)$ and $(1 - c)$ percentages of the population respectively. For an "A" allowable and confidence $c = 0.95$, it will be found that with $n = 3$, $b = 0.70$. When $n = 10$, $b = 0.73$, and when $n = 100$, $b = 0.76$. Thus an approach to design allowables based upon population statistics shows only a slight sensitivity to sample size.

Exactly how significant the differences implied by Eqs. (14) and (15) are may be seen in Fig. 8 which shows the ratio $X_q/\bar{X}_s$ when the population coefficient of variation γ and sample coefficient of variation γ_s take values in the range 0.20 to 0.05. Clearly, the use of population statistics results in higher design allowables being established. Such a concept is

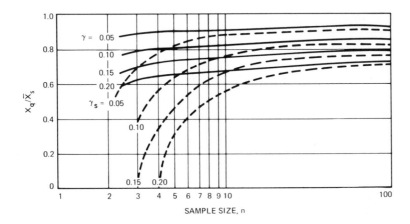

FIG. 8. Design allowables based on population and sample coefficients of variation.

important in evolving design allowables for composite materials, provided the characteristic coefficient of variation of a particular materials system, process, and failure mode is known. Thus variations of lamina orientation, thickness, etc., can be tolerated in optimizing a design without the need to carry out an extensive testing program—simply by using a generic coefficient of variation and the results obtained from a small sample. Typical coefficients for various loading modes may be found in Jones (1969).

D. Minimum Sample Sizes for Design Allowables Determination

No standardized sample sizes presently exist in the statistical definition of design allowables for composites and so it is of value to quote from Moon *et al.* (1966) the guidelines which were laid down in establishing allowables for inclusion in MIL-HDBK-5, one of the most authorative references on metallic materials and elements for aerospace vehicle structures.

Adequate data, normal distribution, direct computation—minimum of 100 individual observations.

Adequate data, nonnormal distribution, direct computation—minimum of 300 individual observations for determining an "A" value.

Inadequate data for direct computation—minimum of 10 pairs of related data.

In actual fact MIL-HDBK-5 values are generally based upon a sample size considerably in excess of that mentioned above.

E. Design Allowables from Computed Strengths

Hadcock (1971) describes a technique for determining design allowables for composites on the basis of ratios of computed strength values and actual test data. The ratio is established from a direct comparison of theory and experiment for some particular loading situation and it is assumed to prevail for other (similar) material configurations. "A" and "B" basis correction factors are obtained using an equation similar to Eq. (14) and these factors are then used to modify the theoretically derived strength values.

F. Fatigue Characterization Using Log-Normal Distribution

It is proposed to review the probabilistic aspects of fatigue as it affects design analysis. No reference to the behavioral characteristics of composites under fatigue will be made; such data is available elsewhere. Since "static" strength data may be viewed as simply being a characteristic strength at a time $t = 0$ in the material load-time history, then most of the probabilistic observations which have been made with implicit reference to the static situation have equal applicability. Under fatigue the life of a structural element should always be qualified with a probability factor and confidence level, i.e., fatigue life is a statistical value and must be evaluated in that context.

Three parameters are generally used to describe fatigue life scatter; *viz,*

(1) mean life,
(2) frequency density or probability distribution, and
(3) standard deviation.

The log-normal distribution is most frequently used to represent fatigue life scatter, in the form:

$$f(\log N_j) = \frac{1}{\sigma (2\pi)^{1/2}} (\exp[-\tfrac{1}{2}[\log N_j - \log \bar{N}]]/\sigma^2)^2$$

where $\log \bar{N}$ is the population mean, and σ is the population standard deviation. However, it is often found that the log-normal distribution is not an accurate representation of fatigue life scatter in the extreme ranges of the distribution which is the region of primary interest in design. Hence, other distributions have been proposed such as Weibull (Guide for Fatigue Testing, 1963) and extreme values (Freudethal and Gumbel, 1954). A fatigue life scatter factor is often defined as:

$$\text{SF} = \bar{N}_c/N_p$$

where $\bar{N}_c$ is the estimate of mean life with confidence level c, and N_p is the life associated with a probability of failure p.

The confidence level c may also be associated with the estimate of the population standard deviation from a data sample. Such statistically defined scatter factors can be used for the specification and verification of fatigue life design requirements in the following manner (Abelkis, 1967).

(i) Specify the required life N_r, where $r = 1 - p$ is the desired reliability and p is the cumulative probability of failure at time N_r.

(ii) By analysis and/or testing establish the mean life N_c for a desired confidence level, c.

(iii) Calculate the life N_p corresponding to the specified probability of failure p, as:

$$N_p = \bar{N}_c / (\text{SF} \mid_p^c)$$

where $\text{SF} \mid_p^c$ is the scatter factor for the specified probability of failure. When the life estimate is based directly on test results and the test spectrum represents the mean life environment, N_p can be calculated directly from the test sample mean life, N_i,

$$N_p = N_i / (\text{SF} \mid_p^c)$$

where $\text{SF} \mid_p^c$ is the scatter factor for the desired confidence level and probability of failure.

(iv) Calculate the fatigue life margin of safety as

$$\text{MS}_{\text{FL}} = (N_p / N_r) - 1 = (\bar{N}_c / N_r \, \text{SF} \mid_p^c) - 1$$

A $\text{MS}_{\text{FL}} \geq 0$ indicates that the design life requirement has been satisfied. If $\text{MS}_{\text{FL}} > 0$, the probability of failure at the required life is less than the specified value and it corresponds to the probability of failure associated with $\text{SF} = \bar{N}_c / N_r$. Also, subject to other strength requirements, a $\text{MS}_{\text{FL}} > 0$ indicates that structural weight can be reduced by increasing the design stress of the structural element to a level which would result in $\text{MS}_{\text{FL}} = 0$. A $\text{MS}_{\text{FL}} < 0$ indicates that the design life requirement has not been fulfilled. The structural element must be redesigned by improving its fatigue quality and/or by reduction of the design stress level.

VI. Factors of Safety and Reliability

It is important to recognize the implications, as far as reliability is concerned, of the use of factors of safety since the latter find widespread application at all levels of design.

There are many definitions of *factor of safety*, F_s, but for illustration it will be assumed that, typically:

$$F_s = \frac{\text{ultimate load on structure}}{\text{design limit load of structure}}$$

As mentioned previously, the terms "ultimate load" and "design limit" should be qualified to account for the variability that will generally be experienced in these quantities. Assume that mean values are used as reference values. Neglecting nonlinearities, the factor of safety may be reduced to the ratio of mean "strength" to mean "stress" (Haughen, 1968)

$$F_s = \bar{S}/\bar{s} \tag{16}$$

Using this definition, it becomes evident why a given factor of safety does not necessarily guarantee a level of reliability. Consider first the Warner diagram, Fig. 9, showing the distribution of strength S and stress s. Since the two distributions overlap, it is evident that a finite possibility of failure exists, the probability increasing as the degree of overlap increases. An indication of the way in which probability of failure may vary—even when the factor of safety defined in Eq. (16) is held constant—may be seen from Fig. 10. It is also apparent that changing the standard deviations of the two distributions can also dramatically change failure probability while maintaining factor of safety constant (Fig. 11). To further emphasize the foregoing points, Table VIII shows the effect on reliability while maintaining factor of safety constant (Eq. (16)) for various values of mean

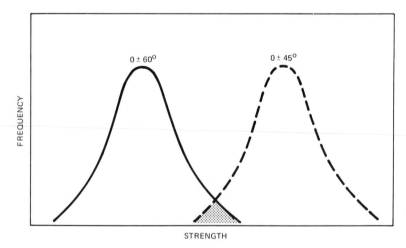

FIG. 9. Warner diagram showing distribution of stress and strength.

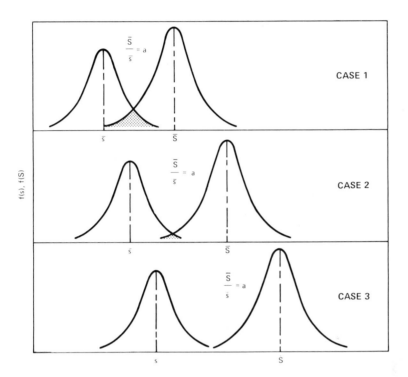

FIG. 10. Effect on probability of failure caused by proportional changes in $\bar{S}$ and $\bar{s}$ resulting in constant factor of safety.

TABLE VIII

SAFETY FACTORS AND RELIABILITIES FOR SPECIFIC STRESS AND STRENGTH DISTRIBUTIONS[a]

Mean strength	Mean stress	Strength standard deviation	Stress standard deviation	F_s	Reliability
25,000	10,000	1000	1500	2.5	0.9999996
25,000	10,000	5000	3000	2.5	0.9949
25,000	10,000	8000	3000	2.5	0.95994
25,000	10,000	5000	7000	2.5	0.95254
25,000	10,000	8000	7000	2.5	0.91406
25,000	10,000	10,000	6000	2.5	0.8997
50,000	20,000	1000	1000	2.5	1.0

[a] After Kececioglu and Cormier (1964).

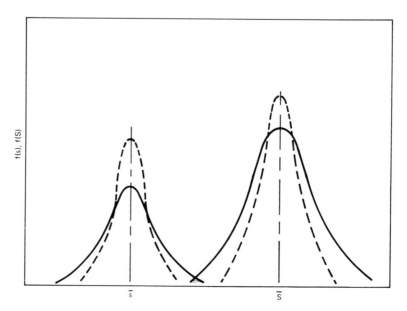

Fig. 11. Effects of changing strength and stress standard deviation while maintaining a constant factor of safety. ———: distribution 1; – – –: distribution 2.

strength, mean stress, strength standard deviation, and stress standard deviation (Kececioglu and Cormier, 1964).

A. Factors of Safety for Comparable Reliability

From the foregoing, it is obvious that a factor of safety, applied without reference to the statistical parameters which define "strength" and "stress," does not ensure a constant level of reliability. Nevertheless, since the concept of factor of safety is well ingrained in structural design, it seems desirable to investigate the relationship between factor of safety, reliability, and whatever statistical parameters are relevant to the problem. In particular, it is proposed to ascertain what the factor of safety should be to achieve the same material reliability as would be exhibited by, say, aluminum. This concept is of significance in relating the statistical characteristics of composite materials and structures to those of conventional materials and structures.

Jones (1969) employs a definition of factor of safety suggested by Leve

(1969), *viz.*,

$$F_s = X_{uq}/X_{dl} \qquad (17)$$

where X_{uq} is the ultimate strength related to the q percentile, and X_{dl} is the applied (design limit) stress, and shows that Eq. (17) can be written as

$$F_s = \frac{1 + \gamma K_{1-q}}{1 + \gamma K_r} \qquad (18)$$

where γ is the population coefficient of variation, K_{1-q} is the value of a standard normally distributed variate exceeded by $1 - q$ percent of the distribution, and K_r is the value of a standard normally distributed variate exceeded by r percent of the population. The quantity r is the reliability level and it specifies the probability that the strength exceeds the applied stress. That is,

$$r = P(X > X_{dl}).$$

Using Eq. (18) it becomes possible to determine the value of the reliability r attained in conventional structures when, say, $Q = 0.01$ (99% probability). If this is known, then the value of F_s to be applied to composite structures to achieve the same reliability may be derived.

Figure 12 shows the factors of safety to be used on materials exhibiting various coefficients of variation and having the same reliability as a con-

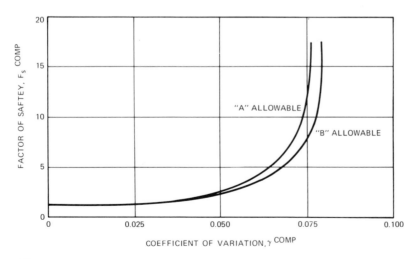

FIG. 12. Factor of safety required in composite structures to equal reliability of aluminum structures. $F_s{}^a = 1.5$, $\gamma^a = 0.03$.

ventional structure designed to a 1.5 factor of safety. The assumed coefficient of variation in the conventional structure is taken to be 0.03, a figure typical of aluminum (Moon *et al.*, 1966).

It is evident from Fig. 12 that the factor of safety increases rapidly if the coefficient of variation of the data is greater than 0.07. To attain an "A"-allowable status, factors of safety some 25% greater than those used for "B" allowables must be employed for coefficients of variation typical of the better class of composites.

This analysis puts the concept of factor of safety on a rational basis. It is evident that the value of, say, 1.5 has meaning only when related to the concept of reliability. The designer should therefore not use traditional factors of safety without careful appraisal of the significance of the data.

B. Reliability When Strength and Stress Are Normally Distributed

Using a theoretical approach, it is possible to compute reliability when the strength and stress distribution are normal (Haughen, 1968). Since the strength characteristics of composite materials may be approximated to such a distribution, the solution, using a difference-function approach, is repeated here.

If s and S are normal random variables for stress and strength respectively, then the density functions are given by

$$f(s) = \frac{1}{\sigma_s(2\pi)^{1/2}} \exp\left[-\frac{1}{2}\left(\frac{s - \bar{s}}{\sigma_s}\right)^2\right]$$

$$f(S) = \frac{1}{\sigma_S(2\pi)^{1/2}} \exp\left[-\frac{1}{2}\left(\frac{S - \bar{S}}{\sigma_S}\right)^2\right]$$

In the present context, let it be assumed that reliability is the probability that strength exceeds stress or

$$S - s > 0$$

If $S - s = \xi$, then the expression for the difference function is

$$f(\xi) = \frac{1}{\sigma_\xi(2\pi)^{1/2}} \exp\left[-\frac{1}{2}\left(\frac{\xi - \bar{\xi}}{\sigma_\xi}\right)^2\right]$$

where $\xi = S - s$ and, $\sigma_\xi = (\sigma_S^2 + \sigma_s^2)^{1/2}$ (σ_s and σ_S are standard deviation estimators). Since the reliability is given by the area under the difference distribution curve between 0 and ∞ $(+ve)$, then

$$R = \frac{1}{\sigma_\xi (2\pi)^{1/2}} \int_0^\infty \exp\left[-\frac{1}{2}\left(\frac{\xi - \bar{\xi}}{\sigma_\xi}\right)^2\right] d\xi$$

Changing variables and limits results in

$$R = \frac{1}{(2\pi)^{1/2}} \int_z^\infty \exp\left[-\left(\frac{z}{2}\right)^2\right] dz$$

where

$$z = (\bar{S} - \bar{s})(\sigma_S^2 + \sigma_s^2)^{-1/2} \tag{19}$$

Equation (19) is called a coupling equation since it probabilistically relates applied and allowable stresses. Once z has been computed, R may be found from tables of the normal probability function.

Consider, as a simple application of the foregoing concepts, a design situation where the stress of a unidirectional glass–polyester rod at ultimate load is defined in terms of a mean $(\bar{S})$ and standard deviation σ_S, i.e.,

$$(\bar{S}, \sigma_S) = (250{,}000, 5000)$$

Similarly, that the applied load stress is defined by

$$(s, \sigma_s) = (230{,}000, 3000)$$

Hence

$$z = \frac{|\,250{,}000 - 230{,}000\,|}{(3000^2 + 5000^2)^{1/2}} = 3.43$$

and so the reliability R is 0.9997.

C. Distribution Functions and Factors of Safety

As discussed, data on composite materials has been represented effectively by both Weibull or normal (log-normal) type distributions. It is of value at this point to consider the sensitivity of the computed factor of safety with distribution function to attain a given material reliability if the characteristic coefficient of variation is changed. This was carried out by Jones (1969). The results are reported in Table IX.

For the purpose of comparison, an old and new design was assumed, the original factor of safety in each case being 1.5. The results suggest that the normal distribution tends to give a more conservative safety factor. This appears worthy of consideration when analyzing data for design application.

TABLE IX

INFLUENCE OF DISTRIBUTION FUNCTION ON FACTOR OF SAFETY

Distribution	Quantity	Original value	New value
Normal	γ	0.12	0.15
	Q	0.01	0.01
	F_s	1.50	1.85
Log-normal	γ	0.12	0.15
	Q	0.01	0.01
	F_s	1.50	1.65
Weibull	γ	0.12	0.15
	Q	0.01	0.01
	F_s	1.50	1.65

Appendix. Estimation of Weibull Parameters for Design Analysis

To estimate efficiently reliability or probability of survival, it is obvious that the distribution parameters must also be ascertained efficiently. The problem may be stated as follows. Let it be assumed that a sample of n items has been randomly selected from a population and is to be subjected to a test representative of the in-service situation. Let it be further assumed that the failure stresses (or times) have a distribution given by Eq. (7) or, alternatively, Eq. (8). Let $X_{1,n} \geq X_{2,n} \geq X_{3,n} \geq \cdots \geq X_{n,n}$ represent the n observed failure stresses in the sample under the assumption that the tests are continued to the nth failure. If, however, at the mth failure the tests are terminated, it becomes necessary to apply point or interval estimation procedures to the m observations in order to establish values for α and β.

Valid techniques are surveyed and compared by, for instance, Mann (1968). As a rule, linear estimation methods are considered the most convenient because only the sample data is required (in terms of logarithms of ordered failure stresses or times) together with a table of weights in order to determine estimates of α and β in the form of weighted sums of the observations. These methods are readily adaptable to computer usage. Asymptotically efficient linear estimators appear to be quite efficient with respect to the best linear invariant estimators—even for fairly small n. Many methods based upon least-squares approximations have been advanced. If the sample size is 10 or greater and if there is little or no censoring, the true least-squares estimates and some approximations thereof are efficient relative to the best linear invariant estimators.

In obtaining graphical approximations to least-squares estimates, plots are made of each ordered observation versus an estimate of the central tendency of the reduced observation and then visual fits are made of the least-squares line. The parameter estimates are then obtained as functions of values of specified properties of the visually fitted line. Such a graphical plot is useful for identifying outliers and in deciding whether observed data are from the two-parameter Weibull distribution assumed. It is generally acknowledged, however, that parameter estimates made by graphical procedures involving a subjective interpretation are not as efficient for estimation as the linear estimates they approximate. The method of moments applied to yield simplified estimators seems to give good results for very small n, but is probably never preferable to the best linear invariant estimates.

Determination of β When α Is Known

Harter and Moore (1965) give a derivation of the maximum likelihood estimator $\hat{\beta}$ (based upon the first m of n ordered observations) of the characteristic scale parameter β of a Weibull distribution of known shape parameter α. This approach is considered one of the most useful and powerful for composite materials in particular, since, as has been established, the value of α will generally be known, to an acceptable level of confidence, in a specific design situation. If the probability density function of a random variable σ having a Weibull distribution with location parameter 0, scale parameter β, and shape parameter α is

$$f(\sigma) = \begin{cases} (\alpha/\beta)(\sigma/\beta)^{\alpha-1} \exp[-(\sigma/\beta)^{\alpha}] & \sigma > 0 \\ 0 & \text{elsewhere} \end{cases}$$

then a maximum likelihood estimator for β, derived by Epstein and Sobel (1953), is given by

$$\hat{\beta} = \{[\beta_{1(n)}^{\alpha} + \beta_{2(n)}^{\alpha} + \cdots + \beta_{m(n)}^{\alpha} + (n-m)\beta_{m(n)}^{\alpha}]1/m\}^{1/2}$$

which may be reduced to

$$\hat{\beta} = \frac{1}{m}\left[\sum_{i=1}^{m} \beta_{i(n)}\right]^{1/\alpha} \tag{20}$$

where n refers to the sample of size n and $\beta_{i(n)}$ $(i = 1, 2, \ldots, m)$ are the first m specimens tested.

An upper confidence bound with confidence level $1 - P$ (lower confidence bound with confidence level P) on β is given by

$$\bar{\beta}_{1-p} = \underline{\beta}_p = \left(\frac{2m}{X^2_{2m,\,p}}\right)^{1/\alpha} \hat{\beta} \tag{21}$$

where X^2 refers to a chi-squared distribution and the first subscript $(2m)$ is the number of degrees of freedom and the second (P) is the cumulative probability. The interval between lower and upper confidence bounds, each with confidence $1 - P$, is the confidence interval with confidence level $1 - 2P$. Equations (20) and (21) remain valid when $m = n$, in which case Eq. (21) is an expression for the conventional confidence bound based on all n observations.

List of Symbols

Italic uppercase

A, B	Constants
F, G	Cumulative distribution function
K	Values of standard normally distributed variates
P	Probability of survivability
S	Strength
X	Design stress

Italic lowercase

k	One-sided tolerance factor
m, n	Sample size
s	stress
t	time
x	random variable

Greek

Γ	Gamma function
α	Shape parameter
β	Location parameter
γ	Coefficient of variation
δ	Ineffective length parameter
σ	Stress; coefficient of variation
ξ	Difference function

Subscripts

p	Truncated distribution
s	Sample
s	Safety
$-$	Lower bound

Superscripts

$^-$	Mean
$^{\wedge}$	Maximum likelihood

References

Abelkis P. R. (1967). Fatigue Life Scatter Factors. Analysis Guidelines No. 67-16, Douglas Aircraft Company, Long Beach, California.

Bombara, E. L. (1961). Reliability of Compliance with One-Sided Specifications Limits When Data Is Normally Distributed, ARGMA TR 2B1R (September).

Boutan, I., Fisk, M., and Trent, D. J. (1968). Quantitative Structural Design Criteria by Statistical Methods, Vol. 11. AFFDL-TR-67-107.

Chen, P. I., and Lin, J. M. (1969). *Mater. Res. Stand.* **2,** no. 8.

Chiu, K. D. (1969). *J. Compos. Mater.* **3,** no. 3.

Davis, A. W., Waddouups, M. E., Wolff, R. V., Cox, E. F., and Wilkins, D. J. (1973). Reliability Review of Composite Structures. General Dynamics (FW), FZM-6098.

Epstein, B. (1948). *J. Appl. Phys.* **19.**

Epstein, B., and Sobel, M. (1953). *J. Amer. Statist. Ass.* **48.**

Frenkel, J. I., and Kontorova, T. H. (1943). *J. Phys. USSR* 7.

Freudenthal, A. M., and Gumbel, E. J. (1954). *J. Amer. Statist. Ass.* **49,** no. 267.

Freudethal, A. M., and Gumbel, M. M. (1954). A Guide for Fatigue Testing and the Statistical Analysis of Fatigue Data. (1963). ASTM Spec. Tech. Publ., ASTM STP 91-A, 2nd ed.

Hadock, R. N. (1971). Design Philosophy for Boron Epoxy Structures. Compos. Tech. Note No. CTN-466-37, Grumman Aerospace Corp.

Halpin, J. C. (1972). *J. Compos. Mater.* **6,** 208–231.

Halpin, J. C., Kopf, J. R., and Goldberg, W. (1970). *J. Compos. Mater.* **4,** 462–474.

Harter, H. L., and Moore, A. H. (1965). *Technometrics* **7,** no. 3.

Haughen, E. B. (1968). "Probabilistic Approaches to Design." Wiley, New York.

Herrman, L. R., Mason, W. E., and Chan, S. T. K. (1967). *J. Compos. Mater.* **1,** no. 3.

Ho, J. Y. L. (1966). Statistical Aspects of Failure, AFML-TR-66-310, Part 1, Air Force Mater. Lab.

Hoffman, O. (1967). *J. Compos. Mater.* **1,** no. 2.

Jacoby, G. H. (1967). Fatigue Life Estimation Processes Under Conditions of Irergularly Varying Loads, AFML-TR-67-215, Air Force Mater. Lab.

Jones, B. H. (1969). Determination of Design Variables for Composite Materials. Composite Materials: Testing and Design, ASTM STP 460, pp. 307–320. STM.

Kaminski, B. E. (1972). Effects of Specimen Geometry on the Strength of Composite Materials. *ASTM Symp. Analysis of Test Methods for Composites, San Antonio, Texas.*

Kececioglu, D., and Cormier, D. (1964). Designing a Specified Reliability into a Component. *Annu. Aerospace Maintainability Conf., 3rd, Washington, D. C.*

Kontorova, T. A. (1940). *J. Tech. Phys. USSR* 10.

Leve, H. L. (1969). Private communication to B. H. Jones.

Mann, N. R. (1968). Point and Interval Estimation Procedures for the Two Parameter Weibull and Extreme-Value Distributions. *Technometrics* **10,** no. 2.

Moon, D. P., Shinn, D. A., and Hyler, W. S. (1966). Use of Statistical Considerations in Establishing Design Allowables for Military Handbook 5. *Reliability Maintainability Conf. 5th, A.I.M.E., S.A.E., A.I.A.A.*

Noyes, J. V., and Jones, B. H. (1968). Crazing and Yielding of Reinforced Composites. Air Force Mater. Lab., A.F.M.L.-TR-68-51.

Petit, P. H. (1967). Ultimate Strength of Laminated Composites. General Dynamics (FW), Contract No. AF33 (615)-5257.

Pierce, F. T. (1926). *J. Textile Inst.* **17.**

Puppo, A. H., and Evensen, H. A. (1971). Strength of anisotropic materials under combined stresses. *AIAA/ASME Struct., Struct. Dynam. Mater. Conf. 12th* Paper 368.

Rosen, B. W. (1964). *AIAA J.* **2,** no. 11.

Rosen, B. W., and Zweben, C. H. (1972). Tensile Failure Criteria for Fiber Composite Materials. NASA CR-2057.

Scop, P. M., and Argon, A. S. (1967). *J. Compos. Mater.* **1,** no. 1.

Scop, P. M., and Argon, A. S. (1969). *J. Compos. Mater.* **3,** no. 1.

Shu, L. S., and Rosen, B. W. (1967). *J. Compos. Mater.* **1,** no. 4.

Structural Design Guide for Advanced Composite Applications. (1971). Air Force
    Mater. Lab.
Tsai, S. W. (1964). Structural Behavior of Composite Materials. NASA CR-71.
Weibull, W. (1939). *Ing. Vetensk. Akad. Handl.* No. 151.
Zweben, C. (1968). *AIAA J.* **2,** no. 12, 1982.

9

Experimental Characterization of Composites

CHARLES W. BERT

School of Aerospace, Mechanical and Nuclear Engineering
The University of Oklahoma
Norman, Oklahoma

I. Introduction

As the use of composite materials in diversified practical structures has increased, so has the need for experimental characterization of such materials. Here experimental characterization means determination of the material behavior by appropriate reduction of experimental data obtained on tests conducted on suitable specimens made of the composite material. The three main uses of experimental characterization data are

(1) to check micromechanics analyses, such as those described in Volume 2 of this treatise,
(2) to obtain data directly for use in subsequent analysis and design of practical structures, and
(3) for quality control purposes.

The experimental characterization for composite materials is generally more complicated than for ordinary homogeneous, isotropic materials because composites behave in much more complicated fashion, due to macroscopic anisotropic effects (properties depending upon orientation) and lamination effects (various other coupling effects). In composites, not only is it necessary to obtain more different kinds of data (since there are more independent material properties), but also it is usually necessary to design the test specimens much more carefully. In fact, Tsai (1971) has indicated that it may be necessary to expend as much effort on the design of suitable test specimens as on the design of the final structural component. Sometimes this requires finite-element stress analyses to evaluate the validity of a proposed specimen design even before the first specimen is built (Rizzo and Vicario, 1972).

Many conferences devoted solely to testing of composites have been held in recent years:

(1) American Society for Testing and Materials/U.S. Navy (1963),
(2) Air Force Materials Laboratory (1966), and
(3) American Society for Testing and Materials (1969, 1972).

In addition, numerous sessions at other meetings have been devoted to experimental characterization of composites. Meetings of the American Institute of Aeronautics and Astronautics, American Society of Civil

Engineers, Society for the Advancement of Materials and Process Engineering, and Society for Experimental Stress Analysis should be mentioned in particular.

In this chapter, the following aspects are emphasized:

(1) selection of suitable type of test specimen,
(2) test specimen design,
(3) appropriate reduction of experimental data.

In particular, details of standard tests and experimental results for specific materials will not be covered. These topics have been covered respectively by Epstein (1969) and the Air Force Material Laboratory's Structural Design Guide for Advanced Composite Applications (1973). Where necessary in connection with analysis of test methods or data reduction, brief explanations of underlying theory are given, along with references to more detailed analyses. Since the testing of composite materials is such a fast-moving field, generally references to work prior to 1962 are excluded.

General treatments of this topic have been presented by: Fried (1963), Yurenka (1963), Barnet and Prosen (1964), Prosen (1965, 1969), Vogt *et al.* (1966), Broutman (1969), Dastin *et al.* (1969), Grimes and Bronstad (1969), Halpin *et al.* (1969), Lenoe (1970), and Shockey (1971).

For purposes of design, it is desirable to characterize experimentally the

TABLE I

Engineering Properties Necessary for Minimum Characterization
of a Thin Layer of Unidirectional Composite Material[a]

Property	Symbol
Longitudinal Young's modulus	E_L
Transverse Young's modulus	E_T
In-plane Poisson's ratio for longitudinal loading	ν_{LT}
In-plane shear modulus	G_{LT}
Longitudinal tensile and compressive strengths	$F_L^{(+)}, F_L^{(-)}$
Transverse tensile and compressive strengths	$F_T^{(+)}, F_T^{(-)}$
In-plane shear strength	F_{LT}
Longitudinal residual stress	$\sigma_L^{(0)}$
Transverse residual stress	$\sigma_T^{(0)}$
Residual in-plane shear stress	$\sigma_{LT}^{(0)}$
Longitudinal thermal-expansion coefficient	α_L
Transverse thermal-expansion coefficient	α_T

[a] Necessary for each fiber volume fraction of interest and for environmental conditions approximating those of anticipated service of the product.

properties of a single ply or layer of the composite material with which one is concerned. Then one can use laminate theory to calculate the properties of laminates consisting of multiple layers with different orientations; see Ashton *et al.* (1969) and Bert (1974a,b). Unfortunately, however, practical considerations often prevent the construction of test specimens consisting of only one ply. Thus, it is necessary to conduct tests on multilayer specimens and use appropriate laminate theory to reduce the results in terms of single-ply properties.

Although some of the experimental methods described in the ensuing sections require only dial gages to measure deflections, most of the methods require the use of metallic electrical-resistance strain gages. The validity of using surface-mounted foil strain gages has been verified by Trantina (1967).

The engineering properties necessary for minimum characterization of a thin layer of unidirectional composite material are listed, along with their symbols, in Table I. In this table, it is assumed that the following reciprocal relation holds among the Young's moduli and Poisson's ratios:

$$\nu_{TL} = \nu_{LT}(E_T/E_L) \tag{1}$$

TABLE II

ADDITIONAL PROPERTIES THAT MAY BE NEEDED UNDER
CERTAIN CIRCUMSTANCES

Property
Poisson's ratio associated with transverse loading (ν_{TL})
Young's and shear moduli and Poisson's ratios under compressive loading
Longitudinal and transverse flexural moduli
Flexural Poisson's ratios
Longitudinal and transverse flexural strengths
Thickness shear moduli
Thickness shear strengths (interlaminar shear strengths)
Strength under combined multiaxial normal stresses and shear stresses
Dependence of mechanical properties on hydrostatic pressure
Complete stress–strain behavior to failure
Fracture toughness data[a]
Fatigue stresses *versus* cycles to failure[a]
Minimum creep rates *versus* nominal stresses
Creep rupture strengths[a]
Dynamic moduli
Damping coefficients

[a] These topics are covered in another volume in this treatise.

TABLE III

THICKNESS-DIRECTION PROPERTIES

Property	Symbol
Young's modulus in thickness direction	E_Z
Poisson's ratio associated with longitudinal-direction loading and strain response in thickness direction	ν_{LZ}
Poisson's ratio associated with transverse-direction loading and strain response in thickness direction	ν_{TZ}
Longitudinal thickness-shear modulus	G_{LZ}
Transverse thickness-shear modulus	G_{TZ}
Tensile and compressive strengths in thickness direction	$F_Z^{(+)}, F_Z^{(-)}$
Longitudinal thickness-shear strength	F_{LZ}
Transverse thickness-shear strength	F_{TZ}
Residual normal stress in thickness direction	$\sigma_Z^{(0)}$
Residual longitudinal thickness-shear stress	$\sigma_{LZ}^{(0)}$
Residual transverse thickness-shear stress	$\sigma_{TZ}^{(0)}$
Thermal-expansion coefficient in thickness direction	α_Z

However, there is some experimental evidence that this does not hold for all composites; see, for instance, Bert and Guess (1972). Also it is assumed that the Young's moduli and Poisson's ratio for compression loading are the same as those for tension loading. Again, this is not true for all composites; see, for instance, Ashton *et al.* (1969, pp. 108–109).

A list of additional properties, which may be necessary in the case of certain composites in some applications, is presented in Table II.

In structures in which the thickness of the composite material is a substantial fraction of the other dimensions, certain of the thickness-direction properties (listed in Table III) may be needed. The exact fractional dimension at which the thickness properties become important depends upon the particular composite material, the geometric configuration, and the type of loading. However, it has been demonstrated in a number of instances that thickness-shear properties become important in a composite material at a smaller ratio of beam or plate thickness than for a structure of the same geometric configuration and type of loading, but made of an ordinary isotropic material; see Chambers and McGarry (1959), Khishchenko (1964), Tarnopol'skii and Roze (1965), and Wu and Vinson (1969).

One of the most important points to keep in mind when selecting the type of test specimen to use in experimental characterization of a composite material is to use a type of specimen which has been made in the same manner as the full-scale, end-product structure. Thus, if the end-product structure is a flat sheet, such as an aircraft wing skin, then flat sheet specimens are preferable. However, if the end-product structure is a filament-wound conical shell, such as a reentry vehicle nose cone, then ring or tube specimens made from filament-wound material are recommended. The reason for this recommendation is that it is usually extremely difficult, if not virtually impossible, to achieve the same fiber volume fraction, fiber spacing, cure conditions, etc., in parts of different geometric configuration (plate vs. tube, etc.) even when made by the same process. Of course, it is obvious that composites made by different processes, even though the geometric configurations of the parts are the same, probably exhibit different properties because they are essentially different materials.

Another pitfall to avoid in experimental characterization of composites is the common assumption that the maximum-principal-strain direction (θ_ϵ) coincides with the maximum-principal-stress direction (θ_σ). Although this assumption is valid for isotropic materials, it can lead to appreciable errors in the case of composite materials because they are macroscopically anisotropic. The magnitude of these errors can be determined from the following equation, derived by Greszczuk (1966a):

$$\tan 2\theta_\epsilon = \frac{(1 - B)G_{\mathrm{LT}}^{-1}\tan\theta_\sigma}{(1 + \nu_{\mathrm{LT}})E_{\mathrm{L}}^{-1}(1 + B\tan^2\theta_\sigma) - (1 + \nu_{\mathrm{TL}})E_{\mathrm{T}}^{-1}(B + \tan^2\theta_\sigma)}$$

(2)

where B is the ratio of the minimum in-plane principal stress to the maximum one.

Figure 1 shows the effect of θ_σ on the difference $\theta_\epsilon - \theta_\sigma$ for typical unidirectional composites subjected to uniaxial tension loading, calculated using Eq. (2) and typical properties listed in Table IV. Figure 1 also shows the effect of the ratio B on $\theta_\epsilon - \theta_\sigma$. Due to the anisotropic nature of composite materials, it is recommended here that the concepts of principal strains and principal stresses be discarded in favor of using normal and shear strains and stresses, all related to the material-symmetry axes (the fiber direction, and two orthogonal directions normal to the fibers).

Still another pitfall is the selection of the proper fiber orientation in composite material specimens. For instance, if one were to select a $\pm 45°$ wrap angle for a filament-wound torsion-tube specimen, no information on the in-plane shear modulus of a ply could be obtained from a torsion test of such a specimen (see Section V).

Finally, it should be mentioned that for structural analysis and design of thin, laminated structures (beams, plates, shells), it is more convenient to use the *reduced elastic stiffness coefficients* (Q_{ij}) instead of the engineering

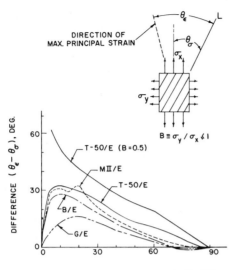

FIG. 1. Difference between directions of maximum principal strain and of maximum principal stress for various unidirectional composites: B/E ~ Narmco 5505 boron–epoxy; G/E ~ S glass–epoxy; MII/E ~ Morganite II graphite–epoxy; T-50/E ~ Thornel 50 graphite–epoxy. Biaxial stress ratio (B) is zero except when otherwise noted. Based on Eq. (2) and material data from Table IV.

TABLE IV

TYPICAL IN-PLANE ELASTIC PROPERTIES FOR SELECTED
UNIDIRECTIONAL COMPOSITES

Symbol	S glass–epoxy[a]	Narmco 5505 boron–epoxy[b]	Thornel 50-E-798 epoxy[b]	Morganite II-2387 epoxy[b]
E_L, msi[c]	8.91	30.0	21.2	19.6
E_T, msi	3.10	3.0	0.85	1.2
ν_{LT}	0.251	0.35	0.31	0.30
G_{LT}, msi	1.28	1.2	0.57	0.59

[a] Data from Greszczuk (1966a).
[b] Data from Whitney *et al.* (1971).
[c] The quantity msi denotes millions of psi.

properties more familiar to engineers. Also for thick structures such as thick-walled cylinders or cones, especially when they are three-dimensionally reinforced (cf. Barton, 1968), it is advisable to use the *Cauchy elastic stiffness coefficients* (C_{ij}). A discussion of these coefficients was presented by Lekhnitskii (1963).

In connection with micromechanics predictions of the macroscopic properties of composites, it is necessary to have available good data for the constituent material properties. However, sometimes this is difficult to obtain, for instance, due to the frailty of fibers. A scheme for obtaining *in situ* constituent material properties from tests on composite materials has been applied successfully to static elastic and plastic-range properties by Papirno and Slepetz (1971) and Bert (1972a) and to dynamic elastic and damping properties by Bert and Chang (1972).

A general method for characterizing composite materials from experimental data and a finite-element computer program have been presented by Kavanagh (1972).

II. Static Uniaxial Tension

It would appear that the static uniaxial tension test is the simplest type of mechanical test. However, for composite materials, there are certain special problems which must be surmounted.

A. *Flat 0° and 90° Specimens*

The flat specimen designs most commonly used for testing composite materials at either 0° or 90° to the fiber direction are shown schematically

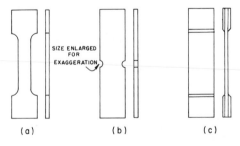

FIG. 2. Types of static uniaxial tensile specimens: (a) dog-bone (Federal Test Method Standard, 1961); (b) straight-sided with slight confluences (Nordby *et al.*, 1965); (c) straight-sided with end tabs (Grimes and Bronstad, 1969).

Fig. 3. Types of end connections for uniaxial tensile specimens: (a) pin type; (b) serrated-jaw type; (c) multihole type—approximately uniform tension (Halpin and Pagano, 1968).

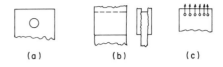

(a)   (b)   (c)

in Fig. 2. Different types of end connections which have been used are shown in Fig. 3.

Most composite materials have low interlaminar shear strengths relative to their tensile strengths. Thus, the dog-bone specimen, Fig. 2a, and the pin-type end connection, Fig. 3a, tend to fail at low loads due to interlaminar shear failure, as shown schematically in Fig. 4.

The straight-sided specimen with slight confluences, Fig. 2b, has a slightly disturbed state of stress at its center which precludes obtaining valid strain-gage readings in that vicinity. Also, although the purpose of the confluences is to prevent failure near the grips, the confluences tend to reduce the tensile strength somewhat.

The multihole-type end connection, Fig. 3c, has been used in research to approximate a uniform distribution of longitudinal tension. However, it is not normally used in full-scale experimental characterization work. Thus, by a process of elimination, it is seen that the most popular flat uniaxial tensile specimen for experimental characterization of composite materials is the straight-sided one with end tabs, Fig. 2c. The most popular end connection, which is used with the Fig. 2c specimen, is the serrated-jaw type, Fig. 3b.

A special precaution which is necessary in testing of unidirectional fiber-reinforced composite materials in the longitudinal direction (i.e., fiber direction) is to make certain that the loading direction does, in fact, coincide with the fiber direction. Otherwise, considerably lower values of both the longitudinal Young's modulus (E_L) and longitudinal tensile strength (F_L) may be obtained than the true ones, since the effect of even one degree of misalignment can be quite severe.

The minimal instrumentation for a uniaxial tensile test consists of a

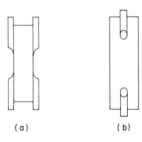

Fig. 4. Interlaminar shear failures of uniaxial tensile specimens made from composite materials. Taken from Shockey (1971).

(a)   (b)

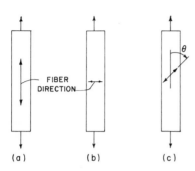

FIG. 5. Fiber orientation in tensile specimens: (a) longitudinal specimen; (b) transverse specimen; (c) off-axis specimen $(0° < \theta < 90°)$.

means of measuring the applied load (usually by means of the load cell in a universal testing machine) and a means of measuring the longitudinal strain, either with an extensometer or an electrical-resistance strain gage, which is more accurate. From these data taken until failure, one can readily obtain a longitudinal or transverse stress–strain curve to failure, depending upon whether the loading direction is parallel or perpendicular to the major material-symmetry axis (fiber direction); see Fig. 5. Both longitudinal and transverse tensile stress–strain curves for several typical fiber-reinforced plastic composites are shown in Fig. 6. Figure 7 shows analogous curves for a metal-matrix composite.

In addition to the instrumentation mentioned above, a strain gage (or extensometer) oriented at 90° to the loading direction is necessary if one

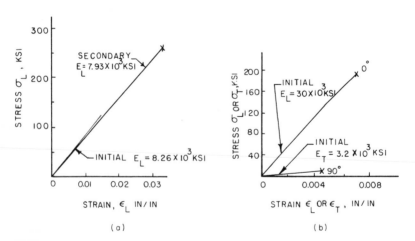

FIG. 6. Longitudinal (0°) and transverse (90°) tensile stress–strain curves for two typical unidirectional fiber-reinforced plastic composites: (a) S glass–epoxy (Ekvall, 1965); (b) boron–epoxy (Ashton *et al.*, 1969).

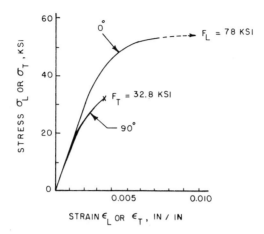

FIG. 7. Longitudinal (0°) and transverse (90°) tensile stress–strain curves for a beryllium wire–X7002 aluminum-alloy matrix composite. From Toy and Dickerson (1967).

wishes to measure the lateral contraction (Poisson's) ratio. For convenience, usually either two strain gages (one at 0° and the other at 90° to the loading direction) or a biaxial strain gage is used when it is desired to measure Poisson's ratio. In this case, it is very important to allow for the transverse-sensitivity factors for the gages in reducing the data. See Baumberger and Hines (1944) and Wu (1962). Otherwise, a large error will be made in the value of Poisson's ratio.

The defining equations for the Poisson's ratios are given below. For longitudinal loading,

$$\nu_{LT} = -\epsilon_T/\epsilon_L \tag{3}$$

For transverse loading,

$$\nu_{TL} = -\epsilon_L/\epsilon_T \tag{4}$$

where ϵ_L and ϵ_T are the transverse-sensitivity-corrected strains in the directions respectively parallel and perpendicular to the fiber direction.

McBride (1960) investigated very small specimens of the type shown in Fig. 2a except that there was no straight-sided region in the center. Weidner (1971) used a very complicated specimen resembling the Fig. 2a specimen in plan view and yet tapered in the side view. Hill (1968) described a composite material combined tension–compression test specimen in which the composite to be tested was bonded to the top and bottom of a thick metal substrate. Of course, the composite on one side is loaded in tension, while that on the other is loaded in compression. A similar speci-

men is the uniaxial sandwich beam test described by Waddoups (1968),
Petit (1969), Lantz and Baldridge (1969), and Lantz (1969). In this
specimen the substrate is hexagonal-cell honeycomb material.

Lenoe *et al.* (1969) made an extensive study of the effects of a variety of
specimen and testing variables on test results obtained on the type of
specimen shown in Fig. 2a: surface preparation in tab region, tab material,
adhesive bond line, strain rate, specimen length, width, and thickness
(number of plies).

Special grips for tensile testing of composites were discussed by Park
(1971), Hancock and Swanson (1971), and Berg *et al.* (1971). The latter
investigators found that the use of a collet-type grip increased the tensile
strength of reduced-test-section tensile specimens by 30 to 40%.

Kreider (1969) discussed some of the problems peculiar to tensile testing
of metal-matrix composites.

Kimball (1962) discussed the testing of reduced-test-section, laminated
block specimens loaded in interlaminar tension, i.e., tension normal to the
plane of the layers.

B. Flat Off-Axis Specimens

It has long been known, both experimentally and theoretically, that the
angle θ between the loading direction and the fiber direction has a significant effect on the values of Young's modulus and Poisson's ratio obtained
from a uniaxial tensile test. Also, it has been clearly demonstrated experimentally that the effect of θ on tensile strength is even more severe. In
many structural components involving uniaxial loading, the loading direction may not be precisely known or it may fluctuate during service use.
Thus, there is considerable interest in obtaining off-axis $(0° < \theta < 90°)$
tensile data, especially tensile strength.

As was pointed out by Ashkenazi and Pozdnyakov (1965), two problems involving off-axis specimens, such as the type shown schematically in
Fig. 8a, are: (1) the problem of cut fibers (which loads up the matrix ex-

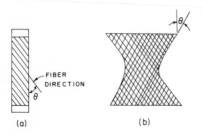

FIBER
DIRECTION

(a)   (b)

FIG. 8. Off-axis tensile specimens: (a)
straight-sided type; (b) bow-tie type.

cessively in shear, causing premature failure), and (2) the problem of obtaining a homogeneous stress state. They pointed out that use of a wide specimen alleviates the first problem, but aggravates the second one. Thus, they recommended that a specimen length/width ratio of at least three be used in order to obtain a nearly homogeneous, uniaxial stress state.

Hackman and Foye (1966) and Dickerson and Di Martino (1966) have described a bow-tie specimen in which the fibers are oriented in two directions, as shown in Fig. 8b. As they realized, this type of specimen goes to the other extreme by giving high strength values simulating an infinite-width specimen, since all of the fibers are loaded directly in the grip region of the specimen.

Pagano and Halpin (1968) demonstrated very vividly, both by simple analysis and by experiments on a very flexible filamentary composite (unidirectional nylon-reinforced rubber), that the type of end constraint plays a major role in off-axis tensile behavior of Fig. 8a type specimens. Specifically, they demonstrated that if the end grips are clamped with respect to rotation in the plane of the specimen, coupling between in-plane shear and tension can result in unusual deformations, as shown exaggerated in Fig. 9a. The work of Pagano and Halpin was continued in experiments by Wu and Thomas (1968) and Richards *et al.* (1969) and in finite-element analyses by Rizzo (1969) and by Richards *et al.* (1969). The latter investigators showed that satisfactory results can be achieved for $\theta = 45°$ by a specimen having a value of 12 for the ratio of the length between grips to the width.

Kreider (1969) carried out off-axis tensile tests on boron–aluminum composite material.

Recently Bert (1972b) carried out an elastic stability analysis which shows that it is theoretically possible to buckle a clamped-end, flat, off-axis specimen subjected to axial tension. The buckling is of the shear type and is caused by the shear produced by the tension-shear coupling discussed above. Although this analysis has not yet been verified quantitatively, it

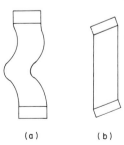

FIG. 9. Exaggerated effects of end constraints in off-axis tensile specimens; (a) grips restrained from in-plane rotation; (b) grips free for in-plane rotation.

(a)   (b)

is analogous to the tension buckling of end-constrained cylindrical shells discussed in Section II,C.

C. Ring and Tube Specimens

In the early days of development of glass-filament-wound reinforced plastic construction, it was recognized that it was not feasible to use flat specimens to measure the properties of such material. Therefore, the Naval Ordnance Laboratory (NOL) introduced ring-type specimens cut from filament-wound tubes; see Erickson *et al.* (1958). In the original work, tension loading was applied by means of a split-D loading device, shown schematically in Fig. 10a. Different variants of this basic idea have been described by Fried (1963). However, tensile strength values determined by split-D-loaded NOL rings were found to be significantly lower than burst strength of internally pressurized tubes; see, for instance, Dallas (1963). Thus, NOL and other laboratories developed means of internally pressurizing NOL rings; see Fig. 10b. This resulted in higher tensile strength values, as reported by Dallas (1963) and Channon and Rubin (1963).

Later it was shown by photoelastic studies that the poor performance of NOL rings under split-D loading was due to high flexural stresses developed in the specimen in the region between the two D's; see Dow (1970). To help alleviate this problem, he investigated a race-track ring specimen shown schematically in Fig. 10c. Although the bending stresses were appreciably reduced, this type of specimen has not been used very widely, probably because it is not a body of revolution and thus is not easily filament wound.

To avoid cut-fiber effects, NOL rings are generally hoop wound, i.e., the fibers are oriented circumferentially. To study width effects and to permit use of specimens with helical winding pattersns ($0° < \theta < 90°$), the Institute of Space and Aeronautical Sciences (ISAS) at the University of Tokyo originated the ISAS cylinder test, which still utilized the split-D loading method; see Fukui *et al.* (1965).

Hanley and Cole (1963) devised a means of internally pressurizing a tube specimen so that only uniaxial hoop stress is developed. They achieved

Fig. 10. Ring-type tensile specimens: (a) original NOL split-D loading device; (b) internal-pressure loading; (c) race-track specimen (Dow, 1970).

(a)   (b)   (c)

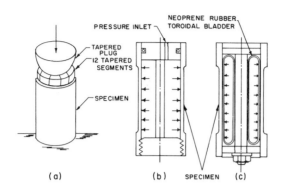

Fig. 11. Tubular-type circumferential tensile specimens: (a) segmented cylinder loading (Hanley and Cole, 1963); (b) hydraulic pressure with axially constrained ends; (c) bladder loading with axial constraint.

this by means of a segmented cylinder inside the tubular specimen; see Fig. 11a. Pure hoop loading was also achieved in a cylindrical specimen reported by Hom *et al.* (1966). In this method, shown schematically in Fig. 11b, an axial rod connected to end caps carries the axial loading due to internal pressure. In still another approach, reported by Burchett *et al.* (1969) and Bert and Guess (1972), the tubular specimen is loaded circumferentially by an internal neoprene bladder, which is restrained from axial movement at its ends, as shown schematically in Fig. 11c. The main advantage of this test method over that of the Fig. 11b type is that sealing problems are neatly avoided.

All of the test specimens described in this section so far are loaded in the circumferential direction. Of course, the simplest type of tension test to run on a tubular-configuration specimen is simply axial tension, used by Yurenka (1963), Hom *et al.* (1966), Feldman *et al.* (1966), and Bert and Guess (1972). Sidorin (1970) made a comparative study of elastic coefficients and tensile strengths obtained from flat and tubular axial-tension specimens and found that those obtained by the former method always were lower than those obtained by the latter.

Usually it is advantageous to use balanced ($\pm\theta$) winding patterns rather than a unidirectional ($+\theta$ only, where $0° < \theta < 90°$) wrap for several reasons:

(1) ease of manufacture by filament winding; otherwise costly hand layup is necessary,

(2) off-axis end-constraint effects, such as those discussed for flat specimens in Section II,B, can be significant, and

(3) buckling due to shear deformations resulting from shear coupling (cross elasticity) may occur, as discussed by Pagano *et al.* (1968).

III. Static Uniaxial Compression

Static uniaxial compression tests are much more difficult to conduct than static uniaxial tension tests, because of the necessity to prevent geometric buckling of the specimen.

A. Flat Plate and Bar Compressive Specimens

For composites, such as fabric-reinforced plastics, which are not so unidirectional, the main requirement in compression testing is to prevent specimen buckling. In the case of a thin, flat laminate, this is usually accomplished by multiple supports which prevent the laminate from buckling out of its plane. This approach was used by Nordby *et al.* (1964) and Romstad (1964b) and is shown schematically in Fig. 12. However, in the case of a highly unidirectional composite, such as unwoven fiber-reinforced composites, loaded in the fiber direction, premature failure occurs by localized "brooming" at the ends as shown in Fig. 13. Unless proper precautions are taken, this problem can occur in metal-matrix composites (Adsit and Forest, 1969) as well as in glass–epoxy (Romstad, 1964b) and boron–epoxy (Hadcock and Whiteside, 1969). It should be mentioned that end brooming even occurs in specimens with a reduced-width test section.

The use of side supports can be avoided by using a block- or bar-type specimen, rather than a plate. For example, Kreider (1969), Dow (1970), Park (1971), and Weidner (1971) all used blocks of either square or rectangular cross section, while Lenoe *et al.* (1969) and Weidner (1971) investigated circular-cross-section blocks. However, as shown by Kreider (1969) and Dow (1970), the block-type specimen is still plagued with the end-brooming problem.

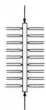

Fig. 12. Side supports to prevent out-of-plane buckling of thin-plate compressive specimens. Taken from Romstad (1964b).

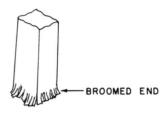

Fig. 13. Premature failure due to end brooming under compressive loading; adapted from Kreider (1969).

One means of reducing end-brooming action is to embed the ends of the specimen by casting them into either a polymer (Romstad, 1964b) or a low-melting-point alloy (Dow, 1970). In Romstad's specimens, the epoxy coating loosened and still permitted premature failure. However, Dow indicated that his "Cerrobend" potted ends were successful. Kritsuk and Emel'yanov (1969) used circular metal collars in connection with square-cross-section specimens.

A more successful method of eliminated brooming is to clamp the ends. Various types of clamping fixtures are shown schematically in Fig. 14.

In determining the compressive modulus and Poisson's ratio, it is desirable to use a straight-sided specimen, i.e., one without a reduced-width test section. For measuring the strain in the direction of loading, it is desirable to use either a compressometer or electrical-resistance strain gages. Testing-machine head travel is not a reliable measure of strain, because there may be some error due to end crushing of the specimen. When it is desired to measure compressive Poisson's ratio, space limitations usually make it mandatory to use electrical-resistance strain gages, either individually mounted or as a rosette.

For compressive strength determination, reduced-center-section specimens are often used in order to ensure that failure does not occur near the ends of the specimen. However, as shown by Fried and Winans (1963), this can induce a splitting-type failure analogous to the tensile type splitting shown in Fig. 4a.

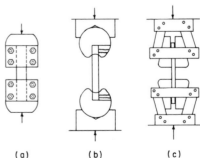

Fig. 14. Compressive-loading clamping fixtures: (a) Romstad (1964b); (b) Hadcock and Whiteside (1969); (c) wedge grip—Fried and Winans (1963).

(a)   (b)   (c)

Again we should mention Hill's (1968) combined tension–compressive test specimen in which the composite to be tested is bonded on the top and bottom of a thick metal substrate. Also, the uniaxial sandwich beam test was applied to determination of compressive properties by Waddoups (1968), Hoggatt (1969), Lantz (1969), and Suarez *et al.* (1972).

One of the advantages of the sandwich method for determination of compressive properties is its convenience for determining off-axis ($\pm\theta$) properties and transverse properties, as shown by Lantz (1969). Transverse compressive properties were determined by use of block specimens by Ekvall (1965) and Ishai *et al.* (1970b).

B. Ring and Tube Compressive Specimens

Two different means of loading an NOL-type ring (see Section II,C) in compression have been investigated by Fried (1963) and Fried and Winans (1963). One method is to use a pad-loading device which is called a reversed split-D device. This method was also used by Elkin (1963). It appears that this method would introduce even higher localized bending stresses than those induced by the split-D tension loading method. The other method uses an external strap, as shown schematically in Fig. 15.

Another means of loading NOL-type rings is to apply external hydraulic pressure, as described by Fried (1963) and by Elkin (1963). The major problem with this means of loading is general buckling of the specimen. One way to sidestep this problem is to compress the specimen uniformly at many different points around the circumference of the specimen. A compressive loading device of this type containing 72 rigid members was described by Prosen *et al.* (1963).

Perhaps the simplest type of compressive specimen to test is the axially compressed tube: It has been used successfully by Yurenka (1963), Card (1965), Hom *et al.* (1966), Feldman *et al.* (1966), and Bert and Guess (1972). The major precaution to be taken is to size the specimen short

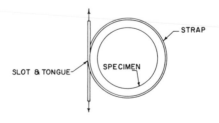

FIG. 15. External-strap loading device (Fried, 1963).

enough and with sufficient wall thickness to prevent general buckling of the specimen. Also care must be exercised to ensure that the specimen is loaded concentrically.

The axial compressive buckling stress (σ_{cr}) of a long, thin-walled, orthotropic circular cylindrical shell can be estimated from the following equation derived from the work of Dow and Rosen (1966):

$$\sigma_{cr} = (h/3R)\varphi(E_x E_y)^{1/2}(1 - \nu_{xy}\nu_{yx})^{-1/2} \tag{5}$$

where φ is a dimensionless factor, given by 1 or $\{2G_{xy}[1 + (\nu_{xy}\nu_{yx})^{1/2}]\}^{1/2}$ $\cdot (E_x E_y)^{-1/4}$, whichever is smaller; h is the wall thickness; R is the mean radius; E_x, E_y = axial and circumferential Young's moduli; and ν_{xy}, ν_{yx} = Poisson's ratios associated with loading in the axial and circumferential directions. For materials which are isotropic, $\varphi = 1$. However, most composites have a low in-plane shear modulus relative to $(E_x E_y)^{1/2}$ and thus have $\varphi < 1$.

IV. Static Uniaxial Bending (Long Beams)

A. Flat Flexural Specimens

The flexural moduli and flexural strengths of a laminated composite depend upon the lamination scheme. These properties also depend upon the number of plies in a much stronger manner than do the tensile properties. Thus, in a certain sense, the flexural properties are not fundamental properties of a composite material ply. Nevertheless, it has become customary to determine the flexural properties of composite materials as data of interest to designers.

The two most popular types of flexural tests are the three-point-load and four-point-load tests depicted schematically in Fig. 16. The three-point test is easier to conduct, yet it has the disadvantage of having high

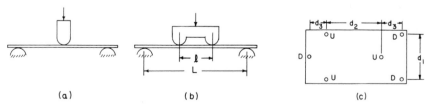

(a)   (b)   (c)

FIG. 16. Flexural loading configurations: (a) three-point-loaded beam; (b) four-point-loaded beam; (c) six-point-loaded plate. D = downward point load; U = upward point load.

thickness shear stresses† along its length (theoretically, uniformly distributed). This promotes premature failure due to the low interlaminar shear strength inherent in most composite materials. The advantage of the four-point test, when properly conducted so that both downward loads are the same, is that theoretically, it induces pure bending (no thickness shear) in the central portion between the two downward loading points. Thus, the only interlaminar shear stresses are induced in the outermost portions of the beam and they can be controlled by increasing the ratio of length l to length L, shown in Fig. 16b.

Customarily flexural strength is determined only for a parallel-laminated specimen. Furthermore, the quantity called flexural strength is not an actually measured stress value at failure. Rather, as pointed out by Romstad (1964a), it is a modulus of rupture, which is a fictitious value computed from the simple flexural stress formula, which is based on the assumption of a straight-line stress–strain relation:

$$\sigma_b = 6M_f/bh^2 \qquad\qquad (6)$$

where M_f = bending moment at failure determined from the failure load and specimen geometry, b = specimen width, and h = specimen depth. From a theoretical standpoint, Eq. (6) is incorrect because it assumes a straight-line stress–strain relation to failure and because it neglects any differences in ply properties (no problem if all plies are identical and have the same orientation, i.e., parallel ply).

In theory, increasing the span-to-depth ratio for a three-point-load specimen should increase the flexural strength (by decreasing the interlaminar shear stresses) until the failure mode changes from interlinear shear to flexural failure at the outer fibers, at which point there should be no further increase in flexural strength. This was verified by Romstad (1964a) who showed that a span-to-depth ratio of at least 32 is necessary to achieve flexural rather than interlaminar failure. However, the higher span-to-depth ratios resulted in much higher deflections, which in turn made it necessary to account for the horizontal forces developed at the supports. Thus, the uncorrected flexural strength values decreased at high span-to-depth ratios. For this reason, Romstad recommended a span-to-depth ratio of 24 for glass–epoxy composites. Romstad also found that the flexural strength increased with increasing nose radius at the midpoint load and recommended a minimum radius of $\frac{3}{4}$ inch. Recently similar work was done by Ogorkiewicz and Mucci (1971).

---

† The term thickness shear is used here, following the terminology of Yu (1959) for plates, rather than transverse shear. Here the term transverse is reserved for the in-plane direction which is perpendicular to the longitudinal direction.

Romstad found that the four-point flexural test required an even higher span-to-depth ratio to ensure outer-fiber flexural failure than for the three-point test. Furthermore, this conclusion held true even when he varied the ratio l/L from 0 (midpoint loading) to 0.44. Romstad showed that the amount of specimen overhang did not affect the measured values of flexural modulus and strength, as was expected.

Lenoe *et al.* (1969) investigated the effects of the following parameters on the flexural strength of boron–epoxy composite material: beam width, number of plies, test temperature, span-to-depth ratio, load-point contact radius, and loading type (three vs. four point).

Rothman and Molter (1969) measured the flexural modulus and strength of graphite–epoxy composite material using four-point loading. They found that more repeatable results were obtained for flexural modulus based upon axial strain-gage readings rather than beam deflection readings. Hammant (1971) discussed advantages of four-point loading.

The problems associated with flexural testing of off-axis fiber-reinforced composites were demonstrated experimentally by Halpin *et al.* (1969) and treated theoretically by Whitney and Dauksys (1970). The shear coupling in such a specimen manifests itself as a bending–twisting coupling or warping effect, which tends to partially lift off the specimen at the supports. However, if one suppresses the lift-off by using double knife edges at each support, additional twisting moments are induced in the specimen. Fortunately, as shown by Ishai *et al.* (1970a) and Lavengood and Ishai (1970), it is possible to minimize the lift-off effect by using a sufficiently narrow specimen and a high span-to-depth ratio.

All of the specimens mentioned in this section have been beams, rather than plates. Usually it is possible to obtain narrow strips, oriented longitudinally and transversely, from sheet material. However, if this is not possible, such as when one wants to leave a plate intact, there is a flexural test for plates: the six-point loading test used by Bergstrasser (1927); see Fig. 16c. This test has been used by Thielemann (1950) and by Hearmon and Adams (1952) for plywood and by Witt *et al.* (1953) for glass–resin laminates. This test is essentially a plate version of the four-point-loaded beam test and supposedly induces pure bending moment in the central portion of the plate.

Generally dial gages, measuring either relative deflection or displacements from a fixed plane, have been used with the six-point-load test. However, Beckett *et al.* (1963) found large discrepancies when this technique was applied to isotropic plates. To remedy this, they made two suggestions: (1) use of a "curvature gage," which measures relative displacement in a small region, and (2) use of a dimension d_2 in Fig. 16c larger than d_1.

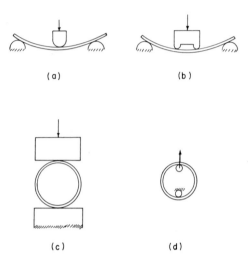

Fig. 17. Ways of experimentally determining the circumferential-direction flexural properties of a filament-wound composite.

B. Curved-Beam and Tube Flexural Specimens

As mentioned previously in Section II,C, it is not convenient to make flat specimens from filament-wound composites. Thus, if the actual part is of this type of construction and is subjected to flexural loading in service usage, it is desirable to have means of accomplishing flexural tests on curved specimens. One such method, suggested by Fried (1963), is to cut circumferential specimens from a filament-wound tube and test them in either three- or four-point loading as shown schematically in Fig. 17a and b. All of the precautions mentioned in Section IV,A apply here.

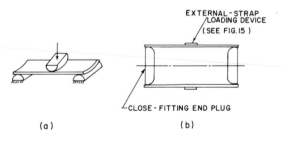

Fig. 18. Methods of determining the axial-direction flexural properties of a filament-wound composite.

Fig. 19. Unsymmetrical axial bending of a filament-wound tube (bending takes place in vertical
plane).

Still another way to obtain the circumferential flexural strength is to
load a complete ring, cut from a filament-wound tube, as shown in Fig.
17c and d. The strength values obtained from specimens of the Fig. 17c
and d types would be expected to be somewhat different than those obtained by specimens of the Fig. 17a and b types. This difference is related
to the circumferential residual stresses built into the composite during
manufacture, but which are at least partially relieved by cutting the Fig.
17a and b type specimens.

The axial flexural strength of the wall of the filament-wound structure
can be measured by testing a beam specimen cut axially from the filament-
wound tube, as suggested by Fried (1963). Such a specimen, shown in
Fig. 18a, is essentially the same as the straight specimens discussed in
Section IV,A, except that it is necessary to take precautions of matching
the tube wall curvature at the loading points.

Perhaps a more satisfactory way of measuring the axial bending strength
of the wall is to use a long filament-wound tube loaded as shown in Fig.
18b.

An entirely different type of axial bending of a tubular specimen is unsymmetrical bending, i.e., bending of the whole tube as a beam (see Fig.
19). This type of specimen was suggested for filament-wound tubes by
Fried (1963) and used by Cervelli (1966) in connection with evaluation of
glass–epoxy filament-wound tubes for aircraft-landing-gear struts.

V. Static Shear

There are more diversified types of specimens in use for determining the
shear moduli and shear strengths than for any other properties; see Adams
and Thomas (1967) and Prosen (1969).

Part of the reason for the diversity of specimen types is that there are
three different kinds of shear loadings:

(1) *in-plane* shear, in which the shear distortion takes place entirely in
the plane of the composite material sheet;

(2) *twisting* shear, in which the cross section of the composite (in either
bar or thin-sheet form) undergoes a twisting-type shear deformation; and

(3) *thickness* shear, sometimes called transverse shear or interlaminar
shear (in the case of a laminate), in which the composite material sheet
undergoes shearing deformation in a plane normal to the plane of the sheet.

In the following subsections, the various types of shear specimens are grouped according to the kind of shear loading which is applied to an element of composite material. However, this is somewhat arbitrary, especially in the case of the torsion-tube specimen, in which the entire cross section of the specimen is subjected to a torque (twisting moment), yet an element of material undergoes a shear deformation in its tangential plane.

It is strongly cautioned that shear tests on angle-ply laminates (alternating $\pm\theta$ orientations) in which individual plies are oriented at $+45°$ and $-45°$ to the shearing plane *cannot* be used to yield shear modulus data for the individual plies (cf. Bert and Guess, 1972).

A. *In-Plane Shear*

1. *Panel Shear (Picture-Frame Loading Fixture)*

The specimen for this panel shear test consists of a thin, flat, square panel to which stiff members are bonded or bolted to each edge. The edge members may or may not be pinned, but they form a four-bar mechanism.

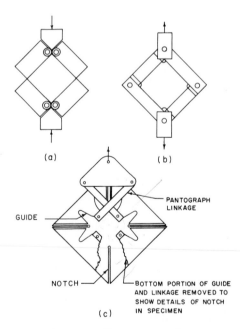

FIG. 20. Various versions of panel-shear test: (a) compression loaded (Youngquist and Kuenzi, 1961); (b) tension loaded (Dastin *et al.*, 1969); (c) modification due to Dickerson and DiMartino (1966).

Then when the four-bar linkage is subjected to either compression or tension loading at diagonally opposite corners, as shown in Fig. 20a or b, the panel is supposed to be subjected to a pure shear state of stress in the plane of the panel (Penton, 1960).

Bryan (1961) made a photoelastic investigation of the stress distribution in the panel-shear specimen and found that the stress distribution deviated substantially from pure shear. Thus, the method is not appropriate for measuring the in-plane shear *modulus*. However, Bryan showed that at the critical region, which is along the edge, the stress state was essentially uniform pure shear and thus he recommended that this should be an accurate method for determining in-plane shear *strength*. Recently photoelastic studies of panel shear specimens of composite materials were made by Liber *et al.* (1971).

Other investigators who have discussed the panel shear test include Youngquist and Kuenzi (1961), Hennessey *et al.* (1965), Adams and Thomas (1967), Dastin *et al.* (1969), and Hadcock and Whiteside (1969). Dickerson and DiMartino (1966) used a modified form of the panel-shear test, shown in Fig. 20c.

The panel should be sized to avoid buckling. However, the buckling load depends upon the shear modulus, which is the quantity being measured. Thus, in sizing the panel, it is necessary to use an estimated value for G_{LT}. Unfortunately, it appears that no general graphical results are available for the buckling of a clamped, square orthotropic plate with clamped edges. Ashton and Whitney (1970) gave an approximate expression, but they showed that it was very unconservative, i.e., it gave buckling-load values which were too high. Thus, it appears that it is necessary to use analytical results for the simply supported case, which would be a conservative approximation of the actual case. The following expression for the applied diagonal force (either tension or compression), necessary to buckle the panel, has been adapted from recent work by Davenport and Bert (1972):

$$P_{cr} = 1.414 \ \pi^2 K D_y / a \qquad (7)$$

where a = length of panel side, D_y = transverse flexural rigidity of the panel itself, and K is a dimensionless buckling coefficient which depends upon D_x/D_y and $\nu_{xy} + (2 D_{xy}/D_y)$ as shown in Table V.

2. Shear Calculated from Tension Data in Conjunction with Transformation Equations

This method of shear calculation was originated by Werren and Gish (1957) and rediscovered by Greszczuk (1966b), Tsai (1967), and Petit

TABLE V

SHEAR BUCKLING COEFFICIENTS FOR SIMPLY SUPPORTED SQUARE
PLATES OF VARIOUS COMPOSITE MATERIALS

Material	D_y/D_x	$\nu_{xy} + (2\,D_{xy}/D_y)$	K
Longitudinal glass cloth–epoxy	0.958	0.424	7.0
Longitudinal boron–epoxy	0.1106	0.950	22.0
Transverse boron–epoxy	9.04	0.704	2.8
Longitudinal graphite–epoxy	0.040	1.248	50.0
Transverse graphite–epoxy	25.0	0.0499	2.0

(1969). From measurements of the uniaxial tension moduli associated with orientations of 0°, 45° (or some other acute angle), and 90°, the following equation is used to calculate G_{LT}:

$$1/G_{LT} = (2\,\nu_{LT}/E_L) + 8\,[(1/E_{11})$$
$$- (m^4/E_L) - (n^4/E_T)](1 - \cos 4\theta)^{-1} \qquad (8)$$

where E_L, E_T, E_{11} are the Young's moduli associated with loading at angles of 0°, 90°, θ with respect to the fiber direction; ν_{LT} is the Poisson's ratio associated with loading at 0°; $m = \cos\theta$; and $n = \sin\theta$.

In the derivation of Eq. (8), it has been tacitly assumed that the reciprocal relation, Eq. (1), holds and that the properties in tension and compression are the same. As discussed in Section I, neither of these assumptions holds in all cases. Therefore, it would be advisable to use the following equation, which is free from these assumptions:

$$1/G_{LT} = (\nu_{LT}^{(+)}/E_L^{(+)}) + (\nu_{TL}^{(-)}/E_T^{(-)})$$
$$+ 8\,[(1/E_{11}^{(+)}) - (m^4/E_L^{(+)} - (n^4/E_T^{(-)})]$$
$$\times (1 - \cos 4\theta)^{-1} \qquad (9)$$

where the superscripts (+) and (−) refer to tension and compression, respectively.

Of course, in testing the 0° < θ < 90° specimen, all of the precautions mentioned in Section II,B apply.

In addition to the investigators mentioned above, this method has been applied to glass–resin by Konstantinov and Strelyaev (1969) and to boron–aluminum by Kreider (1969).

Although this method has been used to predict values of shear strength as well as shear modulus (Werren and Gish, 1957), current practice is to use it for the latter purpose only.

3. Rail Shear (In-Plane)

The rail shear type of test has been widely used to measure the thickness shear properties of various kinds of shear-flexible sandwich core materials. However, it appears that the first suggestion to use it for determining *in-plane* shear properties was made by Hennessey *et al.* (1965). Apparently the first reported experiments of this type were those of Hadcock and Whiteside (1969) on boron–epoxy. Later Balaban and Jackson (1971) used it on glass–epoxy. The test is shown schematically in Fig. 21.

Whitney *et al.* (1971) conducted an extensive theoretical stress analysis of this type of test and concluded that it is a valid means of experimentally determining G_{LT}, provided that the length/width ratio is at least 10. However, for determining the in-plane shear strength, they found that an additional condition is necessary: the major Poisson's ratio with respect to the specimen edges should be less than unity. If this condition is not met, as in a $\pm 45°$ laminate made from unwoven (unidirectional) material, severe shear stress concentration is developed, which results in an excessively low value for the shear stregnth.

As in the case of the picture-frame-loaded panel shear test (Section V,A,1), shear buckling could be a problem, unless it is prevented by means of stabilizing bars, which were used by Balaban and Jackson (1971). The shear stress at which shear buckling occurs in a long, clamped-edge, orthotropic plate can be predicted from the following equation, due to Seydel (1933):

$$\tau_{cr} = (4\beta/hb^2)D_x^{1/4}D_y^{3/4} \tag{10}$$

where b = distance between inside edges of rails, D_x and D_y are the flexural rigidities respectively parallel and perpendicular to the rails, h = plate thickness, and β is a dimensionless coefficient which depends upon the dimensionless parameter γ:

$$\gamma = (D_x D_y)^{1/2}(D_{xy} + 2D_s)^{-1} \tag{11}$$

which was assumed to be greater than unity in writing the form of Eq.

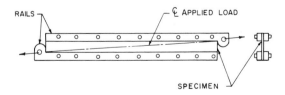

FIG. 21. Rail in-plane shear test.

TABLE VI

MATERIAL PARAMETERS γ FOR SELECTED UNIDIRECTIONAL COMPOSITES
(PROPERTIES FROM TABLE IV)

Composite	Parameter γ
S glass–epoxy	1.606
Narmco 5505 boron–epoxy	2.77
Thornel 50-E-798 epoxy	3.02
Morganite II-2387 epoxy	3.17

(10). In this equation, D_{xy} = Poisson flexural rigidity and D_s = twisting stiffness.

For a parallel-ply plate, we can rewrite Eq. (11) in terms of the engineering elastic properties as follows:

$$\gamma = (E_x/E_y)^{1/2}[\nu_{xy} + 2(1 - \nu_{xy}\nu_{yx})(G_{xy}/E_y)]^{-1} \qquad (12)$$

Seydel presented values of β for selected values of γ over a wide range. However, for isotropic materials $\gamma = 1$ and even for advanced composites, such as unidirectional boron–epoxy and graphite–epoxy, γ does not exceed 4, as shown in Table VI. Thus, the range $1 \leq \gamma \leq 5$, as plotted in Fig. 22, should be sufficient for use in sizing in-plane rail shear specimens to avoid buckling.

It is interesting to note that the parameter γ, Eq. (12), is the same when the fibers are oriented parallel to the loading rails as when they are oriented perpendicular to the rails. However, as can be seen from the stronger dependence on D_y than D_x in Eq. (10), the buckling stress is much higher when the fibers are oriented perpendicular to the rails (i.e., the role of D_x and D_y interchanged).

4. Torsion Tube

Probably the most widely used in-plane shear specimen in use today is the torsion tube. It has been used for filament-wound glass–epoxy by Card (1965), Feldman *et al.* (1966), Cervelli (1966), Grinius (1966, 1967), Dexter (1967), Sidorin (1967), and Wall and Card (1971). Also, it was used by Bert *et al.* (1969a) on glass cloth–epoxy, Grinius (1966, 1967) on filament-wound boron–epoxy, and Bert and Guess (1972) on filament-wound carbon–carbon.

The concept of this test is very simple: a thin-walled circular cross-section tube is subjected to a torque about its longitudinal axis. This subjects the wall of the specimen to a pure shear stress which is uniform around the

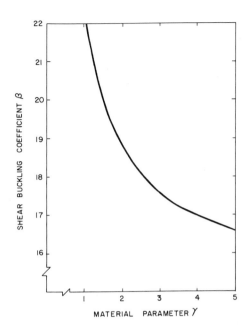

FIG. 22. Effect of material parameter γ on the buckling coefficient for a clamped, orthotropic strip subjected to in-plane shear. Based on numerical results of Seydel (1933), as given by Ashton and Whitney (1970).

circumference and along the length of the specimen. Since the wall thickness is small compared to the mean radius of the tube the shear strain gradient through the thickness is negligible.

Whitney (1967) made a theoretical stress analysis of this specimen and showed that for lamination schemes other than symmetrical (see Ashton et al., 1969), it is not possible to obtain sufficient data to determine the shear properties. Thus, it is recommended that only symmetric layups be used in conjunction with this test. Later Whitney et al. (1971) stated that the torsion tube is the most desirable shear test specimen from an applied mechanics standpoint.

Considerable care should be taken to ensure that only pure torque is applied to the specimen. To prevent the development of bending moments, the specimen must be mounted concentrically. To avoid inducing axial force as the specimen undergoes shearing deformation, the specimen must be free to move axially.

The instrumentation required is an accurate means for determining the applied torque and electrical-resistance strain gages to determine the shear strain. Since an electrical-resistance strain gage cannot measure shear strain directly, one must use a strain gage at 45° to the tube axis, from which the shear strain can be calculated by use of the Mohr strain circle.

To prevent failure of the bond between the specimen and the end attachment through which the torque is applied, it is preferable to use a long adhesive joint bonded on both the inside and outside surfaces of the tube.

To avoid buckling of the specimen, it is necessary to provide either sufficient wall thickness or keep the length short. Bert *et al.* (1969a) carried out a limited number of tests which indicated that the measured values of shear modulus and shear strength were unaffected by specimen length, provided of course that the length was short enough to prevent buckling. The critical shear stress at which buckling occurs in a clamped-clamped, parallel-ply, orthotropic tube of moderate length may be predicted from the following equation, derived from the analysis by Simitses (1967):

$$\tau_{\mathrm{cr}} = \tfrac{1}{3} E_x^{3/8} [E_y/(1 - \nu_{xy}\nu_{yx})]^{5/8} h^{5/4} L^{-1/2} R^{-3/4} \tag{13}$$

where E_x and E_y are the Young's moduli in the axial (x) and circumferential (y) directions, ν_{xy} and ν_{yx} are the Poisson's ratios due to loading in the x and y directions, h = wall thickness, L = clamped length, and R = mean radius.

Although Eq. (13) was originally intended for moderate-length shells, it gives a conservative prediction for short-length shells. Inspection of Eq. (13) shows that circumferentially wrapped tubes ($E_y > E_x$) are less susceptible to torsional buckling than those with the fibers oriented axially.

5. Sandwich Cross Beam and Sandwich Plate

This test, shown schematically in Fig. 23, is essentially a sandwich beam version of the plate twist test described in Section V,B,1. However, the composite material facings are thin relative to the honeycomb core and thus are located at a large distance, relative to the facing thickness, from the midplane of the sandwich plate. Thus, the composite material is probably subjected to more of an in-plane shear than a twisting type.

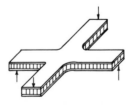

Fɪɢ. 23. Cross-beam sandwich test (Waddoups, 1968).

This test has been applied to boron–epoxy material (Waddoups, 1968; Petit, 1969; Lenoe, 1970; Shockey, 1971) and to graphite–epoxy (Petit, 1969).

A variation of this idea is actually to use a sandwich plate subjected to a plate twist test. Thus, the specimen would look just like the one shown in Fig. 24a, except that the plate would have thin composite material facings separated by a honeycomb core.

B. Twisting Shear

1. Plate Twist

The plate twist test configuration is shown schematically in Fig. 24a. It has been in use for some time, having been used in the early 1950s to determine the twisting stiffnesses for plywood by Thielemann (1950) and Hearmon and Adams (1952) and for glass–reinforced-plastic laminates by Witt *et al.* (1953).

Assuming that the plate deflects into a saddle shape, the twisting stiff-

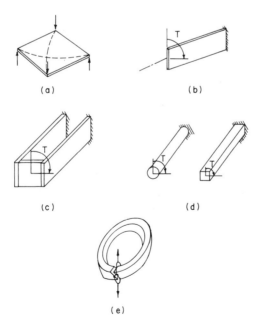

FIG. 24. Types of twisting shear specimens: (a) plate; (b) strip; (c) double strip; (d) round or square bars; (e) split ring loaded out of plane.

ness can be calculated from the plate deflection. In fact, the comments on the six-point-loaded plate test in Section IV,A apply equally well to the present test.

This test has been used by numerous investigators in the 1960s: Hennessey *et al.* (1965), Grinius (1966, 1967), Sidorin (1967), Konstantinov and Strelyaev (1969), and Rothman and Molter (1969).

In a geometrically nonlinear (large-deflection) analysis of a homogeneous, isotropic plate in plate twisting, Foye (1967) showed that a bifurcation type of instability occurs at corner deflections of about five times the plate thickness. He also showed that the linear analysis traditionally used to reduce test data can be erroneous by 30% at corner deflections of only twice the plate thickness. Presumably, analogous results would be obtained in the case of an orthotropic plate, which has not yet been analyzed in this manner.

In linear analyses, Whitney (1967, 1968) made theoretical investigations of the applicability of this test to plates with various simple lamination schemes.

2. Torsion Strip

Apparently this relatively new test was first suggested as a material test by Dai (1965) in connection with cross-rolled beryllium sheet. Its analytical basis was further investigated by Semenov (1968), Lempriere *et al.* (1969), and Shlenskii (1970). Recently it was applied to testing of unidirectional glass–epoxy by Bracco *et al.* (1971) and Spies and de Jong (1971).

Figure 24b shows schematically the specimen and loading. Recently Slepetz (1971) suggested a double-strip test, depicted in Fig. 24c, which has not yet been evaluated.

3. Torsion Bar

Although the twisting of a round bar has been a standard way of determining the shear modulus of metals, apparently it was not used for composites until 1967 (Adams *et al.*, 1967; Adams and Thomas, 1967). They investigated S glass–epoxy, using both molded rods and rods machined from plate. This type of specimen, shown schematically in Fig. 24d, was also mentioned by Semenov (1968) and Konstantinov and Strelyaev (1969). It was used by Lenoe *et al.* (1969) and Lenoe (1970) on boron-epoxy and by Hanna and Steingiser (1969), Novak (1969), and Hancox and Wells (1970) on graphite–epoxy.

The cross section may either be round or square, the latter being more convenient when the rod is machined from plate. In reducing the test data, care must be taken to use the correct equations from anisotropic elasticity theory (Lekhnitskii, 1963), which are quite different from the isotropic ones except when the fibers are oriented parallel to the axis of the specimen when the equations coincide.

4. Split Ring Loaded Out of Plane

This test, originated by Greszczuk (1968, 1969), is shown schematically in Fig. 24e. This test is intended for use on filament-wound materials. It has the following advantages:

(1) It does not require as much material as does a torsion-tube test.

(2) Loading is easily accomplished on a universal testing machine.

(3) The instrumentation is a simple linear dial indicator to measure the relative out-of-plane displacement between the two loading points.

The disadvantages of this testing method are:

(1) It cannot be used to determine the torsional strength, since the ring cross section is loaded by a combination of torque and bending moment.

(2) Since about 5 to 16% of the out-of-plane deflection is due to bending action, it is necessary to know the circumferential bending stiffness (or the corresponding Young's modulus) in order to reduce the split-ring load-deflection data to shear modulus. However, since bending makes such a small contribution to the total deflection, a large error in Young's modulus introduces only a small error in measured shear modulus.

Originally, this test was intended to be used for only orthotropic rings, i.e., those made from either hoop-wound, axial layup, or cross-ply layup. However, by using the results of anisotropic torsion bar theory (Lekhnit-skii, 1963), Guess and Bert (1971) extended the data-reduction procedure so that it is applicable to many-layered, bihelically-wound ($\pm\theta$) rings. Such rings can be cut from tubes made by conventional filament winding. Guess and Bert checked out the method on S glass–epoxy composite by comparing the resulting values of shear modulus with those obtained from torsion-tube tests. Good agreement was obtained and later the method was used in characterization of filament-wound carbon–carbon composite (Bert and Guess, 1972).

C. Thickness Shear

1. Block and Notched Specimens

The background for block and notched specimens goes back to methods developed at the Forest Products Laboratory for measuring interlaminar shear strengths of wood and plywood, as reported by Youngquist and Kuenzi (1961), for instance. For unidirectional glass–resin composite, Romstad (1964c) evaluated the use of the two types of block shear depicted schematically in Fig. 25a and b, as well as the types of notched shear specimens shown in Fig. 25c–g. He obtained good agreement between the block single and double shear specimens only for the case of longitudinal thickness shear strength. The various notched shear specimens were subjected to considerable scatter due to the inability to achieve adequate control of critical notch parameters. Thus, Romstad concluded that the shear strength measured by using any of the specimen types shown in Fig. 25a–g was lower than the shear strength under pure shear conditions.

Davis (1964) used the types of specimens shown in Figs. 25c and d and 26a and b in evaluating unidirectional glass–resin composites. As in the case of Romstad's work, Davis found considerable variability from one type of specimen to another as well as with the same type of specimen. In further work on glass–resin composites, Dexter (1967) used the Fig. 25c type specimen, while Jacobs (1967) used the Fig. 25f type specimen.

In connection with more advanced composites, Elkin *et al.* (1969) and

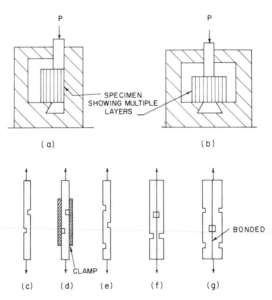

FIG. 25. Selected types of thickness-shear specimens: (a) block single shear; (b) Johnson block double shear; (c) staggered two-notch (unclamped); (d) staggered two-notch (clamped); (e) staggered three-notch; (f) double two-notch; (g) double three-notch (bonded). Adapted from Romstad (1964c).

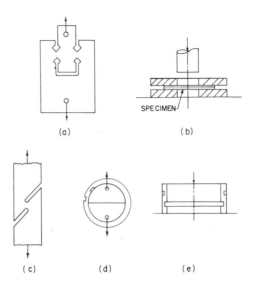

Fig. 26. Additional thickness-shear specimens: (a) double shear (Davis, 1964); (b) punch shear (Davis, 1964); (c) slanted two-notch (Kreider, 1969); (d) circumferential-thickness shear test on notched ring, loaded by split-D device (Fried, 1963); (e) axial thickness shear test on notched tube (Yurenka, 1963).

Hancox and Wells (1970) used the Fig. 25c type specimen for graphite–resin composites, while Kreider (1969) used the Fig. 26c type specimen for boron–aluminum.

The tubular or ring versions of the Fig. 25c specimens are shown in Fig. 26d and e.

2. *Short-Beam Shear*

The short-beam shear test has been the most widely used for shear testing of composite materials. Essentially this is the same test as the bending test discussed in Section IV, except that here the specimen is sized with a low ratio of span length to beam depth, to induce a thickness shear ("interlaminar") failure. The various kinds of specimens used include:

(1) *three-point-loading straight beam*; see Fig. 16a; used by Davis (1964), Romstad (1964c), Dexter (1967), Hanna and Steingiser (1969), Hoggatt (1969), Lenoe *et al.* (1969), Rothman and Molter (1969), Sattar and Kellogg (1969), Hancox and Wells (1970), Daniels *et al.* (1971), Mullin and Knoell (1970);

FIG. 27. Five-point-loading short-beam shear test.

(2) *four-point-loading straight beam*; see Fig. 16b; used by Dexter (1967) and Mullin and Knoell (1970);

(3) *five-point-loading straight beam*; see Fig. 27; proposed by Langley (1968) for measuring thickness-shear stiffness;

(4) *three-point-loading curved beam*; see Fig. 17a; used by Roskos and Pflederer (1963), Elkin (1965), and Dexter (1967).

Of the above investigations, the extensive experimental program on boron–epoxy carried out by Lenoe *et al.* (1969) was especially good. However, in spite of the large body of research carried out on this type of test to date, it still cannot be considered to be a very valid test for material characterization purposes, although it may be useful for quality control.

3. Rail Shear (Thickness)

As previously mentioned in Section V,A,3, the rail shear method has been used for measuring the shear stiffness of adhesives and sandwich core materials (Youngquist and Kuenzi, 1961). However, it has only recently been applied to thin, laminated, filamentary composites by Zabora and Bell (1971). They called it the slip-plane shear test and have applied it to parallel-ply, cross-ply, and ±45° boron–epoxy laminates.

VI. Static Multiaxial Loading

The materials in structural components are often subjected to multiaxial loading in service. However, in contrast to the extensive experimental data on biaxial-stress behavior of isotropic aerospace structural alloys (Bert *et al.*, 1966), there is a dearth of information on composite materials under these conditions. Perhaps this is surprising, since the first large-scale structural application of modern composite material (filament-wound glass–resin) was for closed-end internal-pressure vessels. The first vessels of this type were small gas-storage bottles for aircraft applications. This small-scale application was followed by intensive development of glass–epoxy and the associated filament-winding process for solid-propellant rocket-motor casings (cf. Rosato and Grove, 1964, and Bert and Hyler, 1966). Although many burst tests were conducted on subscale and full-scale pressure vessels in the Polaris missile program, many of the failures occurred at discontinuities present in practical casings, i.e., end fittings, nozzle ports, ignitor bosses, etc. Also, the stress distribution and even the multiaxial stress state depend very much upon the meridional shape of the vessel, including the end domes. Thus, very little data on composite *material* behavior under multiaxial loading were obtained.

In isotropic materials uniaxial loading results in the same behavior regardless of the loading orientation in the material, by definition. Of course, in practice there are some small differences due to orientation, i.e., rolling effects, etc., especially in the plastic range. In contrast, filamentary composite materials, due to their inherent anisotropic nature on a macroscopic basis, behave quite differently at different loading orientations (θ) with respect to the fiber direction (L). This difference in behavior is due to the fact that uniaxial loading at an acute angle θ induces both biaxial normal stresses and a shear stress with respect to the LT coordinate system, which is the important one for composite material behavior. Thus, in filamentary composites, a type of multiaxial loading is induced even in the off-axis uniaxial loading mentioned in Sections II,B and III,A. However, this is a limited kind of biaxial loading in these two respects:

(1) The biaxial normal stresses are always of the same sign, i.e., either both tension or both compression.

(2) There is always some concomitant shear stress. In other words, the ratios σ_T/σ_L and σ_{LT}/σ_L cannot be varied independently (σ_L, σ_T = normal stresses parallel and transverse to the filaments, σ_{LT} = shear stress on the LT plane).

A great variety of theoretical and semiempirical equations for predicting the strength of filamentary composites under multiaxial stress conditions have been proposed. These are reviewed extensively in this treatise by Wu in "Empirical Strength Criteria," Chapter 9 of Volume 2, by Chamis in "Micromechanics Strength Theories," Chapter 3 of Volume 5, and Vicario and Toland in "Failure Criteria and Failure Analysis of Composite Structural Components," Chapter 2 of Volume 7. Thus, it suffices to mention here only these two facts concerning unidirectional filamentary composites:

(1) The shear strength is an independent material property and the behavior also depends upon the *sign* of the shear stress (i.e., the direction of the applied shear stress, see Pagano and Chou, 1969).

(2) Most of the equations proposed predict very nearly the same

strength behavior under the kind of biaxial stress state produced by off-axis uniaxial loading.

In view of the above considerations, it is clear that there is a need for experimental means of applying more general multiaxial stress states, especially those in which the stress components σ_L, σ_T, and σ_{LT} can be varied independently. Various approaches for achieving such stress states are described below.

A. Plate-Type Biaxial-Loading Specimens

Reiterating what was stated previously, if one is concerned with a flat-panel structure, it is desirable to conduct tests on plate specimens. Apparently the first biaxial-stress tests on composites in a plate configuration were those reported by Grimes *et al.* (1967). A schematic diagram of their specimen and method of loading is shown in Fig. 28a. Unfortunately, since

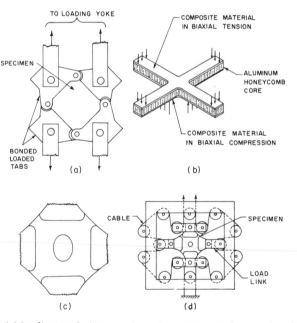

FIG. 28.   Biaxial-loading techniques using plate-type specimens: (a) Southwest Research Institute (Grimes *et al.*, 1967); (b) General Dynamics–IIT Research Institute (Waddoups, 1968); (c) University of Okalahoma specimen; (d) loading device for specimen c (Bert *et al.*, 1969a).

there was no reduced-thickness region, all of the specimens failed at the edge.

Another means of conducting a biaxial-stress test on a plate specimen is to use the sandwich cross-beam specimen discussed previously in Section V,A,5, except that now the loadings are different, as shown in Fig. 28b. This approach was reported by Waddoups (1968) and Shockey (1971). It has the advantage of being capable of determining strength under biaxial compression loading and a combination of tension and compression, as well as biaxial tension. Some disadvantages of this method are: (1) stress concentrations at the corner fillets, (2) possible effects of the core-to-facing bond on the strength of the composite material facing, and (3) no reduced-thickness test section.

A third kind of plate-type composite material specimen for determining biaxial strength is a specially designed specimen with a reduced-thickness test section and loaded by means of four bonded loading tabs, as shown in Fig. 28c. This concept was originated by Bert et al. (1969a, b). A specially designed loading fixture with cables operating over sixteen pulleys was used to provide biaxial tension loads of either 1:1 or 1:2 ratio; see the schematic diagram in Fig. 28d. The major features of this loading fixture are its reliability and elimination of hydraulic control problems which would have existed if the loads had been applied by hydraulic rams. The major disadvantage of this setup is the limitation of only two biaxial-stress ratios (1:1 and 1:2), both in tension only.

B. Shell-Type Specimens

Oblate spheroidal shells have been used in burst tests of filament-wound composite materials, cf. Vogt et al. (1966). However, the circular cylindrical shell configuration has been used much more extensively, cf. Ely (1965), Protasov and Kopnov (1965), Vogt et al. (1966), Herring et al. (1969), Jones (1969), Weng (1969), Sidorin (1970), Cole et al. (1971), Bert and Guess (1972), and Whitney et al. (1972).

Perhaps the first theoretical analysis of composite material tubes under combined tension or compression, internal pressure, and torque was due to Whitney and Halpin (1968). Using Donnell's approximate shell theory, they concluded that a uniform stress state can be achieved if the specimen is symmetrically laminated and if one end is free to rotate. Later, using both classical and finite-element analyses, Vicario and Rizzo (1970) studied the effect of tube length and showed that the effects of end constraint are limited to small regions near the ends of the tube. They concluded that the Whitney and Halpin analysis was sufficiently accurate provided that wall thickness/diameter < 0.05 and length/diameter > 3.

More recently Pagano and Whitney (1970), Pagano (1971), and Whitney (1971) have presented various theoretical analyses which bear upon the geometric design of tubular specimens. Their recommendations can be summarized as follows:

(1) It is practically impossible to come anywhere near to achieving a uniform strain distribution in a tubular specimen laid up from helically oriented unidirectional material; thus, such specimens should be avoided.

(2) For a symmetric, orthotropic laminate, which is approximated by a $\pm\theta$ filament-wound cylinder having many layers (say ≥ 6), it is possible to achieve a nearly uniform strain distribution provided that the mean diameter/wall thickness ratio is 20 or more.

(3) A specimen length of two times the mean diameter plus the desired gage length is recommended.

(4) Under certain conditions, ordinary thin-shell theory is not sufficiently accurate to make reasonable predictions of the strain distribution within a specimen. For an extensive discussion of the various composite material shell theories, the reader is referred to Bert (1974b).

Using a refined shell theory, Bert and Guess (1972) presented equations for reduction of experimental data from tubular specimens made of material which is not assumed *a priori* to be symmetric, i.e., Eq. (1) does not necessarily hold. Applying their equations to test data of a filament-wound carbon–carbon composite, they found that there was a statistically significant difference between ν_{LT}/E_L and ν_{TL}/E_T, i.e., Eq. (1) did not hold.

VII. Systematized Experimental Programs for Complete Characterization of Static Properties

Apparently among the first attempts to develop programs to characterize static properties completely was the work of Hearmon and Adams (1952) and Witt *et al.* (1953). They used plate bending tests (Section IV,A) at orientations of 0° and 90° to determine E_L, E_T, and ν_{LT}. However, it should be pointed out that these were all obtained in flexure, rather than in the generally more desirable direct tension. The above investigators used the plate twist test (Section V,B,1), with the fiber direction parallel to one set of plate edges, to measure the shear modulus G_{LT}. It is noted that this is a measure of the twisting shear modulus, rather than the generally more desirable in-plane shear modulus.

Tsai and Springer (1963) suggested a simplification in the procedure mentioned above in that their technique requires a total of only two tests, using a total of only two specimens, rather than the three tests using three specimens in the procedure previously described. Tsai's two tests were: (1) long-beam bending at an orientation of *either* 0° or 90°, (2) plate twisting at an orientation of 22.5°. The first test obtains either E_L or E_T directly, and the second provides sufficient information when used in conjunction with E_L or E_T, to obtain the remaining elastic properties. Later Tsai (1965) modified the technique to consist of one test on each of these three specimens: (1) *either* 0° or 90° long-beam (not plate) bending to obtain E_L or E_T, (2) plate twisting at 0° to obtain G_{LT}, and (3) plate twisting at 45° from which the remaining elastic properties can be obtained. The major improvement of Tsai's approach is in terms of saving material, since beam and plate twist specimens use considerably less material than plate bending specimens. However, his approach still suffered from the fact that the normal stress properties obtained were flexural and the shear modulus was twisting, rather than in-plane.

For circular cylindrical specimens, Card (1965) used axial compression, torsion, and internal-pressure tests to obtain data for characterizing the elastic behavior. In the data reduction, all bending–stretching coupling effects were neglected and each set of two helical half-layers was considered as a single orthotropic layer, as first suggested by Clark (1963).

Feldman *et al.* (1966) used the refined theory of laminated cylindrical shells due to Cheng and Ho (1963) to reduce data obtained from axial tension and compression, torsion, and internal-pressure tests on filament-wound tubular specimens. This provided complete characterization of the elastic properties, assuming the reciprocal relation to hold and assuming circumferential properties in tension and compression to be identical.

Hom *et al.* (1966) conducted axial tension and compression and circumferential internal and external pressure tests to obtain data for determining the circumferential and axial Young's moduli and Poisson's ratios. They found that the reciprocal relation, Eq. (1), held for their glass–epoxy composite. Although they did not mention any differences between the tension and compression properties, the tests they conducted would have allowed these to be determined for both the axial and circumferential directions. Since Hom *et al.* did not measure the shear properties, they did not completely characterize the composite.

Bert and Guess (1972) obtained data in axial tension and compression, torsion, circumferential internal pressure, and a combination of axial tension and circumferential internal pressure. Since the carbon–carbon specimens consisted of many filament-wound layers (alternating $+\theta$ and $-\theta$), they were assumed to be orthotropic and homogeneous through the thickness (i.e., bending–stretching effects were neglected). The data were reduced using the refined shell theory due to Langhaar and Boresi (1958), extended to orthotropic material in which the reciprocal relation is not assumed *a priori* to hold. The data reduced in this manner showed that Eq. (1) did not hold for this composite. Limited data in axial compression resulted in properties the same as those in axial tension, within experimental accuracy. Thus, no further attempt was made to include the differences between tension and compression properties.

The author knows of no complete characterization of the elastic properties of any composite. For example, each of the experimental programs mentioned above fell short of this in one way or another. However, the means for conducting such a program for filament-wound tubes are available. Such a program would consist of the following tests:

(1) Axial tension (to obtain E_{11}^{+} and ν_{12}^{+})
(2) Axial compression (to obtain E_{11}^{-} and ν_{12}^{-})
(3) Circumferential tension (to obtain E_{22}^{+} and ν_{21}^{+})
(4) Circumferential compression (to obtain E_{22}^{-} and ν_{21}^{-})
(5) Torsion (to obtain G_{12}).

In the above listing, superscripts $(+)$ and $(-)$ denote tension and compression, respectively, and subscripts 1 and 2 denote the axial and circumferential directions, respectively. For instance, if the specimen is hoop-wound, $E_{11} \rightarrow E_{\mathrm{L}}$, $E_{22} \rightarrow E_{\mathrm{T}}$, etc. If the specimen is wound at a helix angle $(\pm\theta)$, the transformations of anisotropic elasticity (see Ashton *et al.*, 1969) can be used to transform the measured properties (relative to 1, 2 axes) to individual-layer material-symmetry-axis properties (relative to L, T axes). This was done by Bert and Guess (1972), for example.

VIII. Dynamic Properties

The dynamic properties discussed here include the dynamic stiffness coefficients and the associated damping coefficients. Of the various techniques described in the remainder of this section, most are at least potentially suitable for determining both dynamic stiffness and damping coefficients. However, in some instances, practical considerations prevent a given technique from being used to determine one class of properties or the other. For example, it has not yet been possible to measure ultrasonic attenuation with sufficient accuracy to determine reliably the damping coefficients (Martin, 1969).

Many of the dynamic methods have been used extensively in connection with nondestructive testing (NDT) to determine the presence of various kinds of flaws in composite materials (cf. Martin, 1969). However, the present discussion is limited to characterization of the dynamic stiffness and damping properties.

For a complete discussion of the theoretical micromechanics aspects of the dynamic behavior of composite materials, the reader is referred to the chapter by Achenbach, "Waves and Vibrations in Directionally Reinforced Composites" in Volume 2 of this treatise, and also the chapter by Moon, "Wave Propagation and Impact in Composite Materials," in Volume 7.

A. Ultrasonic Pulse Propagation

Ultrasonic measurements in filamentary composite materials date back at least to the work of Dietz (1961), who measured the propagation velocity and attenuation of microsecond pulses in glass–epoxy. However, he did not interpret his results in terms of stiffness or damping.

Apparently the first work in which ultrasonic pulse propagation was used to determine elastic moduli of composites was due to Abbott and Broutman (1966). By means of the through-transmission technique they measured both tensile and compressive pulses in slender-bar specimens, for fibers oriented either parallel or perpendicular to the longitudinal axis of the bar. In these cases, the longitudinal and transverse Young's moduli, E_L and E_T, are related to the corresponding propagation velocities, v_L and v_T, as follows:

$$E_L = \rho v_L{}^2 \qquad E_T = \rho v_T{}^2 \tag{14}$$

where ρ is the mean density of the composite.

Strictly speaking, Eqs. (14) are applicable only for excitation frequencies resulting in wavelengths, transverse to the bar, which are much longer than the largest cross-sectional dimension of the bar. As pointed out by Reynolds (1971), for example, when the transverse wavelength is of the same order of magnitude as the bar width, the propagation velocity changes to that of a bulk wave (v_B), which is related to the Cauchy stiffness coefficient associated with normal stresses in the direction of the bar axis (direction 1) as follows:

$$C_{11} = \rho v_B{}^2 \tag{15}$$

For the case of fibers oriented parallel to the axis of the bar, the material can be considered to be transversely isotropic with its plane of isotropy being the cross-sectional plane.† Then C_{11} and E_L are related as follows:

$$E_L = C_{11} - 2C_{12}^2(C_{23} + C_{33})^{-1} \qquad (16)$$

where

$$C_{12}(C_{23} + C_{33})^{-1} = \nu_{12} \qquad (17)$$

is the Poisson's ratio associated with loading in the axial direction and deformation in the transverse direction (direction 2). Since ν_{12} is approximately one-half and since C_{12}/C_{11} is very small (≈ 0.03), Reynolds showed that C_{11} is only slightly larger than E_L. Also, the change from bar velocity to bulk velocity occurs at extremely high frequencies, since the ratio of the transverse to the longitudinal wavelength is given by

$$\lambda_2/\lambda_1 = (C_{22}/C_{11})^{1/2} \qquad (18)$$

which is considerably smaller than unity for unidirectional filamentary composites.

Numerous studies have been made on the through-transmission technique for measurement of bulk velocity and subsequent use in determining the stiffness. For instance, Zurbrick and Schultz (1966), Schultz (1967), and Zurbrick (1968) investigated the variability due to processing variables. Zurbrick (1969) and Hastings (1970) found that the following simple relationship holds:

$$\rho v_B^2 = 0.0124\ \bar{E} \qquad (19)$$

where $\bar{E}$ is the so-called isotropic modulus given by

$$\bar{E} = \tfrac{1}{2}(E_L + E_T) \qquad (20)$$

Zurbrick (1969) and Schultz (1971) reported measurements of E_{11} versus the angular orientation (θ) as determined from the following approximate relationship:

$$E_{11} = \rho v_B^2 \qquad (21)$$

As previously discussed, strictly speaking Eq. (15) should have been used instead of Eq. (21), but the error due to the use of Eq. (21) is on the order of 3% for many advanced composites. These investigators used circular-disk specimens and measured the propagation across diameters at various orientations.

Use of the through-transmission technique requires physical access to

---

† In the terminology of crystal physics, the transversely isotropic case is known as the hexagonal crystal class.

two opposite surfaces of the specimen. Often, in the case of practical structural components, access is available to only one surface. In such cases, the technique of single-surface sounding or interval velocity may be used (Potapov, 1968; Schultz, 1971).

By generating both types of waves (i.e., bulk and shear) in specimens at various orientations, Markham (1970) and Zimmer and Cost (1970) were able to characterize completely the elastic coefficients of filamentary composites. The plan they used is listed in Table VII. The equations necessary to calculate the five independent stiffness coefficients from the five measured velocities listed can be found from the following general expression for harmonic wave propagation in a transversely isotropic continuum (Hearmon 1961; Markham, 1970):

$$\{[\rho v^2 - C_{66} - n^2(C_{11} - C_{66})][\rho v^2 - C_{66} - (1 - n^2)(C_{33} - C_{66})]$$

$$-n^2(1 - n^2)(C_{12} + C_{66})^2\}\{\rho v^2 - C_{66} - \tfrac{1}{2}(1 - n^2)(C_{33} - C_{23} - 2C_{66})\}$$

$$= 0 \qquad (22)$$

where n is the direction cosine of the wave normal to direction 1 (the fiber direction). The resulting equations are as follows (Reynolds, 1971):

$$C_{11} = \rho v_{11}^2$$

$$C_{33} = C_{22} = \rho v_{22}^2$$

$$C_{23} = C_{33} - 2\rho v_{23}^2 \qquad (23)$$

$$C_{55} = C_{66} = \rho v_{21}^2$$

$$C_{13} = C_{12} = -C_{66} + [4C_{11}C_{33} + C_{11}C_{66} + C_{33}C_{66} + C_{66}^2$$

$$-2(C_{11} + C_{33} + 2C_{66})\rho v_s^2 + (2\rho v_s^2)^2]^{1/2}$$

TABLE VII

PLAN FOR COMPLETE CHARACTERIZATION OF DYNAMIC ELASTIC COEFFICIENTS
BY ULTRASONIC-PULSE-VELOCITY MEASUREMENTS

Propagation direction	Mode	Velocity designation
1 (fiber direction)	Bulk	v_{11}
2 (transverse to fiber)	Bulk	v_{22}
2	Shear (polarized in 21 plane)	v_{21}
2	Shear (polarized in 23 plane)	v_{23}
45° to 1 axis	Shear (polarized in the plane formed by intersection of propagation direction with the 1 axis)	v_s

Equations (22) and (23) are written in terms of the standard coordinate system and elastic constant designations for composite materials,† namely, axis 1 is the fiber direction and axes 2 and 3 are orthogonal to axis 1 and to each other. Constants C_{11}, C_{22}, C_{33} are the normal stress stiffness coefficients corresponding to the 1, 2, 3 axes, respectively; constants C_{44}, C_{55}, C_{66} are the shear stress stiffness coefficients associated with shearing action in the 23, 31, and 12 planes. Constants C_{ij} (ij = 12, 13, 23) are normal stress stiffness coefficients for normal stresses acting in direction i due to normal strain in direction j.

Zimmer and Cost (1970) used equations equivalent to the above to characterize a unidirectional glass–epoxy composite, while Markham (1970) used them to characterize a unidirectional carbon–fiber reinforced plastic. Potapov (1968) presented equations equivalent to those presented above and applied them to a characterization of a glass–resin composite. He found that there was considerably less scatter in the dynamic elastic coefficients than in the static ones. Spintsis (1970) presented similar equations for the special case of a thin layer.

In a parallel-ply laminate, the fiber-to-fiber spacing may be different in the in-plane transverse direction than in the thickness direction. Thus, the properties in these two directions are not the same and the composite is orthotropic‡ (with nine independent elastic coefficients) rather than transversely isotropic (five independent coefficients).

Another situation in which the material may behave orthotropically is three-dimensionally reinforced material. Neighbours and Schacher (1967) have presented equations for all symmetry classes; however, even in the case of an orthotropic material, the general equations are quite complicated. In fact, even when one knows the material-symmetry planes (from the geometry of the material), only six elastic coefficients can be obtained from pure-mode propagation along the material-symmetry axes. Thus, impure modes must be used to obtain data for determining the remaining three independent coefficients. Apparently the first use of ultrasonic-

---

† Hearmon (1961) and Markham (1970) both used the coordinate system which is standard in the field of crystal physics and in which the plane of isotropy was the 12 plane. Zimmer and Cost (1970) used the coordinate system which is standard in the field of composite materials and in which the plane of isotropy was the 23 plane. However, they used a nonstandard designation of the shear coefficients; namely they interchanged the role of C_{66} and C_{44}. Both the coordinate system and the stiffness coefficient designations used in the present work are identical with those of Ashton *et al.* (1969), which are considered to be the standards in the field of composite materials.

‡ In crystal-physics parlance, the orthotropic case is called the orthorhombic crystal class.

velocity measurements to completely characterize experimentally a composite material which is orthotropic rather than transversely isotropic was made recently by Tauchert and Güzelsu (1971) for various fabric-reinforced composites.

In the terminology of higher-order elasticity theory (cf. Smith and Stephens, 1964), the ordinary linear elasticity theory embodied in the generalized Hooke's law is called first-order theory but the corresponding elastic stiffness coefficients are called second-order elastic coefficients. To include the effect of hydrostatic pressure, which is obviously important in connection with materials used in deep-diving submersible vehicles, the appropriate theory is second-order elasticity theory. This theory contains third-order elastic coefficients as well as the ordinary (second-order) ones. Thurston (1965) and Brugger (1965) have presented equations which can be used to determine these third-order elastic coefficients from ultrasonic-velocity measurements on media subjected to various initial (static) stress states. Thurston pointed out that if one uses the concept of effective elastic coefficients which are stress-dependent, then the familiar symmetry relations of classical infinitesimal elasticity no longer hold. Apparently the first experimental characterization of hydrostatic-pressure effects on filamentary composites is Lamberson's (1969).

Recently Tauchert and Moon (1971) and Tauchert (1971) measured the velocity and attenuation of ultrasonic pulses in various composites. Of course, since the material damping is small, elastic coefficients could be obtained directly from the measured velocities. For the same composites, they made separate forced vibration tests to measure the damping coefficients. Then they used these values of the damping coefficient in a Fourier integral solution for a linear viscoelastic solid to predict the attenuation versus distance traveled. They obtained reasonably good agreement between this prediction and the measured attenuation. Unfortunately, to date no one has inverted the analysis to permit direct computation of the damping coefficient.

B. Free Vibration

Free vibration has generally been used in experimental characterization in conjunction with resonant forced vibration in the following manner. First the specimen is excited in a desired resonant mode by an appropriate exciter, then the power to the excitation is cut off, and finally the decaying time history of the ensuing free vibration is measured by an appropriate transducer and recorded. The direct measure of damping used is the logarithmic decrement δ, defined as follows:

$$\delta \equiv \ln(a_i/a_{i+1}) \tag{24}$$

where a_i and a_{i+1} are the amplitudes of the ith and $(i + 1)$th decaying cycles.

In many materials, the decay per cycle is so small that it cannot be detected with sufficient accuracy to give reliable values for logarithmic decrement as calculated by Eq. (24). Thus, it is more expedient to calculate δ using the following expression:

$$\delta = (1/n) \ln(a_i/a_{i+n}) \tag{25}$$

where n is any convenient integer, such as 10, for example. Equation (25) was derived assuming that the logarithmic decrement is independent of vibration amplitude.

It should be apparent that the successful use of the technique described above requires that the decay time for the excitation power should be an order of magnitude smaller than that of the test specimen. The logarithmic decrement of actual materials depends upon the mode of vibration and the frequency. The resonant frequency corresponding to a given mode can be changed by changing the specimen geometry, i.e., the length in the case of a bar-configuration specimen.

Among the earliest uses of free vibration to determine the logarithmic decrement of a composite material were the free–free beam experiments reported by Bert *et al.* (1967). The specimens were sandwich beams with glass–epoxy facings and hexagonal-cell honeycomb cores of either aluminum or glass–phenolic. Good correlation was obtained between the measured values of δ and those predicted by an energy analysis of a Timoshenko beam, which includes thickness-shear flexibility and rotatory inertia. However, the complexity of the analysis prevented explicit determination of the δ's of the facings and core.

Later Schultz and Tsai (1968, 1969) used free flexural vibration of very thin cantilever beams to determine δ for glass–epoxy in two configurations: (1) unidirectional with the fibers at an arbitrary orientation θ with respect to the longitudinal axis of the beam, and (2) symmetrically laminated quasi-isotropic layups (layer orientations of $0°$, $-60°$, $60°$, $60°$, $-60°$, $0°$ and of $0°$, $90°$, $45°$, $-45°$, $-45°$, $45°$, $90°$, $0°$). In the $\theta \neq 0°$, $90°$ case, the coupling between bending and twisting significantly invalidated the simple flexural theory used in the data reduction.

Pottinger (1970) measured the temporal decay of axial vibrations of bars of unidirectional filamentary composites (glass–epoxy and boron–aluminum).

C. Sinusoidally Forced Vibration

Forced vibration has several advantages over free vibration in characterizing the dynamic behavior of composites:

(1) Both dynamic stiffness and damping types of coefficients can be measured directly.

(2) The accuracy in measuring the damping is considerably improved.

Perhaps the earliest work of this type was that of Schultz and Tsai (1968, 1969), who determined the resonant frequencies (and thus the stiffness) of cantilever beams by the usual peak-amplitude method and the dimensionless damping ratios† (ζ) from the half-power-point bandwidth ($\omega_2 - \omega_1$), using the following expression:

$$\zeta = (\omega_2 - \omega_1)/(2\omega_n) \qquad (26)$$

where ω_n is the resonant frequency falling between ω_1 and ω_2. As in the case of their free vibration work, the specimens were unidirectional at various θ's and quasi-isotropic (see Section VIII, B). They calculated values for the Young's moduli using elementary Bernoulli–Euler beam theory, i.e., no corrections were made for thickness shear, rotatory inertia, or the bending–twisting coupling present in the off-axis unidirectional specimens.

Apparently the first application of corrections for higher-order effects in composite material resonant-vibration data was made by Behrens (1968). He used rectangular-cross-section bars with fibers parallel to the longitudinal axis of the bar. He presented equations which reduce to the following for the transversely isotropic case.

For longitudinal vibration, the natural frequencies are

$$f_{nL} = \frac{n}{2L}\left(\frac{E_{11}}{\rho K_L}\right)^{1/2} \qquad (27)$$

where L/n is the wavelength, ρ is the mean density of the composite, E_{11} is the longitudinal Young's modulus, and K_L is a correction factor given by

$$K_L = 1 + \frac{1}{3}\left(\frac{n\pi\nu_{12}}{2L}\right)^2 (a^2 + b^2) \qquad (28)$$

where ν_{12} is the major Poisson's ratio and a and b are the cross-sectional dimensions.

---

† This measure of damping is defined as the ratio of the damping coefficient to the critical damping coefficient.

For flexural vibration, the natural frequencies are

$$f_{n\text{B}} = \frac{a}{4\pi}\left(\frac{m_n}{L}\right)^2\left(\frac{E_{11}}{3\rho K_{\text{B}}}\right)^{1/2} \tag{29}$$

where m_n, for free-free or clamped-clamped ends, is given by the roots of the following equation:

$$\cos m_n \cosh m_n = 1 \tag{30}$$

and K_{B} is a correction factor given by

$$K_{\text{B}} = 1 + \frac{1}{2}\left(\frac{a}{L}\right)^2 m_n\varphi_n(m_n)\left\{1 + \frac{m_n}{6}\,\varphi_n(m_n)\right.$$

$$+ \frac{1}{5}\frac{E_{11}}{G_{12}}\left[m_n\varphi_n(m_n) - 2\right]\right\}$$

$$- \left(\frac{m_n a}{L}\right)^4\frac{E_{11}}{120\,G_{12}} \tag{31}$$

where

$$\varphi_n(m_n) = \begin{cases} \tanh(m_n/2) & \text{when } n \text{ is odd} \\[2mm] \coth(m_n/2) & \text{when } n \text{ is even} \end{cases} \tag{32}$$

For torsional vibration, the natural frequencies are

$$f_{n\text{T}} = \frac{n}{L}\left(\frac{G_{12}}{\rho K_{\text{T}}}\right)^{1/2}\{F[(1 + a^2 b^{-2})^{-1}]\}^{1/2} \tag{33}$$

where

$$F(x) = x^{-1}\left\{1 - \frac{6}{x}\left(\frac{2}{\pi}\right)^5\sum_{k=0}^{\infty}\frac{\tanh(2k + 1)(\pi x/2)}{(2k + 1)^5}\right\} \tag{34}$$

It is noted that Behrens took the correction factor K_{T} to be equal to unity.

By suitably selecting values of E_{11}, ν_{12}, and G_{12}, Behrens was able to match each set of measured frequencies within 0.2% for a steel fiber–aluminum matrix composite. The resulting elastic-property values were slightly higher ($\approx$0.5%) than the static ones. This is thermodynamically valid since the dynamic values would be expected to be appropriate for adiabatic conditions while the static ones would be appropriate for iso-thermal conditions.

Adams *et al.* (1969) conducted flexural and torsional resonant vibration tests to obtain Young's and shear moduli and the corresponding damping ratios for glass–epoxy and carbon–epoxy. The magnetic-coil-driven inertia bar was located at the center of the bar to excite flexure and at one end to excite torsion.

Wells *et al.* (1969) conducted resonant vibration tests on free-free beams of graphite–epoxy. In reducing their data to dynamic moduli, they used simple Bernoulli–Euler beam theory. Later Dudek (1970) showed that when their values were corrected for thickness shear and rotatory inertia by means of the exact solution to the Timoshenko beam equations due to Huang (1961), the resulting values became essentially independent of frequency. This was in qualitative agreement with Dudek's own experimental results for magnetically-driven cantilever beams of graphite–epoxy having a different fiber volume fraction.

Gustafson *et al.* (1970) and Mazza *et al.* (1971) conducted resonant-vibration tests on double cantilever beams driven by an electrodynamic shaker. They tested homogeneous aluminum, glass–epoxy (0° unidirectional and cross-ply) and boron–epoxy (0° and 90° unidirectional, and ±45° laminated). They used elementary Bernoulli–Euler theory and obtained very good correlation with results of other investigators for 2024-T4 aluminum. In this case, the effect of thickness shear would be very small, since the material is isotropic ($E/G \approx 2.7$). However, for advanced composites, E_{11}/G_{12} is very high (≈ 30 for boron–epoxy) and the thickness-shear correction can be significant. These experimenters investigated the effect of air damping on the measured damping values and found it to be quite strong, especially for the unidirectional composites.

Tauchert and Moon (1971) and Tauchert (1971) conducted forced vibration tests on circular-cross-section cantilever beams made of the same composites on which they had conducted the pulse-propagation tests mentioned in Section VIII,A. For all four of the composite materials tested, the moduli obtained in this fashion fell between those obtained statically and by pulse propagation. Damping was obtained from the half-power points, using Eq. (26).

Keer and Lazan (1961) and Kern and Skinner (1962) measured the energy dissipated per cycle at resonance as the measure of damping. For the case of a Kimball–Lovell material (Kimball and Lovell, 1927), which has a logarithmic decrement that is unaffected by displacement amplitude, the damping energy is proportional to the square of the stress amplitude. This behavior was obtained experimentally by Keer and Lazan (1961) for double-cantilever sandwich beams with glass-reinforced plastic facings and excited by an electrodynamic shaker.

Ekstein and Schiffman (1956) proposed the use of cubic specimens to measure the natural frequencies and thus deduce the elastic properties of isotropic materials. Recently Demarest (1971) extended their analysis to the case of anisotropic materials and demonstrated its use by applying it to a small cube of fused quartz. Square-plate transducers, in contact with the faces, edges, or corners of the cube, were used to excite various modes. The measured frequencies agreed with calculated ones based on published elastic constants to within 0.42%. This demonstrated the validity of the method and associated data-reduction analysis; however, apparently it has not yet been used for composite materials.

Recently Clary (1972) conducted some forced vibration tests which, although not intended for material characterization purposes, did illustrate some refined techniques which could be applied to material characterization. He used the Kennedy–Pancu technique, as modified by Pendered and Bishop (1963), to determine the natural frequencies and the associated modal damping of long plates made of unidirectional boron–epoxy material. It is necessary to measure phase as well as amplitude. Then the criterion for resonance is a maximum $\Delta s/\Delta\omega$ for a fixed increment of frequency $\Delta\omega$, where Δs is the increment in arc length on the Argand diagram (amplitude *versus* phase φ) associated with $\Delta\omega$. The modal damping ratio ζ is calculated by use of the following expression:

$$\zeta = [\omega_R(d\varphi/d\omega)_R]^{-1} \tag{35}$$

where ω_R is the resonant frequency for the mode concerned and $(d\varphi/d\omega)_R$ is the rate of change in phase with respect to frequency at ω_R.

Using composite ply properties (stiffness and damping) generated by a micromechanics analysis made by Bert and Chang (1972) based on experimentally determined properties of the constituents, Siu and Bert (1973) made a forced vibrational analysis of Clary's (1972) boron–epoxy plates and obtained very close agreement with the measured resonant frequencies, modal damping ratios, and nodal patterns. Furthermore, Clary, as well as Bert and Siu, showed that for these plates, there was very little difference between the resonant frequencies determined on the basis of the peak-amplitude and the modified Kennedy–Pancu resonance criteria.

IX. Concluding Remarks

This chapter has been concerned with experimental characterization of composites, with particular emphasis on (1) the test methods which either have been used or are appropriate and presently available, and (2) the available analytical solutions valid for reducing experimental data to composite properties. The state of the art in both of these aspects is in a rapid state of flux as new test methods are devised and new analytical solutions obtained. Much more work needs to be done in both of these areas, as well as in correlating the results obtained by various test methods. Special challenges are presented by randomly reinforced composites and three-dimensionally reinforced composites.

Acknowledgments

The author wishes to thank the many people who have contributed to this chapter, either by providing information or reports or by discussing various aspects of the problems involved. Special thanks are due to Dr. James M. Whitney of the Nonmetallic Materials Division, Air Force Materials Laboratory, Wright-Patterson AFB, Ohio; T. R. Guess of the Composite Research and Development Department, Sandia Laboratories, Albuquerque, New Mexico; L. B. Greszczuk of McDonnell–Douglas Astronautics Company, Western Division, Huntington Beach, California; and Dr. Davis M. Egle of the School of Aerospace, Mechanical and Nuclear Engineering, University of Oklahoma, Norman. Partial support in the form of a National Aeronautics and Space Administration research grant, monitored by R. R. Clary of Langley Research Center, is also gratefully acknowledged.

List of Symbols

a	Specimen length (plate)	f	Failure
B	Ratio of minimum to maximum in-plane stress	L	Longitudinal
		R	Resonant
b	Specimen width or distance between rails	s	Shear
		T	Transverse
C	Cauchy stiffness coefficient	x	Axial
D	Flexural or twisting rigidity	y	Circumferential
E	Young's modulus	σ	Principal stress
F	Tensile strength	ϵ	Principal strain
f	Natural frequency		
G	Shear modulus		
h	Specimen depth or wall thickness	**Greek**	
K	Dimensionless buckling coefficient, frequency factor		
L	Length	β	Dimensionless coefficient
M	Bending moment	γ	Dimensionless stiffness parameter
m	$\cos \theta$	δ	Logarithmic decrement
n	$\sin \theta$, direction cosine of wave normal	ϵ	Transverse-sensitivity-corrected strain
P	Applied diagonal force	ν	Poisson's ratio
R	Mean radius	ρ	Mean density
s	Arc length	θ	Angle
v	Propagation velocity	φ	Factor in Eq. (5); phase angle
		τ	Shear stress
Subscripts		ω	Frequency
		σ	Stress
B	Bulk wave	ζ	Modal damping ratio
cr	Critical buckling		

References

Abbott, B. W., and Broutman, L. J. (1966). *Proc. Ann. Tech. Conf., Soc. Plast. Ind. Reinforced Plast. Div., 21st.* Sect. 5-D.

Adams, D. F., and Thomas, R. L. (1967). *In Advances in Structural Composites (Nat. SAMPE Symp.)*, Vol. 12, Paper AC-5.

Adams, D. F., Doner, D. R., and Thomas, R. L. (1967). Mechanical Behavior of Fiber-Reinforced Composite Materials. Air Force Mater. Lab., AFML-TR-67-96, AD-654056.

Adams, R. D., Fox, M. A. O., Flood, R. J. L., Friend, R. J., and Hewitt, R. L. (1969). *J. Compos. Mater.* **3**, 594.

Adsit, N. R., and Forest, J. D. (1969). *In* Composite Materials: Testing and Design. Amer. Soc. Testing Mater., Spec. Tech. Publ. 460, pp. 108–121.

Air Force Materials Laboratory (1966). Testing Techniques for Filament Reinforced Plastics, held at Dayton, Ohio, Sept. 21–23, 1966. AFML-TR-66-274, AD-801547.

Air Force Materials Laboratory (1973). Structural Design Guide for Advanced Composite Applications. Wright-Patterson AFB, Ohio.

American Society for Testing and Materials (1963). *Symp. Std. Filament-Wound Reinforced Plast., Naval Ord. Lab., White Oak, Silver Spring, Maryland, June 6–7, 1962* Spec. Tech. Publ. 327.

American Society for Testing and Materials (1969). *Conf. Compos. Mater. Testing Design, New Orleans, Louisana, Feb. 11–13, 1969.* Spec. Tech. Publ. 460.

American Society for Testing and Materials (1972). *Conf. Compos. Mater. Testing Design, 2nd, Anaheim, California, April 20–22, 1971* Spec. Tech. Publ. 497.

Ashkenazi, E. K., and Pozdnyakov, A. A. (1965). *Ind. Lab.* **31**, 1559.

Ashton, J. E., and Whitney, J. M. (1970). Theory of Laminated Plates. Technomic, Westport, Connecticut.

Ashton, J. E., Halpin, J. C., and Petit, P. H. (1969). Primer on Composite Materials: Analysis. Technomic, Westport, Connecticut.

Balaban, M. M., and Jackson, W. T. (1971). *Exp. Mech.* **11**, 224.

Barnet, F. R., and Prosen, S. P. (1964). *Mater. Protect.* **3**, 32.

Barton, R. S. (1968). *SPE J.* **24**, 31.

Baumberger, R., and Hines, F. (1944). *Proc. SESA* **2**, pt. 1, 113.

Beckett, R. E., Dohrmann, R. J., and Ives, K. D. (1963). *In* "Experimental Mechanics" (*Proc. Int. Congr. Exp. Mech., 1st, New York, 1961*) (B. E. Rossi, ed.), pp. 129–148. Pergamon, Oxford.

Behrens, E. (1968). *Textile Res. J.* **38**, 1075.

Berg, C. A., Melton, R., Kalnin, I., and Dunn, T. (1971). *J. Mater.* **6**, 683.

Bergsträsser, M. (1927). *Z. Tech. Phys.* **8**, 355.

Bert, C. W. (1972a). Plasticity and Creep Analysis of Filamentary Metal-Matrix Composites, SC-DR-720055. Sandia Lab., Albuquerque, New Mexico.

Bert, C. W. (1972b). Unpublished analysis.

Bert, C. W. (1974a). *In* "Composite Materials" (L. J. Broutman and R. H. Krock, eds.), Vol. 7, Structural Design and Analysis, Part I (C. C. Chamis, ed.). Academic Press, New York and London.

Bert, C. W. (1974b). *In* "Composite Materials" (L. J. Broutman and R. H. Krock, eds.), Vol. 7, Structural Design and Analysis, Part I (C. C. Chamis, ed.). Academic Press, New York and London.

Bert, C. W., and Chang, S. (1972). In-Plane, Flexural, Twisting and Thickness-Shear

Coefficients for Stiffness and Damping of a Monolayer Filamentary Composite. Final Rep., Part I, on NASA Grant NGR-37-003-055. Univ. of Oklahoma Res. Inst., Norman, Oklahoma. NASA CR-112141.

Bert, C. W., and Guess, T. R. (1972). Mechanical Behavior of Carbon/Carbon Filamentary Composites. *In Conf. Compos. Mater. Testing Design, 2nd* Amer. Soc. Testing Mater., Spec. Tech. Publ. 497, pp. 89–106.

Bert, C. W., and Hyler, W. S. (1966). *Advan. Space Sci. Technol.* **8,** 65–194.

Bert, C. W., Mills, E. J., and Hyler, W. S. (1966). Mechanical Properties of Aerospace Structural Alloys under Biaxial-Stress Conditions. Air Force Mater. Lab., AFML-TR-66-229, AD-488304.

Bert, C. W., Wilkins, D. J., Jr., and Crisman, W. C. (1967). *J. Eng. Ind. Trans. ASME* **89B,** 662.

Bert, C. W., Mayberry, B. L., and Ray, J. D. (1969a). Behavior of Fiber-Reinforced Plastic Laminates under Uniaxial, Biaxial, and Shear Loadings. U.S. Army Aviat. Mat. Lab., USAAVLABS-TR-68-86, AD-684321.

Bert, C. W., Mayberry, B. L., and Ray, J. D. (1969b). *In* Composite Materials: Testing and Design. Amer. Soc. Testing Mater., Spec. Tech. Publ. 460, pp. 362–380.

Bracco, A., Mannone, G., and Sattin, M. (1971). *In* Composite Materials. NATO, AGARD, AGARD-CP-63-71, AD-732741, Paper No. 7.

Broutman, L. J. (1969). *In* "Composite Engineering Laminates" (A. G. H. Dietz, ed.), pp. 125–151. MIT Press, Cambridge, Massachusetts.

Brugger, K. (1965). *J. Appl. Phys.* **36,** 768.

Bryan, E. L. (1961). *In Symp. Shear Torsion Testing* Amer. Soc. Testing Mater., Spec. Tech. Publ. 289, pp. 90–94.

Burchett, O. J., Theis, J. D., and Curlee, R. M. (1969). Failure of Some Carbon-Carbon Cylinders Under Hoop Stress, Rep. SC-TM-69-123. Sandia Lab., Albuquerque, New Mexico.

Card, M. F. (1965). Experiments to Determine Elastic Moduli for Filament-Wound Cylinders. NASA TN D-3110.

Cervelli, R. V. (1966). *In* Testing Techniques for Filament Reinforced Plastics. Air Force Mater. Lab., AFML-TR-66-274, AD-801547, pp. 369–434.

Chambers, R. E., and McGarry, F. J. (1959). *ASTM Bull.* No. 238, 38.

Channon, S. L., and Rubin, L. (1963). *In Symp. Std. Filament-Wound Reinforced Plast.* Amer. Soc. Testing Mater., Spec. Tech. Publ. 327, pp. 187–196.

Cheng, S., and Ho, B. P. C. (1963). *AIAA J.* **1,** 892.

Clark, S. K. (1963). *Textile Res. J.* **33,** 295.

Clary, R. R. (1972). *In Conf. Compos. Mater. Testing Design, 2nd* Amer. Soc. Testing Mater., Spec. Tech. Publ. 497, pp. 415–438.

Cole, B. W., Cornish, R. H., Finlayson, L. A., and Liber, T. (1971). Biaxial Testing of Composite Materials. Amer. Soc. Mech. Eng. Design Eng. Conf. Paper.

Dai, P. K. (1965). Mechanical Considerations in Utilization of Beryllium Structural Systems. Air Force Mater. Lab., AFML-TR-64-395.

Dallas, R. N. (1963). *In Symp. Std. Filament-Wound Reinforced Plast.* Amer. Soc. Testing Mater., Spec. Tech. Publ. 327, pp. 123–132.

Daniels, B. K., Harakas, N. K., and Jackson, R. C. (1971). *Fibre Sci. Technol.* **3,** 187.

Dastin, S., Lubin, G., Munyak, J., and Slobodzinski, A. (1969). *In* Composite Materials: Testing and Design. Amer. Soc. Testing Mater., Spec. Tech. Publ. 460, pp. 13–26.

Davenport, O. B., and Bert, C. W. (1972). *J. Aircr.* **9,** 477.

Davis, J. W. (1964). *Proc. Ann. Tech. Conf., Soc. Plast. Ind. Reinforced Plast. Div., 19th.* Sect. 19-A.

Demarest, H. H., Jr. (1971). *J. Acoust. Soc. Amer.* **49**, 768.

Dexter, H. B. (1967). Correlation of Three Standard Shear Tests for Unidirectional Glass–Epoxy Composites. M.S. thesis, Virginia Polytechnic Inst., Blacksburg, Virginia.

Dickerson, E. O., and DiMartino, B. (1966). *In Advan. Fibrous Reinforced Compos.* (*Nat. SAMPE Symp.*) **10**, H23–H50.

Dietz, A. G. H. (1961). *J. Eng. Mech. Div. Proc. ASCE* **87** (EM 3), 31.

Dow, N. F. (1970). *In* "Mechanics of Composite Materials" (F. W. Wendt, H. Liebowitz, and N. Perrone, eds.), pp. 23–46. Pergamon, Oxford.

Dow, N. F., and Rosen, B. W. (1966). *AIAA J.* **4**, 481.

Dudek, T. J. (1970). *J. Compos. Mater.* **4**, 232.

Ekstein, H., and Schiffman, T. (1956). *J. Appl. Phys.* **27**, 405.

Ekvall, J. C. (1965). *In AIAA Struct. Mater. Conf., 6th, Palm Springs, California,* pp. 250–263. AIAA, New York.

Elkin, R. A. (1963). *In Symp. Std. Filament-Wound Reinforced Plast.* Amer. Soc. Testing Mater., Spec. Tech. Publ. 327, pp. 66–82.

Elkin, R. A. (1965). *Proc. Ann. Tech. Conf., Soc. Plast. Ind. Reinforced Plast. Div., 20th.* Sect. 1-B.

Elkin, R. A., Fust, G., and Hanley, D. P. (1969). *In* Composite Materials: Testing and Design. Amer. Soc. Testing Mater., Spec. Tech. Publ. 460, pp. 321–335.

Ely, R. E. (1965). Biaxial Fracture Stresses for Graphite, Ceramic, and Filled and Reinforced Epoxy Tube Specimens. Redstone Arsenal, RR-TR-65-10, AD-469036.

Epstein, G. (1969). *In* "Handbook of Fiberglass and Advanced Plastics Composites" (G. Lubin, ed.), pp. 661–707. VanNostrand-Reinhold, Princeton, New Jersey.

Erickson, P. W., Sr., Silver, I., and Perry, H. A., Jr. (1958). *Plast. Technol.* **4**, 1017.

Federal Test Method Standard (1961). Plastics: Methods of Testing. Std. No. 406.

Feldman, A., Stang, D. A., and Tasi, J. (1966). *Exp. Mech.* **6**, 385.

Foye, R. L. (1967). *J. Compos. Mater.* **1**, 194.

Fried, N. (1963). *In Symp. Std. Filament-Wound Reinforced Plast.* Amer. Soc. Testing Mater., Spec. Tech. Publ. 327, pp. 13–39.

Fried, N., and Winans, R. R. (1963). *In Symp. Std. Filament-Wound Reinforced Plast.* Amer. Soc. Testing Mater., Spec. Tech. Publ. 327, pp. 83–95.

Fukui, S., Kawata, K., Kobayashi, A., Takada, N., Hashimoto, S., Otani, N., and Hondo, A. (1965). *In Proc. Int. Symp. Space Technol. Sci., 6th, Tokyo* pp. 467–470.

Greszczuk, L. B. (1966a). *In* Orientation Effects in the Mechanical Behavior of Anisotropic Structural Materials. Amer. Soc. Testing Mater., Spec. Tech. Publ. 405, pp. 1–13.

Greszczuk, L. B. (1966b). *In* Testing Techniques for Filament Reinforced Plastics. Air Force Mater. Lab., AFML-TR-66-274, AD-801547, pp. 95–124.

Greszczuk, L. B. (1968). *Proc. Ann. Tech. Conf., Soc. Plast. Ind. Reinforced Plast./Compos. Div., 23rd,* Sect. 17-D.

Greszczuk, L. B. (1969). *In* Composite Materials: Testing and Design. Amer. Soc. Testing Mater., Spec. Tech. Publ. 460, pp. 140–149.

Grimes, G. C., and Bronstad, M. E. (1969). *In* "Handbook of Fiberglass and Advanced Plastics Composites" (G. Lubin, ed.), pp. 708–743. VanNostrand-Reinhold, Princeton, New Jersey.

Grimes, G. C., Pape, B. J., and Ferguson, J. H. (1967). Investigation of Structural Design Concepts for Fibrous Aircraft Structures. Vol. III, Technology Appraisal—Experimental Data and Methodology. Air Force Flight Dynam. Lab., AFFDL-TR-67-29, Vol. III, AD-824228.

Grinius, V. G. (1966). Micromechanics—Failure Mechanism Studies. Air Force Mater. Lab., AFML-TR-66-177, AD-638921.

Grinius, V. G. (1967). Micromechanics—Experimental and Analytical Studies. Air Force Mater. Lab., AFML-TR-67-148, AD-659166.

Guess, T. R., and Bert, C. W. (1971). Split Ring Test for Measuring the Shear Modulus of Helically-Wound Composites. *St. Louis Symp. Advan. Compos., 5th, April 6–7.*

Gustafson, A. J., Mazza, L. T., Rodgers, R. L., and McIlwean, E. H. (1970). Development of Test Methods for Measuring Damping of Fiber-Reinforced Materials. U.S. Army Aviat. Mater. Lab., USAAVLABS TR 70-42, AD-873990.

Hackman, L. E., and Foye, R. (1966). *In* Testing Techniques for Filament Reinforced Plastics. Air Force Mater. Lab., AFML-TR-66-274, AD-801547, pp. 435–465.

Hadcock, R. N., and Whiteside, J. B. (1969). *In* Composite Materials: Testing and Design. Amer. Soc. Testing Mater., Spec. Tech. Publ. 460, pp. 27–36.

Halpin, J. C., and Pagano, N. J. (1968). *J. Compos. Mater.* **2**, 68.

Halpin, J. C., Pagano, N. J., Whitney, J. M., and Wu, E. M. (1969). *In* Composite Materials: Testing and Design. Amer. Soc. Testing Mater., Spec. Tech. Publ. 460, pp. 37–47.

Hammant, B. (1971). *Composites* **2**, 246.

Hancock, J. R., and Swanson, J. R. (1971). *J. Compos. Mater.* **5**, 414.

Hancox, N. L., and Wells, H. (1970). *In* "Carbon Composite Technology" (*Proc. Ann. Symp., 10th, Albuquerque, New Mexico, Jan. 29–30, 1970*), pp. 35–53.

Hanley, D. P., and Cole, C. K. (1963). *In Symp. Std. Filament-Wound Reinforced Plast.* Amer. Soc. Testing Mater., Spec. Tech. Publ. 327, pp. 207–215.

Hanna, G. L., and Steingiser, S. (1969). *In* Composite Materials: Testing and Design. Amer. Soc. Testing Mater., Spec. Tech. Publ. 460, pp. 182–191.

Hastings, C. H. (1970). *In* "Carbon Composite Technology" (*Proc. Ann. Symp., 10th, Albuquerque, New Mexico, January 29–30, 1970*), pp. 195–212.

Hearmon, R. F. S. (1961). "An Introduction to Applied Anisotropic Elasticity." Oxford Univ. Press, London and New York.

Hearmon, R. F. S., and Adams, E. H. (1952). *Brit. J. Appl. Phys.* **3**, 150.

Hennessey, J. M., Whitney, J. M., and Riley, M. B. (1965). Experimental Methods for Determining Shear Modulus of Fiber Reinforced Composite Materials. Air Force Mater. Lab., AFML-TR-65-42, AD-623316.

Herring, H. W., Baucom, R. M., and Pride, R. A. (1969). Mechanical Behavior of Boron-Epoxy Filament-Wound Cylinders under Various Loads. NASA TN D-5050.

Hill, R. G. (1968). *Exp. Mech.* **8**, 75.

Hoggatt, J. T. (1969). *In* Composite Materials: Testing and Design. Amer. Soc. Testing Mater., Spec. Tech. Publ. 460, pp. 48–61.

Hom, K., Couch, W. P., and Willner, A. R. (1966). Elastic Material Constants of Filament-Wound Cylinders Fabricated from E-HTS/E787 and S-HTS/E787 Prepreg Rovings. David Taylor Model Basin, Rep. 1823, AD-630318.

Huang, T. C. (1961). *J. Appl. Mech.* **28**, 579.

Ishai, O., Anderson, R. M., and Lavengood, R. E. (1970a). *J. Mater.* **5**, 184.

Ishai, O., Moehlenpah, A. E., and Preis, A. (1970b). *J. Eng. Mech. Div. Proc. ASCE* **96** (EM 5), 739.

Jacobs, R. G. (1967). *Exp. Mech.* **7**, 176.

Jones, E. R. (1969). *SPE J.* **25**(3), 50.

Kavanagh, K. T. (1972). *Exp. Mech.* **12**, 50.

Keer, L., and Lazan, B. J. (1961). Damping and Fatigue Properties of Sandwich Configurations in Flexure. Aeronaut. Syst. Div., ASD TR 61-646, AD-272016.

Kern, E. L., and Skinner, S. M. (1962). *J. Appl. Polym. Sci.* **6**, 404.

Khishchenko, Yu. M. (1964). *Ind. Lab.* **30**, 937.

Kimball, K. E. (1962). Interlaminar Properties of Five Plastic Laminates. Forest Products Lab. Rep. 1890, Madison, Wisconsin.

Kimball, A. L., and Lovell, D. E. (1927). *Phys. Rev. (Ser. 2)* **30**, 948.

Konstantinov, V. A., and Strelyaev, V. S. (1969). *Ind. Lab.* **35**, 1034.

Kreider, K. G. (1969). *In* Composite Materials: Testing and Design. Amer. Soc. Testing Mater., Spec. Tech. Publ. 460, pp. 203–214.

Kritsuk, A. A., and Emel'yanov, R. F. (1969). *Ind. Lab.* **35**, 1696.

Lamberson, D. L. (1969). The High Pressure Equation of State of Tantalum, Polystyrene, and Carbon Phenolic Determined from Ultrasonic Velocities. Air Force Inst. Tech., Doctoral Dissertation, AD-734764.

Langhaar, H. L., and Boresi, A. P. (1958). *In Proc. U.S. Nat. Congr. Appl. Mech., 3rd* pp. 393–399.

Langley, M. (1968). *Aeronaut. J.* **72**, 442.

Lantz, R. B. (1969). *J. Compos. Mater.* **3**, 642.

Lantz, R. B., and Baldridge, K. G. (1969). *In* Composite Materials: Testing and Design. Amer. Soc. Testing Mater., Spec. Tech. Publ. 460, pp. 94–107.

Lavengood, R. E., and Ishai, O. (1970). *J. Mater.* **5**, 684.

Lekhnitskii, S. G. (1963). "Theory of Elasticity of an Anisotropic Elastic Body." Pergamon, Oxford.

Lempriere, B. M., Fenn, R. W., Jr., Crooks, D. D., and Kinder, W. C. (1969). *AIAA J.* **7**, 2341.

Lenoe, E. M. (1970). *J. Eng. Mech. Div. Proc. ASCE* **96** (EM 6), 809.

Lenoe, E. M., Knight, M., and Schoene, C. (1969). *In* Composite Materials: Testing and Design. Amer. Soc. Testing Mater., Spec. Tech. Publ. 460, pp. 122–139.

Liber, T., Daniel, I. M., and Ahimaz, F. J. (1971). Presented at *Amer. Soc. Testing Mater. Conf. Compos. Mater. Testing Design, 2nd, Anaheim, California.*

Markham, M. F. (1970). *Composites* **1**, 145.

Martin, G. (1969). *In Aerosp.—AFML Conf. NDT Plast./Compos. Struct., Dayton, Ohio* AD-708146, Paper No. 2.

Mazza, L. T., Paxson, E. B., and Rodgers, R. L. (1971). Measurement of Damping Coefficients and Dynamic Modulus of Fiber Composites. U.S. Army Aviat. Mater. Lab., USAAVLABS-TN-2, AD-869025.

McBride, R. J. (1960). An Evaluation of Macro-Test Procedures for Determining the Mechanical Properties of Reinforced Plastics. Wright Air Develop. Center, WADC TR 59-605, AD-236127.

Mullin, J. V., and Knoell, A. C. (1970). *Mater. Res. Std.* **10** (12), 16.

Neighbours, J. R., and Schacher, G. E. (1967). *J. Appl. Phys.* **38**, 5366.

Nordby, G. M., Noyes, J. V., and Crisman, W. C. (1964). Research in the Field of Fiberglass-Reinforced Sandwich Structure for Airframe Use. U.S. Army Transportation Res. Command, TRECOM TR 64-37, AD-607339.

Nordby, G. M., Crisman, W. C., and Bert, C. W. (1965). The Effect of Resin Content and Voids on the Strength of Fiberglass-Reinforced Plastics for Airframe Use. U.S. Army Aviat. Mater. Lab., USAAVLABS-TR-65-66, AD-627362.

Novak, R. C. (1969). *In* Composite Materials: Testing and Design. Amer. Soc. Testing Mater., Spec. Tech. Publ. 460, pp. 540–549.

Ogorkiewicz, R. M., and Mucci, P. E. R. (1971). *Composites* **2**, 139.

Pagano, N. J. (1971). *J. Compos. Mater.* **5**, 260.

Pagano, N. J., and Chou, P. C. (1969). *J. Compos. Mater.* **3**, 166.

Pagano, N. J., and Halpin, J. C. (1968). *J. Compos. Mater.* **2**, 18.

Pagano, N. J., and Whitney, J. M. (1970). *J. Compos. Mater.* **4**, 360.

Pagano, N. J., Halpin, J. C., and Whitney, J. M. (1968). *J. Compos. Mater.* **2**, 154.

Papirno, R., and Slepetz, J. M. (1971). *In* Composite Materials. NATO, AGARD, AGARD-CP-63-71, AD-732741, Paper No. 10.

Park, I. K. (1971). *Int. Conf. Carbon Fibres, Their Compos. Appl.* Plastics Inst., London, Paper No. 23.

Pendered, J. W., and Bishop, R. E. D. (1963). *J. Mech. Eng. Sci.* **5**, 345.

Penton, A. P. (1960). *SPE J.* **16**, 1246.

Petit, P. H. (1969). *In* Composite Materials: Testing and Design. Amer. Soc. Testing Mater., Spec. Tech. Publ. 460, pp. 83–93.

Potapov, A. I. (1968). An Investigation of the Elastic Characteristics of Fiberglass Reinforced Plastics by the Pulse Acoustic Method. Foreign Technol. Div., FTD-MT-24-47-68, AD-681578.

Pottinger, M. G. (1970). Material Damping of Glass Fiber-Epoxy and Boron Fiber-Aluminum Composites. Aerosp. Res. Lab., Rep. ARL 70-0237, AD-721191.

Prosen, S. P. (1965). *In* "Filament Structures Technology" (*Proc. Ann. Tech. Symp., 6th, ASME, New Mexico Sect. Univ. of New Mexico, Dec. 3–4, 1965*), pp. 180–214.

Prosen, S. P. (1969). *In* Composite Materials: Testing and Design. Amer. Soc. Testing Mater., Spec. Tech. Publ. 460, pp. 5–12.

Prosen, S. P., Karpe, S., Kinna, M. A., Mueller, C., Perry, H. A., and Barnet, F. R. (1963). *In Symp. Std. Filament-Wound Reinforced Plast.* Amer. Soc. Testing Mater., Spec. Tech. Publ. 327, pp. 105–122.

Protasov, V. D., and Kopnov, V. A. (1965). *Polym. Mech.* **1** (5), 39.

Reynolds, W. N. (1971). *Int. Conf. Carbon Fibres, Their Compos. Appl.* Plastics Inst., London, Paper No. 52.

Richards, G. L., Airhart, T. P., and Ashton, J. E. (1969). *J. Compos. Mater.* **3**, 586.

Rizzo, R. R. (1969). *J. Compos. Mater.* **3**, 202.

Rizzo, R. R., and Vicario, A. A. (1972). *In Conf. Compos. Mater. Testing Design, 2nd* Amer. Soc. Testing Mater., Spec. Tech. Publ. 497, pp. 68–88.

Romstad, K. (1964a). Investigation of Methods for Evaluating Unwoven Glass-Fiber-Reinforced Plastic Laminates in Flexure. Forest Products Lab., Res. Note FPL-024, Madison, Wisconsin.

Romstad, K. (1964b). Methods for Evaluating Tensile and Compressive Properties of Plastic Laminates Reinforced with Unwoven Glass Fibers. Forest Products Lab., Res. Note FPL-052, Madison, Wisconsin.

Romstad, K. (1964c). Methods for Evaluating Shear Strength of Plastic Laminates Reinforced with Unwoven Glass Fibers. Forest Products Lab., Res. Note FPL-033, Madison, Wisconsin.

Rosato, D. V., and Grove, C. S., Jr. (1964). "Filament Winding." Wiley (Interscience), New York.

Roskos, T. G., and Pflederer, F. R. (1963). *In Symp. Std. Filament-Wound Reinforced Plast.* Amer. Soc. Testing Mater., Spec. Tech. Publ. 327, pp. 96–104.

Rothman, E. A., and Molter, G. E. (1969). *In* Composite Materials: Testing and Design. Amer. Soc. Testing Mater., Spec. Tech. Publ. 460, pp. 72–82.

Sattar, S. A., and Kellogg, D. H. (1969). *In* Composite Materials: Testing and Design. Amer. Soc. Testing Mater., Spec. Tech. Publ. 460, pp. 62–71.

Schultz, A. W. (1967). *Mater. Res. Std.* **7**, 341.

Schultz, A. W. (1971). *SAMPE Quart.* **2** (2), 31.

Schultz, A. B., and Tsai, S. W. (1968). *J. Compos. Mater.* **2**, 368.

Schultz, A. B., and Tsai, S. W. (1969). *J. Compos. Mater.* **3,** 434.

Semenov, P. I. (1968). *Polym. Mech.* **2,** 17.

Seydel, E. (1933). *Ing.-Arch.* **4,** 169.

Shlenskii, V. F. (1970). *Sov. Appl. Mech.* **3** (4), 76.

Shockey, P. D. (1971). *In* "Experimental Mechanics" (*Proc. Ann. Symp., 11th, Albuquerque, New Mexico, February 11–12, 1971*), pp. 9–14.

Sidorin, Ya. S. (1967). *Ind. Lab.* **32,** 723.

Sidorin, Ya. S. (1970). Experimental Investigation of Anisotropy of Fiberglass-Reinforced Plastics. Foreign Technol. Div., Air Force Syst. Command, Transl. FTD-HT-23-208-70, AD-710345.

Simitses, G. J. (1967). *AIAA J.* **5,** 1463.

Siu, C. C., and Bert, C. W. (1973). *J. Eng. Ind. Trans. ASME* **96B,** 603.

Slepetz, J. M. (1971). *In* Composite Materials. NATO, AGARD, AGARD-CP-63-71, AD-732741, Paper No. 8.

Smith, R. T., and Stephens, R. W. B. (1964). *Progr. Appl. Mater. Res.* **5,** 39–64.

Spies, G. J., and de Jong, T. (1971). *In* Composite Materials. NATO, AGARD. AGARD-CP-63-71, AD-732741, Paper No. 2.

Spintsis, I. A. (1970). *Polym. Mech.* **3,** 110.

Suarez, J. A., Whiteside, J. B., and Hadcock, R. N. (1972). *In Conf. Compos. Mater. Testing Design, 2nd* Amer. Soc. Testing Mater., Spec. Tech. Publ. 497, pp. 237–256.

Tarnopol'skii, Yu. M., and Roze, A. V. (1965). *Polym. Mech.* **1,** 69.

Tauchert, T. R. (1971). *J. Compos. Mater.* **5,** 456.

Tauchert, T. R., and Güzelsu, A. N. (1971). *J. Compos. Mater.* **5,** 549.

Tauchert, T. R., and Moon, F. C. (1971). *AIAA J.* **9,** 1492.

Thielemann, W. (1950). Contribution to the Problem of Buckling of Orthotropic Plates, with Special Reference to Plywood. NACA TM 1263.

Thurston, R. N. (1965). *J. Acoust. Soc. Amer.* **37,** 348, 1147.

Toy, A., and Dickerson, E. O. (1967). *In Advan. Struct. Compos.* (*Nat. SAMPE Symp.*) **12,** Paper D-6.

Trantina, G. G. (1967). Preliminary Investigation of Measurement of Elastic Moduli of Composites Using Strain Gages. Univ. of Illinois, Dept. of Theor. and Appl. Mech., T&AM Rep. 271, AD-664690.

Tsai, S. W. (1965). *J. Eng. Ind. Trans. ASME* **87B,** 315.

Tsai, S. W. (1967). A Test Method for the Determination of Shear Modulus and Shear Strength. Air Force Mater. Lab., AFML-TR-66-372, AD-652217.

Tsai, S. W. (1971). *In* "Experimental Mechanics" (*Proc. Ann. Symp., 11th, Albuquerque, New Mexico, February 11–12, 1971*), pp. 1–8.

Tsai, S. W., and Springer, G. S. (1963). *J. Appl. Mech.* **30,** 467.

Vicario, A. A., and Rizzo, R. R. (1970). *J. Compos. Mater.* **4,** 273.

Vogt, C. W., Haniuk, E. S., and Trice, J. M., Jr. (1966). *In* Testing Techniques for Filament Reinforced Plastics. Air Force Mater. Lab., AFML-TR-66-274, AD-801547, pp. 185–251.

Waddoups, M. E. (1968). *In* Composite Materials Workshop (S. W. Tsai, J. C. Halpin, and N. J. Pagano, eds.), pp. 254–308. Technomic, Stamford, Connecticut.

Wall, L. D., and Card, M. F. (1971). Torsional Shear Strength of Filament-Wound Glass-Epoxy Tubes. NASA TN D-6140.

Weidner, J. C. (1971). New Tensile and Compressive Test Specimens for Unidirectional Reinforced Graphite Epoxy Composites. Air Force Mater. Lab., AFML-TR-70-264.

Wells, H., Colclough, W. J., and Goggin, P. R. (1969). *Proc. Ann. Tech. Conf., Soc. Plast. Ind. Reinforced Plast./Compos. Div., 24th.* Sect. 2-C.

Weng, T. L. (1969). *AIAA J.* **7,** 851.

Werren, F., and Gish, M. (1957). Supplement to Directional Properties of Glass-Fabric-Base Plastic Laminate Panels of Sizes That Do Not Buckle. Forest Products Lab., Rep. 1803-C, Madison, Wisconsin.

Whitney, J. M. (1967). *Exp. Mech.* **7,** 447.

Whitney, J. M. (1968). Application of the Plate Twist Test to Laminated Composites. Air Force Mater. Lab., AFML-TR-67-407, AD-668477.

Whitney, J. M. (1971). *J. Compos. Mater.* **5,** 340.

Whitney, J. M., and Dauksys, R. J. (1970). *J. Compos. Mater.* **4,** 135.

Whitney, J. M., and Halpin, J. C. (1968). *J. Compos. Mater.* **2,** 360.

Whitney, J. M., Stansbarger, D. L., and Howell, H. B. (1971). *J. Compos. Mater.* **5,** 24.

Whitney, J. M., Pagano, N. J., and Pipes, R. B. (1972). *In Conf. Compos. Mater. Testing Design, 2nd.* Amer. Soc. Testing Mater., Spec. Tech. Publ. 497, pp. 52–67.

Witt, R. K., Hoppmann, W. H., II, and Buxbaum, R. S. (1953). *ASTM Bull.* No. 194, 53.

Wu, C. T. (1962). *Exp. Mech.* **2,** 338.

Wu, E. M., and Thomas, R. L. (1968). *J. Compos. Mater.* **2,** 523.

Wu, C. I., and Vinson, J. R. (1969). *Fibre Sci. Technol.* **2,** 97.

Youngquist, W. G., and Kuenzi, E. W. (1961). *In Symp. Shear Torsion Testing* Amer. Soc. Testing Mater., Spec. Tech. Publ. 289, pp. 75–89.

Yu, Y. Y. (1959). *J. Appl. Mech.* **26,** 679.

Yurenka, S. (1963). *In Symp. Std. Filament-Wound Reinforced Plast.* Amer. Soc. Testing Mater., Spec. Tech. Publ. 327, pp. 314–329.

Zabora, R. F., and Bell, J. E. (1971). A Test Technique to Study Interlaminar Shear Phenomena of Laminated Composites. Air Force Flight Dynam. Lab., AFFDL-TR-71-67, AD-729872.

Zimmer, J. E., and Cost, J. R. (1970). *J. Acoust. Soc. Amer.* **47,** 795.

Zurbrick, J. R. (1968). *Proc. Ann. Tech. Conf., Soc. Plast. Ind. Reinforced Plast./Compos. Div., 23rd.* Sect. 7-B.

Zurbrick, J. R. (1969). *In Aerosp.-AFML Conf. NDT Plast./Compos. Struct., Dayton, Ohio* AD-708146, Paper No. 18.

Zurbrick, J. R., and Schultz, A. W. (1966). *In* Testing Techniques for Filament Reinforced Plastics. Air Force Mater. Lab., AFML-TR-66-274, AD-801547, pp. 675–700.

10

Analysis of Discontinuities, Edge Effects, and Joints

GLENN C. GRIMES

Department of Structural Research
Southwest Research Institute
San Antonio, Texas

LOWELL F. GREIMANN

Department of Civil Engineering
Iowa State University
Ames, Iowa

I. Introduction

The purpose of this chapter is to acquaint the reader with the phenomena of edge effects and discontinuities in composites under load and to provide some attachment analysis techniques which have not been published in the literature.

Discontinuities covered in Section II are partly a macrofracture mechanics problem and partly one of a micromechanical discontinuity. Edge effects presented in Section III are found to be closely related to the lamination sequence and are usually significant only within one laminate thickness distance of the free edge. Attachment efficiency and cost and adhesive bonded joint analysis techniques are presented in Section IV showing that nonlinear analysis techniques accurately predict bonded joint strengths. Mechanically fastened joints are reviewed in Section V; typical experimental behavior and the lack of research in this area are discussed.

In some respects it will be seen that discontinuities and edge effects are closely related to joints and their behavior under load; thus incorporating them into a single chapter is logical.

II. Discontinuities

Discontinuities (on the macroscale) can be defined as abrupt changes in geometry or material type in a load bearing structural member causing changes in the load paths and/or stress intensities. A hole or step in the laminate thickness is an example of a geometric discontinuity. A material discontinuity, for example, would occur when a metal insert is added to a laminate at the time it is made. However, this section will cover only geometric discontinuities since material changes almost always result in a bonded or mechanical joint, the analyses of which are covered in other sections of this chapter. Discontinuities are of two types: precise and random. Precise discontinuities may be molded in or mechanically cut into the laminate, whereas random discontinuities are induced by external forces causing damage (a bullet hole, for example). Methodology and insight will be provided selectively on some of these problems, but concentrating on precise round hole discontinuities.

On the microscale discontinuities can be described as fiber breaks, resin matrix cracking or crazing, and delaminations or voids. Such microdiscontinuities may be caused by the processing and/or tooling used or by

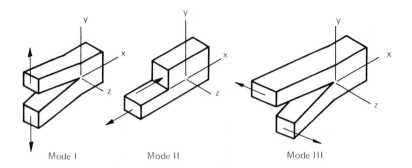

Fig. 1. The basic modes of crack surface displacements.

load or thermally induced stresses (strains). Only load induced discontinuities will be discussed with some prediction techniques presented.

In the discussion of discontinuities in composite material structural members, standard methods of describing stress fields near crack tips or intense energy regions will be used. These are shown in Fig. 1, illustrating the three classic modes. Only Mode I will be discussed in any depth for composites.

A. Holes

This type of discontinuity in composite materials has not received a great deal of attention in the open literature at this writing. Empirical work in fitting elastic fracture mechanics formulas to composites behavior by experimental observations has received some attention. In addition, several purely analytical approaches have been used which show promise. Several of these empirical and analytical techniques will be reviewed relative to application on composite structures.

1. *Empirical Approach*

For the case of composite uniaxial tension members with a hole, Waddoups *et al.* (1971) utilize an empirical procedure within the confines of linear elastic fracture mechanics. The fracture model used is shown in Fig. 2. Tension test data on [0/90]c and [0/±45]c symmetric graphite–epoxy composite specimens with circular holes was utilized for correlation. Development of the empirical technique involved analysis of the test data in a fashion to demonstrate an equivalence of energy rate and stress intensity in fracture using a plane strain Mode I crack. Using anisotropic materials

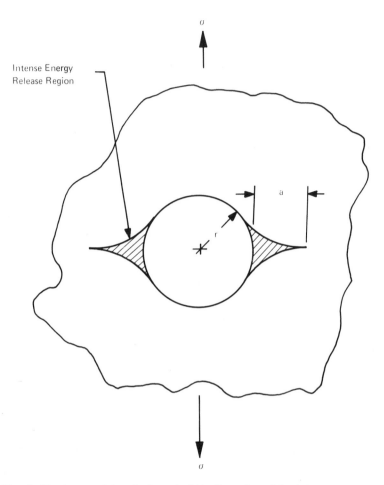

Fɪɢ. 2. Fracture model. *a* is characteristic dimension of the intense energy region.

crack extension formulas, which are assumed to be analogous with the isotropic case defined by Paris and Sih (1965), are at least applicable to a homogeneous orthotropic lamina according to Wu (1968) and, with the empirical modification of Waddoups *et al.* (1971), to a laminate. This formula for the energy available for crack extension is

$$G_I = \frac{(1 - \nu^2)\pi}{E} K_I^2 \tag{1}$$

The intense energy region and the crack analysis are assumed symmetric with the characteristic length, *a*, based upon a $1/(r)^{1/2}$ type of singularity.

In order to define the stress intensity factor, Paris and Sih (1965) was used to give:

$$K_I = \sigma(\pi a)^{1/2} f(a/r) \tag{2}$$

Substituting Eq. (2) into Eq. (1) yields

$$(G_I)^{1/2} = \left[\pi\left(\frac{a(1 - \nu^2)}{E}\right)^{1/2}\right]\sigma f(a/r) \tag{3}$$

Now assume that the material behaves like an ideal (brittle) (Griffith, 1920) solid so that G_I will be a material constant, i.e., the composite is taken to be homogeneous for this analysis. For this homogeneous, elastic, and anisotropic case the stress concentration factor K_T at the edge of any round hole is 3.0 as shown by Bowie (1956). By comparison, the [0/45]c graphite–epoxy material with a round hole has a stress concentration factor K_T of 2.98 according to Waddoups *et al.* (1971), i.e., the use of empirically modified formulas will be sufficiently accurate for use in analysis. Another assumption necessary is that the characteristic length (a) be small but finite. Now Eq. (2) is solved for stress:

$$\sigma_c = \frac{K_{Ic}}{(\pi a)^{1/2} f(a/r)} \tag{4}$$

and for a specimen with no hole:

$$\sigma_0 = \sigma_c \big|_{a/r=a} = \frac{K_{Ic}}{(\pi a)^{1/2}(1.00)} \tag{5}$$

Therefore,

$$\sigma_0/\sigma_c = f(a/r) \tag{6}$$

This ratio has been parametrically evaluated in Waddoups *et al.* (1971) for a [0/±45]c laminate which is shown in Fig. 3. Note that the experimental points superimposed on the parametric curves correlate well with them. Waddoups *et al.* (1971) explain that the experimental behavior coincides with a constant characteristic length of $a = 0.040$ in. Because of the internal (microscopic) structure of the composite, no macroscopically measureable crack was present. However, an intense energy region (high stress intensity) apparently exists because the material fractures catastrophically under load, starting at this point when the critical energy level is attained.

Further verification of the concept of an intense energy region is shown by Waddoups *et al.* (1971) in Fig. 4. Strains are measured from the inside of a hole in a tensile specimen along a transverse line toward the edge and plotted as a function of the distance from the centerline of the hole divided

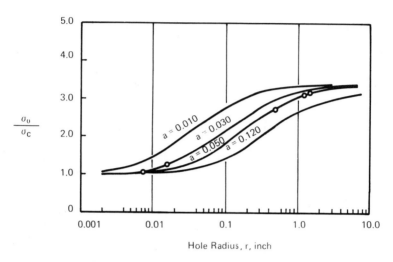

FIG. 3. Parametric study of $[0/\pm45]_{2S}$ graphite–epoxy.

by the hole radius. The values shown in Fig. 4 illustrate the high strains occurring in the intense energy regions, i.e., the assumption of such an area
next to a hole is reasonable. The experimental data correlation with the
fracture analysis led Waddoups et al. (1971) to conclude that G_I is a measure of the energy available to resist a crack, and that it remains constant as
the stress intensity factor K_I varies as a function of r. Therefore, fracture
behavior of such orientations† of graphite–epoxy is similar to a Griffith
(brittle) solid under static loading conditions. Under fatigue loading conditions, however, this is not true. There is no evidence of nucleation and
growth of through (macro) cracks as exhibited in metals; as a result the
composite material exhibits very high 10^7 cycle endurance limit strength.‡
This phenomena is not characteristic of either metals or the theoretical
Griffith (brittle) solid typified by most ceramics.

Generally, the procedure for applying linear elastic fracture mechanics to
composite materials is to define the values of a/r and a using two types of
experimental specimens: one having an induced stress concentration and
one having none. Once this is established Waddoups et al. (1971) postulate
that the reduced specimen strength σ_c can be predicted for other stress
concentrations of a similar geometry. Figure 3 provides information in this

† Waddoups et al. (1971) also include $[0/90]_C$ graphite–epoxy laminates as exhibiting
such behavior.
‡ Ranging from 50 to 80% of static ultimate depending on the composite material
and orientation.

area by relating hole radius r to the strength ratio σ_0/σ_c [assumed to be equal to $f(a/r)$] for various values of the intense energy region characteristic dimension, a. For example, in Waddoups et al. (1971) for the case of a round hole in a $[0/\pm45]_c$ graphite–epoxy specimen subjected to uniaxial tension, an average value is $a = 0.04$. However, a stricter interpretation of Fig. 3 shows that small holes ($r < 0.05$ in.) have values closer to $a = 0.03$ and large holes ($r > 0.3$ in.) have values closer to $a = 0.05$ in with the $a = 0.04$ value assumed to apply to the $0.05 \leq r \leq 0.30$. The experimental data plotted in Fig. 3 corroborate this for the $[0/\pm45]_c$ graphite–epoxy material A purely experimental approach could also be used, i.e., test one or more specimens, each with and without holes, and use the strength ratios of the two to establish the $f(a/r)$ value.

Illustrating the use of this technique for a $[0/\pm45]_c$ graphite–epoxy laminate, assume there are several tensile specimens with holes of radii r, as shown in the first column of Table I. Then from Fig. 3 the values in the second, third, and fourth columns can be obtained. The values in the fifth column are obtained from Fig. 5 using the a/r inputs of Table I. Note the closeness of the values in the fourth and fifth columns. Figure 5 was plotted from analytically derived data taken from Paris and Sih (1965) for a hole in a uniaxial tension loaded plate (isotropic or anisotropic). Obviously, then, either Fig. 3 or Fig. 5 could be used to obtain $f(a/r)$ values now that

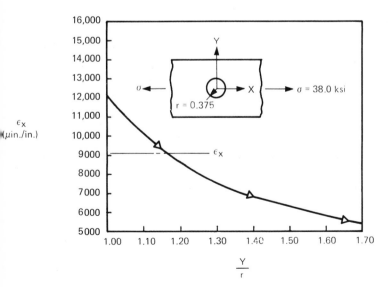

FIG. 4. Strain profile at net section. e_x is the ultimate for an unnotched control specimen of $[0/+45]_{2S}$ graphite–epoxy.

TABLE I

STRENGTH REDUCTION FACTORS FOR A TENSILE MEMBER WITH A ROUND HOLE

Hole radius r, in.	Intense energy characteristic dimension a, in.	a/r	$\sigma_0/\sigma_c = f(a/r)$	Stress intensity factor coefficient $= f(a/r)$	K_I at 50,000 psi, psi $\sqrt{\text{in.}}$	Working design allowables stress level with a hole, psi
0.01	0.03	3.0	1.10	1.13	16,884	45,455
0.10	0.04	0.4	2.00	1.97	35,449	25,000
1.00	0.05	0.05	3.05	2.98	60,439	16,393

the characteristic dimension a has been defined. Therefore, for any given or desired operating stress level σ, the stress intensity factor K_I may be calculated using Eq. (2). At a material design allowable stress level of $\sigma = 50,000$ psi the K_I values are shown in Table I. Thus, the stress intensity factor is shown to increase with increasing hole size at a given tension member al-

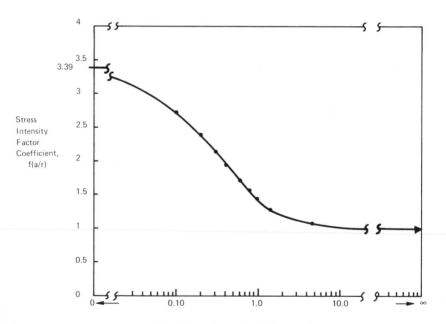

Size of Energy Intense Region (in terms of hole radius)

FIG. 5. Geometry effects on stress intensity.

lowable stress level. Therefore, the working design allowable stress level must be reduced according to the equation:

$$\sigma_c = \frac{\sigma_0}{f(a/r)} \tag{7}$$

These values are shown in the last column of Table I. This then provides an indication of the decreased material allowable stresses available when a hole is present in a composite material tension member.

Another method of utilizing this information would be to use Eq. (4) to predict the failure strength or design allowables of similar tensile specimens keeping in mind that changing the hole geometry or the allowable stress (or strength) will change the K_I value.

A purely experimental approach was used by Daniel and Rowlands (1971) to determine the strain (stress) concentration around a hole in a tension loaded anisotropic plate by moiré techniques. The results for both

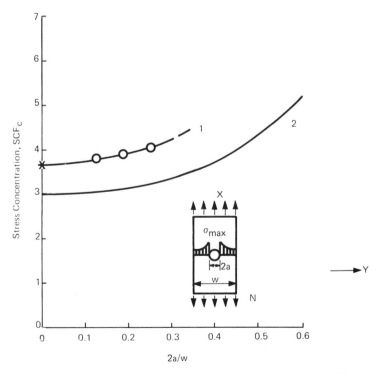

FIG. 6. Stress concentration factor as a function of hole diameter to width ratio. 1. [90/0/90/0]$_S$ glass–epoxy; 2. isotropic; $\bigcirc$ experimental; * theoretical. SCF$_c = \delta_{max}/N$.

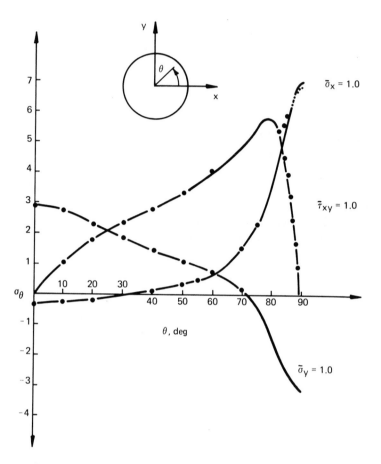

Fig. 7. Stress distributions for boron–epoxy lamina (orthotropic). $E_x = 30.0$, $E_y = 3.0$, $G_{xy} = 1.0$, $\nu_{xy} = 0.336$ ·—·— Reference solution; ··· Finite-element solution.

isotropic and anisotropic stress concentration factors are shown in Fig. 6. The theoretical calculations were made based on the Lekhnitskii (1963) and Savin (1961) formulas:

$$\text{SCF}_c = 1 + \left\{ 2\left[\left(\frac{E_x}{E_y}\right)^{1/2} - \nu_{xy} \right] + \frac{E_x}{G_{xy}} \right\}^{1/2} \tag{8}$$

where

E_x, E_y = moduli in the longitudinal and transverse direction, respectively,

ν_{xy} = Poisson's ratio,

G_{xy} = shear modulus related to the values of Young's modulus and Poisson's ratio by the relation:

$$\frac{1}{G_{xy}} = \frac{4}{E_{xy}} - \frac{1 - 2\nu_{xy}}{E_x} - \frac{1}{E_y}$$

E_{xy} = modulus at 45° to the principal axis.

2. Analytical Approaches

Rybicki and Hopper (1972) investigated stress concentrations due to holes by utilizing linear elastic plane stress conditions with a finite-element solution. These results were compared to a Lekhnitskii (1968) solution. The results are plotted for a circular hole in a plate for a unit stress of 1.0. The tangential stress σ_θ at the hole edge is then plotted against angular location, θ. Results for an orthotropic case boron–epoxy lamina are shown in Fig. 7 for $\bar{\sigma}_x$, $\bar{\tau}_{xy}$, $\bar{\sigma}_y$ applied stresses of 1.0. The σ_θ values, then, become

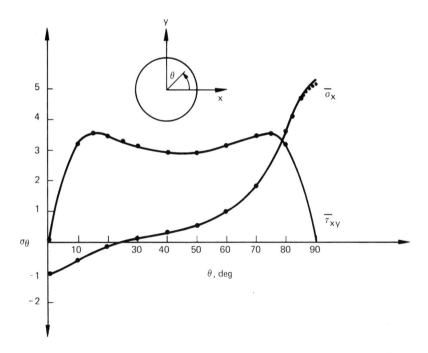

FIG. 8. Stress distributions for a (90/0/0/90) boron–epoxy laminate (orthotropic). $E_x = E_y = 6.5757$, $\nu_{xy} = 0.0606$, $G_{xy} = 0.4$. $\cdots$ Reference solution; —·—Finite-element solution.

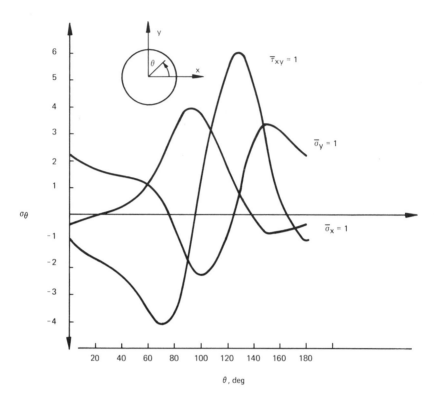

FIG. 9. Stress distributions for a (45/0/0/−45) boron–epoxy laminate (anisotropic). ──── Finite-element solution.

stress concentration factors at the hole's edge. Figure 8 presents the σ_θ *versus* θ results for a boron–epoxy orthotropic case $[90/0]_s$ laminate for $\bar\sigma_x$ and $\bar\tau_{xy}$ equal to 1.0. Note that the finite-element solution and the Lekhnitskii (1968) elasticity solution are in excellent agreement. Figure 9 gives the σ_θ versus θ results of an anisotropic finite-element solution only for $\bar\sigma_x$, $\bar\tau_{xy}$, and $\bar\sigma_y$ applied stresses of 1.0 for a $[+45/0]_s$ boron–epoxy laminate. It can be observed in Fig. 10 that stress concentrations are considerably lower in an isotropic material under the same stresses.

Greszczuk's (1972) analysis gives results which are nearly identical with those of Rybicki and Hopper (1972) for boron–epoxy plates. In addition, unidirectional laminates with circular holes are analyzed at various uniaxial loading angles and under biaxial loadings. Stress concentration factors of a unidirectional laminate with a circular hole are shown in Fig. 11 for a biaxial loading and in Fig. 12 for a uniaxial loading at various angles to the reinforcement direction. Note the ⊗ designated points on the curves of these figures which locate the predicted failure stress concentration. Greszczuk (1972) used the Henky von Mises distortional energy theory to predict failures.

Figure 13 shows the predicted effect of a cutout on a unidirectional laminate's strength with uniaxial loading at various angles to the reinforcement. An interesting phenomenon can be observed in Fig. 13: while the laminate with a hole loaded parallel to the fibers has only 10% of the tensile strength of one without, at loading angles of 45° and above, the laminate with a hole has approximately 40% of the tensile strength of one without a hole. Such results obviously do not correlate with the maximum stress concentration factors shown in Figs. 11 and 12 but with the ⊗ designated stress concentration factor points which are lower and at a different angular location. Greszczuk's (1972) analysis shows that orthotropic and anisotropic plates containing holes will fail as a result of the interaction of various stress components rather than a maximum stress concentration as happens in isotropic plates.

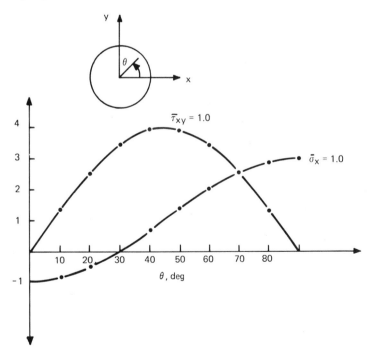

FIG. 10. Stress distribution around a circular hole in an isotropic material. $E_x = E_y = 3.0$, $\nu_{xy} = 0.2$, $G_{xy} = 1.25$. —·— Reference solution; —— Finite-element solution.

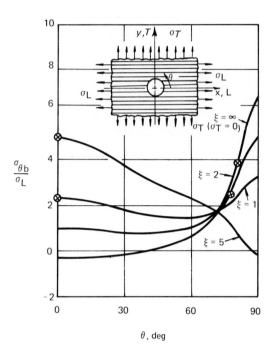

FIG. 11. Stress concentrations in biaxially loaded boron–epoxy plates. The predicted location of failure as well as stress concentration at that point are noted. $\sigma_{\theta b}$ is the circumferential stress at the edge of the opening. $\xi = \sigma_L/\sigma_T$.

TABLE II

PROPERTIES OF BORON–EPOXY LAMINA USED TO OBTAIN NUMERICAL RESULTS

Property	Value
Young's modulus of fiber, E_f, 10^6 psi	60
Poisson's ratio of fiber, ν_f	0.20
Young's modulus of resin, E_r, 10^6 psi	0.50
Poisson's ratio of resin, ν_r	0.35
Young's modulus of composite in the fiber direction, E_L, 10^6 psi	41.0
Young's modulus of composite in transverse direction, E_T, 10^6 psi	3.45
Shear modulus of composite, G_{LT}, 10^6 psi	1.50
Major Poisson's ratio of composite, ν_{LT}	0.27
Minor Poisson's ratio of composite, ν_{LT}	0.023
Strength of composite in the fiber direction, F_L, 10^3 psi	180
Strength of Composite in transverse direction, F_T, 10^3 psi	20
Shear strength of composite, F_{LT}, 10^3 psi	10

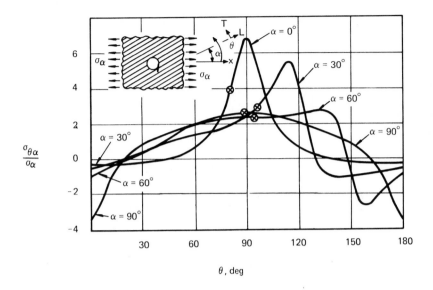

FIG. 12. Stress concentrations in anisotropic boron–epoxy plates. $\sigma_{\theta\alpha}$ is the circumferential stress at the edge of the opening. $\otimes$ denotes the predicted location of failure and the stress concentration at that point.

Figure 14 shows the reasonably good correlation of the experimental results with the theory on a unidirectional laminate with a hole for a uniaxial stress applied at 30° to the reinforcement. Table II gives the boron–epoxy lamina properties used in the calculations. While the formulas developed in Greszczuk (1972) are lengthy, they are in closed form and can readily be used either in hand or computer calculations. The numerical plots shown herein will provide the reader with accurate stress concentration and failure information on boron–epoxy plates with holes. However, different composite materials will have different characteristics so their stress concentration factors will not be the same. Thus they should be calculated.†

B. Micromechanical Discontinuities

Three types of load induced discontinuities are possible: fiber breaks, matrix resin cracks, and fiber–matrix interface separations. However, with the high quality materials and processes available today, load induced

† SCF values may be obtained from the previous discussions in this chapter or from Greszczuk's (1972) formulas.

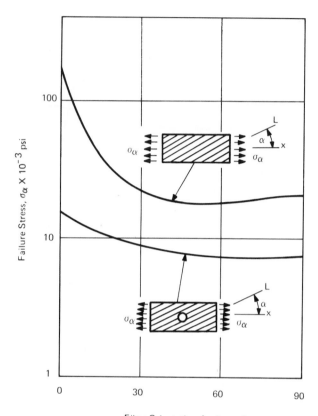

Fig. 13.   Effect of cutout and fiber orientation on the strength of boron–epoxy composite plates. F_L = 180 ksi (allowable strength in L direction); F_T = 20 ksi (allowable strength in T direction); F_{LT} = 10 ksi (allowable shear strength).

interface separation is seldom a significant factor in subsequent loading behavior or cause of failure, so it will not be considered here. The other two types of discontinuities will be considered here, i.e., fiber breaks and resin cracks. Fiber breaks will be considered in terms of their stress concentration factors induced on the fiber and on the resin matrix. Resin cracks will be considered only as lamina cracking (in the matrix) parallel to the fibers and perpendicular to the principal stress causing them.

In addition, a maximum strain criterion as an intermediate and ultimate failure prediction technique for composite materials will be presented. The importance of this criterion to the subject of discontinuities results from

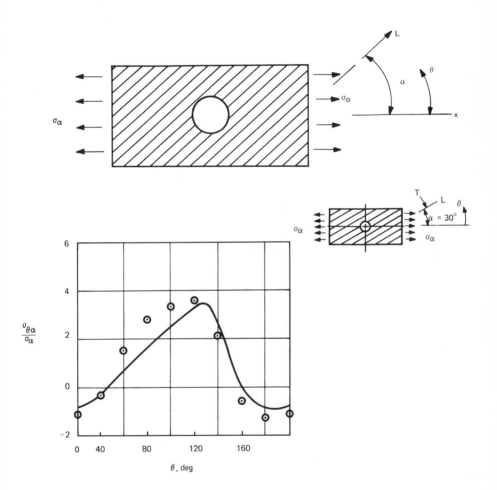

FIG. 14. Test theory comparison of stress concentrations in anisotropic plate. — Theory; ⊙ Test results; $\sigma_{\theta\alpha}$ is the stress around the circumference of the cutout. Properties of the plate are: $E_L = 4.525 \times 10^6$ psi, $E_T = 1.825 \times 10^6$ psi, $G_{LT} = 0.733 \times 10^6$ psi, $\nu_{LT} = 0.270$.

the fact that most proportional limits and ultimate strength values are controlled by load induced micromechanical discontinuities. These discontinuities are caused by the strain incompatibility of discrete elements of the composite, i.e., the fiber and matrix of two or more different lamina orientations within a laminate. Most of these limitations can be accurately described by limiting uniaxial strain values of each lamina. Techniques for determining these strain values for each lamina and then combining them into a laminate's strength envelope by continuum mechanics will be discussed.

1. *Fiber Breaks*

Barker and McLaughlin (1971) investigated the effect of a continuous fiber discontinuity on the fiber and matrix stress concentration factors (SCF) and their relation to the gross composite stress. Using linear elastic micromechanics they developed the fiber-to-composite stress relationship in a unidirectional composite without a discontinuity as:

$$\frac{\bar{\sigma}_f}{\bar{\sigma}_0}\left[V_f + \frac{E_m}{E_f}(1 - V_f)\right] = 1 \tag{9}$$

and for the matrix-to-composite stress relationship:

$$\frac{\bar{\sigma}_m}{\bar{\sigma}_0}\left[\frac{E_f}{E_m}V_f + (1 - V_f)\right] = 1 \tag{10}$$

However, when a discontinuity is present the left-hand sides of these equations will be different from unity because the fiber and matrix stresses deviate from their average values. Equations (9) and (10) will then become stress concentration factor equations if it is assumed that the applied normal matrix and fiber stresses are principal stresses. Thus

$$\text{SCF}_f = \frac{\sigma_f}{\bar{\sigma}_0}\left[V_f + \frac{E_m}{E_f}(1 - V_f)\right] \tag{11}$$

and

$$\text{SCF}_m = \frac{\sigma_m}{\bar{\sigma}_0}\left[\frac{E_f}{E_m}V_f + (1 - V_f)\right] \tag{12}$$

If E_f/E_m is greater than 20, then Eqs. (11) and (12) reduce to

$$\text{SCF}_f = \frac{V_f\sigma_f}{\bar{\sigma}_0} \tag{13}$$

and

$$\text{SCF}_m = \frac{E_f}{E_m}\frac{V_f\sigma_m}{\bar{\sigma}_0} \tag{14}$$

These formulas are independent of fiber gap length within the range expected of load induced damage (i.e., $4d$ or less). The fiber SCF_f is also independent of fiber/matrix modulus ratios above 20, whereas the matrix SCF_m is almost directly proportional to this ratio. Barker and MacLaughlin (1971) verify their work with a finite-element analysis, the results of which are shown in Fig. 15. Note the fiber volume fraction V_f has little effect on the SCF values. From these equations it can be seen that a continuous fiber discontinuity can be extremely detrimental if the matrix resin has a low

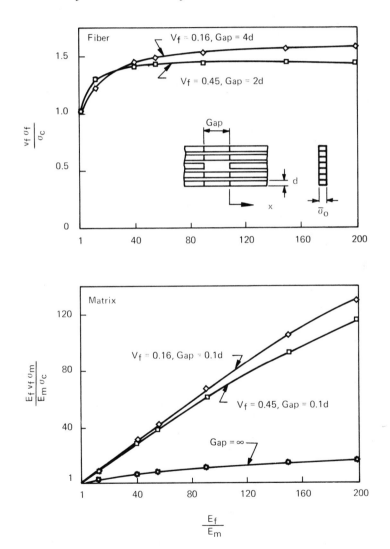

FIG. 15. Stress concentrations in fiber and matrix *versus* modulus ratio.

TABLE III

TRANSFORMED LAMINA STIFFNESS MATRICES

$$\bar{Q}_{11} = U_1 + U_2 \cos(2\theta) + U_3 \cos(4\theta)$$
$$\bar{Q}_{22} = U_1 - U_2 \cos(2\theta) + U_3 \cos(4\theta)$$
$$\bar{Q}_{12} = U_4 - U_3 \cos(4\theta)$$
$$\bar{Q}_{66} = U_5 - U_3 \cos(4\theta)$$
$$\bar{Q}_{16} = -\tfrac{1}{2} U_2 \sin(2\theta) - U_3 \sin(4\theta)$$
$$\bar{Q}_{26} = -\tfrac{1}{2} U_2 \sin(2\theta) + U_3 \sin(4\theta)$$

where

$$U_1 = \tfrac{1}{8}(3Q_{11} + 3Q_{22} + 2Q_{12} + 4Q_{66})$$
$$U_2 = \tfrac{1}{2}(Q_{11} - Q_{22})$$
$$U_3 = \tfrac{1}{8}(Q_{11} + Q_{22} - 2Q_{12} - 4Q_{66})$$
$$U_4 = \tfrac{1}{8}(Q_{11} + Q_{22} + 6Q_{12} - 4Q_{66})$$
$$U_5 = \tfrac{1}{8}(Q_{11} + Q_{22} - 2Q_{12} + 4Q_{66})$$

where

$$Q_{11} = E_{11}/(1 - \nu_{12}\nu_{21})$$
$$Q_{22} = E_{22}/(1 - \nu_{12}\nu_{21})$$
$$Q_{12} = \nu_{21} E_{11}/(1 - \nu_{12}\nu_{21}) = \nu_{12} E_{22}/(1 - \nu_{12}\nu_{21})$$
$$Q_{66} = G_{12}$$

elongation prior to the onset of pronounced nonlinearity (Chamis *et al.*, 1973). The situation also worsens as the fiber/matrix modulus ratio increases. Most modern matrix resins have at least some elongation so that the SCF_m will be somewhat reduced from that calculated for linear elastic conditions.

2. *Lamina Matrix Cracking and Maximum Strain Criterion*

Matrix discontinuities occur because of principal stresses induced in a lamina perpendicular to its fiber direction. When such stresses cause transverse strain in excess of the lamina strain capability the matrix cracks. Such micromechanical damage does not necessarily cause ultimate failure under static conditions but may be the cause of fatigue failures which exceed this stress value. The phenomenon was observed by Grimes *et al.* (1972) with further elaboration by Grimes and Whitney (1972).

In this reference the point was made that failures of composite material structures under load are either matrix controlled or filament controlled and that such failures can be related to the lamina principal axis strength values. This is done through the use of a maximum strain criterion failure surface which will be developed in the following paragraphs.

Utilizing the standard coordinate system and notation of Ashton *et al.* (1969), the stress–strain relationships of a generally orthotropic lamina are given by the stiffness matrix:

$$
\begin{bmatrix} \sigma_x \\ \sigma_y \\ \tau_{xy} \end{bmatrix}^k = \begin{bmatrix} \bar{Q}_{11} & \bar{Q}_{12} & \bar{Q}_{16} \\ \bar{Q}_{12} & \bar{Q}_{22} & \bar{Q}_{26} \\ \bar{Q}_{16} & \bar{Q}_{26} & \bar{Q}_{66} \end{bmatrix}^k \begin{bmatrix} \epsilon_x \\ \epsilon_y \\ \gamma_{xy} \end{bmatrix} \tag{15}
$$

where the $\bar{Q}_{ij}$ are reduced stiffnesses for plane stress. The formulas necessary for the calculation of these values are given in Table III.

By selecting lamina ultimate strength values for those properties which are linear to failure and proportional limit strength values for those properties which are nonlinear above this point, a set of lamina properties based on linear behavior is established. A similar set of linear behavior reduced design allowable values could also be selected if desired. It will be necessary to obtain longitudinal and transverse lamina tension and compression strength values and a shear strength value to use here. This approach is not bad for graphite–epoxy laminates which exhibit linear lamina stress–strain behaviors in all modes except edgewise shear, which is highly nonlinear, and transverse compression, which is slightly nonlinear.

The strain–stress relations of a homogeneous anisotropic lamina are defined by the compliance matrix as

$$
\begin{bmatrix} \epsilon_1 \\ \epsilon_2 \\ \gamma_{12} \end{bmatrix} = \begin{bmatrix} S_{11} & S_{12} & S_{16} \\ S_{12} & S_{22} & S_{26} \\ S_{16} & S_{26} & S_{66} \end{bmatrix} \begin{bmatrix} \sigma_1 \\ \sigma_2 \\ \tau_{12} \end{bmatrix} \tag{16}
$$

where the S_{ij} values are defined in Ashton *et al.* (1969) and shown in Table IV. For a unidirectional material the S_{16} and S_{26} values vanish. By moving the basic material elastic constants, the S_{ij} values can be calculated and the

TABLE IV

Components of the Lamina Compliance Matrix

$$
\begin{aligned}
S_{11} &= 1/E_{11} \\
S_{22} &= 1/E_{22} \\
S_{12} &= -\nu_{12}/E_{11} = -\nu_{21}/E_{22} \\
S_{66} &= 1/G_{12} \\
S_{16} &= S_{26} = 0
\end{aligned}
$$

strain values which correspond to the properties selected above can be calculated for the four failure surface quadrants at zero shear. In addition, the pure shear strain value can be calculated. These values may now be used in the maximum strain criterion to obtain the permissible lamina and laminate loads and stresses.

The governing constitutive equations for a homogeneous anisotropic laminate of symmetric construction subjected to in-plane loadings are given by the extensional stiffness matrix of Ashton *et al.* (1969) as:

$$
\begin{bmatrix} A_x \\ A_y \\ A_{xy} \end{bmatrix} = \begin{bmatrix} A_{11} & A_{12} & A_{16} \\ A_{12} & A_{22} & A_{26} \\ A_{16} & A_{26} & A_{66} \end{bmatrix} \begin{bmatrix} \epsilon_x{}^0 \\ \epsilon_y{}^0 \\ \gamma_{xy}^0 \end{bmatrix} \tag{17a}
$$

where

$$
A_{ij} = \sum_{k=1}^{n} (\bar{Q}_{ij})_k (h_k - h_{k-1})
$$

or in more convenient form:

$$
\begin{bmatrix} \bar{\sigma}_x \\ \bar{\sigma}_y \\ \bar{\tau}_{xy} \end{bmatrix} = \begin{bmatrix} Q_{11}^* & Q_{12}^* & Q_{16}^* \\ Q_{12}^* & Q_{22}^* & Q_{26}^* \\ Q_{16}^* & Q_{26}^* & Q_{66}^* \end{bmatrix} \begin{bmatrix} \epsilon_x{}^0 \\ \epsilon_y{}^0 \\ \gamma_{xy}^0 \end{bmatrix} \tag{17b}
$$

where $\bar{\sigma}_x = H_x/h$, $\bar{\sigma}_y = H_y/h$, $\bar{\tau}_{xy} = H_{xy}/h$, and

$$
Q_{ij}^* = \frac{1}{h} \int_{-h/2}^{h/2} \bar{Q}_{ij} \, dz
$$

For uniaxial tensile loading in the x direction of symmetric composites in which the in-plane stiffness matrix is orthotropic (i.e., $A_{16} = A_{26} = 0$), the constitutive equations of Eq. (17a) in inverted form become

$$
\epsilon_x{}^0 = \bar{S}_{11} H_x, \qquad \epsilon_y{}^0 = \bar{S}_{12} H_x, \qquad \gamma_{xy}^0 = 0 \tag{18}
$$

where $\bar{S}_{ij}$ are elements of the inverse matrix of Q_{ij}^* and are given by

$$
\bar{S}_{11} = \frac{Q_{22}^*}{Q_{11}^* Q_{22}^* - Q_{12}^{*2}}, \qquad \bar{S}_{12} = -\frac{Q_{12}^* \bar{S}_{11}}{Q_{22}^*}
$$

Using Eq. (18) in conjunction with the standard strain transformation equations yields the following relationships for applying the maximum strain criterion:

$$\sigma_0{}^* = \begin{cases} \dfrac{\bar{\epsilon}_1}{m^2 \bar{S}_{11} + n^2 \bar{S}_{12}} \\[3ex] \dfrac{\bar{\epsilon}_2}{m^2 \bar{S}_{12} + n^2 \bar{S}_{11}} \\[3ex] \dfrac{\bar{\gamma}_{12}}{2mn(\bar{S}_{11} - \bar{S}_{12})} \end{cases} \tag{19}$$

where $\sigma_0{}^* = \bar{\sigma}_x = \text{const}$, $m = \cos\theta$, $n = \sin\theta$. First ply† or ultimate† failure corresponds to the lowest value of $\sigma_0{}^*$ as determined from Eqs. (19) using the appropriate maximum strain value.

For pure shear loading of symmetric orthotropic laminates, Eq. (17b) can be written in the form

$$\bar{\tau}_{xy} = \text{const} = \tau_0{}^* = Q_{66}^* \gamma_{xy}^0 \tag{20}$$

or in the inverse form

$$\gamma_{xy}^0 = \bar{S}_{66}\tau_0{}^* \tag{21}$$

where $\bar{S}_{66} = 1/Q_{66}^*$. Equation (21) in conjunction with the standard strain transformation equations yields the following relationships for applying the maximum strain criterion:

$$\tau_0{}^* = \begin{cases} -\dfrac{\bar{\epsilon}_1}{mn\bar{S}_{66}} \\[3ex] \dfrac{\bar{\epsilon}_2}{mn\bar{S}_{66}} \\[3ex] \dfrac{\bar{\gamma}_{12}}{(m^2 - n^2)\bar{S}_{66}} \end{cases} \tag{22}$$

Again the lowest value of $\tau_0{}^*$ as determined from Eqs. (22) corresponds to the first ply or ultimate failure depending on the maximum strain value used.

After ultimate failure is reached in a lamina (a microdiscontinuity in the laminate) the ply is assumed to unload through a steep negative tangent

† These are two different values.

TABLE V

COMPARISON OF PREDICTED AND EXPERIMENTAL LAMINATE STRENGTH PROPERTIES
(Graphite–Epoxy: HTS[a]/ERL-2256[b])[c]

| | General orientation code | | | |
| | [0/90]c | | [±45]c | |
Type of value	Predicted psi	Experimental psi	Predicted psi	Experimental psi
Tension—P.L.	49,668	49,050	10,324	9070
—Ult.	97,274	74,230	—	19,900
Compression—P.L.	69,185	62,210	14,381	10,150
—Ult.	—	84,070	—	22,200
Shear—P.L.	1,470	1180	—	—
—Ult.	13,400	23,400	47,975	—

[a] Hercules, Inc. tradename.
[b] Union Carbide tradename.
[c] F.V. = 60%, V.V. = 1%, density = 0.0571 lb/in.³, ply thickness = 0.0084 in., meter length fiber. Material form: Prepreg prepared by Fiberite Corp. and designated HY-E-1371B.

modulus. Total laminate failure is assumed to occur when the Q_{ij}^* matrix becomes singular or when a negative sign appears on the diagonal. This is the same procedure used by Petit and Waddoups (1969).

Grimes and Whitney (1972) compared this approach with experimental data for [0/90]c and [±45]c laminates of HTS/ERL-2256 graphite–epoxy material. Comparison of the computed strengths based on the maximum strain criterion with experimentally measured values is given in Table V for these orientations. Correlation is reasonable.

III. Edge Effects

In this section the behavior of finite width laminated composites with free edges that are subjected to uniaxial loads will be presented. In Section III,A the effects of lamination sequence on this behavior are discussed and found to be primarily a free edge problem. Calculations for predicting such free edge effects are presented in Section III,B.

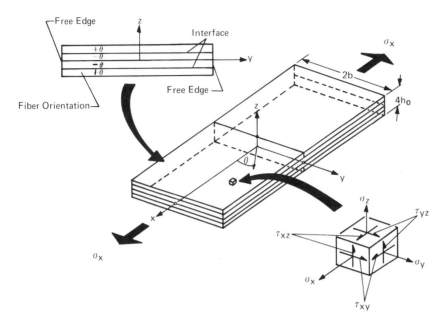

FIG. 16. Laminate geometry.

A. Stacking Sequence

Edge effects in composite structures result from interlaminar stresses which increase substantially near a free edge. The most common cause is a uniaxial tension member with sides unconstrained. The magnitude of these stresses has been found to be a function of lamina orientation and stacking sequence in a laminate. Puppo and Evenson (1970) studied interlaminar shear showing that it can be calculated using linear elastic theory (plane stress) if the interlaminar layer is modeled as a bondline. Pipes and Pagano (1970) investigated the same phenomenon using three-dimensional elasticity but using a finite difference technique for determining angleply laminate properties. Using a four-ply $[\pm\theta]_s$ laminate the geometry is shown in Fig. 16. Results were shown for a $\theta = 45°$, i.e., $[\pm 45]_s$ laminate of finite width, $b = 8h_0$, with the following graphite–epoxy lamina properties:

$$E_{11} = 20.0 \times 10^6 \text{ psi}, \qquad G_{12} = G_{13} = G_{23} = 0.85 \times 10^6 \text{ psi}$$

$$E_{22} = E_{33} = 2.1 \times 10^6 \text{ psi}, \qquad \nu_{12} = \nu_{13} = \nu_{23} = 0.21$$

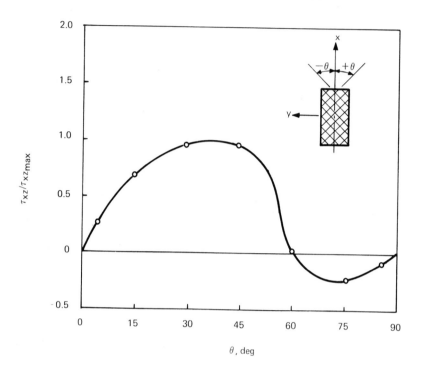

Fig. 17. Interlaminar shear stresses as a function of fiber orientation. $\tau_{xz\,max} = \tau_{xz}$ at $\sigma \cong 35_x$.

Pipes and Pagano (1970) show that the interlaminar shear stresses for this laminate become very large near the free edge† and are of significant size only for a distance of one laminate thickness in from this edge. Maximum interlaminar stress is shown to occur at $z/h_0 = 1.0$ with a magnitude of $\tau_{xz}/\epsilon_x > 2.0$ at the free edge $(y/b = 1.0)$. Pipes and Pagano (1970) show the results of $[\pm\theta]_s$ laminates as θ varies from 0° to 90° plotted as a function of $\tau_{xz}/\tau_{xz\,max}$ with the value occurring at $\theta = 35°$. Figure 17 shows this plot which indicates that the interlaminar stresses are high for laminates of $[\pm15]_s$ to $[\pm55]_s$ with an abrupt drop to zero stress for a laminate of $[\pm60]_s$. Pipes and Pagano compared the results of their technique to that of Puppo and Evensen (1970) as shown in Fig. 18 for σ_x, τ_{xy}, and τ_{xz}. The largest difference in the two methods is shown for interlaminar shear stresses with Puppo and Evensen (1970) showing a finite value of $\tau_{xz}/\epsilon_x = 1.0$ at the free edge.

† Actually a singularity is suspected at the free edge by these authors.

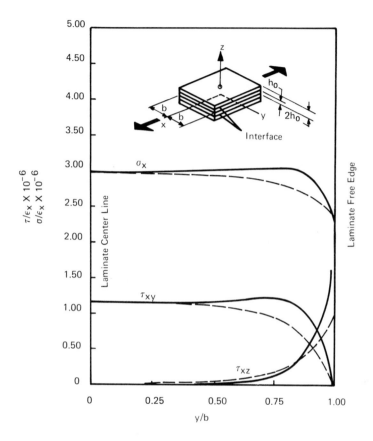

Fɪɢ. 18. Comparison of results at interface. $b = 8h$, $\theta = +45°$. —— Pipes–Pagano; — — — Puppo–Evenson.

Pagano and Pipes (1971) further delineate the problem of edge effects as related to a stacking sequence in a boron–epoxy angleply laminate under uniaxial extension with built-in thermal stresses assumed. Results of an approximate method show that the interlaminar tensile stress, σ_z, is the probable cause of failure, starting at the free edge. This normal tensile stress is highest in a $[\pm15/\pm45]_s$ laminate, becoming much lower in a $[15/\pm45/-15]_s$ orientation. A $[\pm45/\pm15]_s$ orientation gives the highest normal compressive stresses, but a $[45/\mp15/-45]_s$ orientation is optimum because both interlaminar shear and normal stresses are kept to a minimum. Tensile fatigue specimens of some of these orientations were observed to fail by delamination at the edge by Foye and Baker (1970) with strength depending on the stacking sequence (as above).

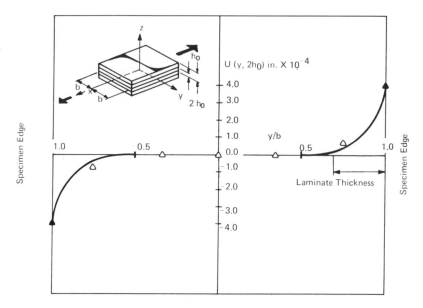

Fig. 19. Axial displacement distribution at the laminate surface $z = 2h_0$. —— Elasticity results; △ Moiré analysis.

Further experimental verification for the interlaminar stresses at the edge is given by Pipes and Daniel (1970), showing that a graphite–epoxy $[+25_4/-25_8/+25_4]_T$ laminate exhibits the edge effects previously shown by deviations in axial displacement near the free edge. Stress–displacement relations with appropriate symmetry conditions are

$$\mu = (\epsilon_x)x + U(y, z) \qquad (23)$$

with $z = 2h_0$. Under a uniaxial loading the experimental moiré surface axial strains caused by $U(y, z)$ displacements are plotted on the analytical curve produced by the Pipes and Pagano (1970) technique as shown in Fig. 19. Correlation is very good, showing that these secondary displacements which cause interlaminar stresses are not of significant magnitude except in the region, one laminate thickness in from the free edge.

Rybicki and Hopper (1972) use three-dimensional finite-element techniques for studying finite width laminates of bidirectional and angleply orientations. They show close agreement with the interlaminar shear results of Pipes and Pagano (1970) and verify the interlaminar normal stress characteristics postulated in Pagano and Pipes (1971).

Pipes (1972) performed a rather complete three-dimensional elastic finite difference analysis of four-ply $[0/90]_s$ and $[90/0]_s$ orientations and the general six-ply $[0/\pm\theta]_s$ sequence to determine the laminate's interlaminar shear and normal stresses while under axial extension. Pipes (1972) says that the interlaminar stresses at the free edge of a finite width laminate loaded axially are a consequence of the equilibrium requirements of the anisotropic laminated system. Two modes of interlaminar stress transfer are shown to exist: (1) the interaction of the in-plane shear stress τ_{xy} and the interlaminar shear stress τ_{xz} are induced by the shear coupling characteristics of the off-axis laminae in angleply laminates, and (2) the interaction between the transverse normal stress σ_y and the other two interlaminar stresses, τ_{yz} and σ_z, is caused by the response of the bidirectional laminae. The first mode interlaminar stress transfer applies to $[\pm\theta]_s$ and $[0/\pm\theta]_s$

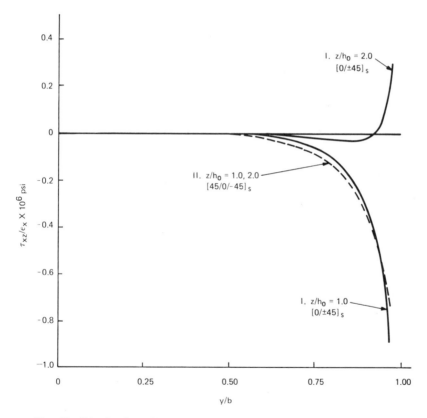

Fig. 20. Distribution of interlaminar shear stress τ_{xz} with two stacking sequences. $b = 15h_0$.

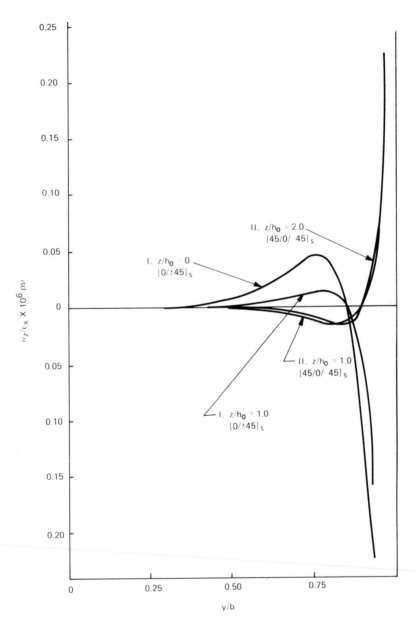

Fig. 21.   Distribution of interlaminar normal stress σ_z with two stacking sequences. $b = 15h_0$.

angleply orientations, while the second mode describes this type of stress transfer in bidirectional [0/90]s and [90/0]s lamination sequences.

While [±θ]s laminates were previously discussed, Pipes (1972) concentrates on the [0/±θ]s orientations for first-mode interlaminar stress transfer. With θ = 45° the two stacking sequences: I, [0/±45]s and II, [45/0/−45]s are used to illustrate these stresses. Figure 20 shows the interlaminar shear stress as a function of y/b for these two sequences. Both show large negative sign interlaminar shear stresses but only the second one shows some positive sign stresses of this type. While this may not mean much at first, a look at Fig. 21 does delineate the interlaminar normal stresses as a function of y/b for these two sequences. Obviously, orientation sequence I goes into large magnitude interlaminar normal compressive stresses near the free edge, whereas the II sequence goes into large magnitude interlaminar normal tensile stresses in this zone. Now the postulation of Pagano and Pipes (1971) (discussed above) makes sense. Interlaminar

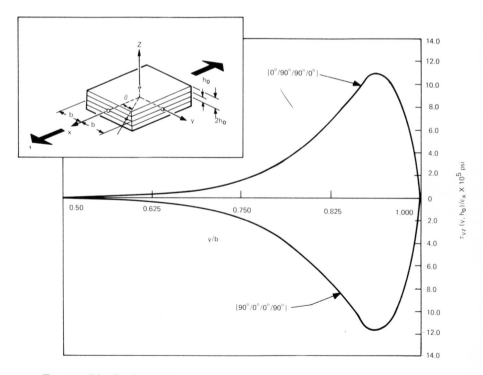

FIG. 22. Distribution of the interlaminar shear stress at the interface. Bidirectional laminate, $b/h_0 = 16$.

normal strength in tension is not as high as in compression for polymer matrix laminates. Therefore, laminate I will achieve higher stresses than laminate II before interlaminar failure occurs at the free edge.

For the second mode of stress transfer [0/90]s and [90/0]s stacking sequences were used by Pipes (1972) to show the interlaminar stresses. As seen in Fig. 22 both sequences show high interlaminar shear stresses near the free edge but dropping to zero suddenly at this edge. Figure 23 shows the interlaminar normal stresses which indicate that the [90/0]s stresses go compressive near the free edge, whereas the [0/90]s stresses become large tensile stresses. Again the laminate with the large normal tensile stress will fail first. Because of suspected singularities the actual magnitude of σ_z normal stress at the free edge could not be determined. However, Pipes (1972) developed a finer mesh for his finite difference technique and calculated a value at the free edge and compared it with a converged solution as shown in Fig. 24.

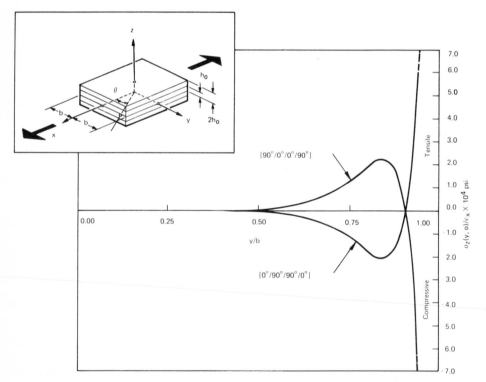

FIG. 23. Distribution of the interlaminar normal stress at the midplane. Bidirectional laminate, $b/h_0 = 16$.

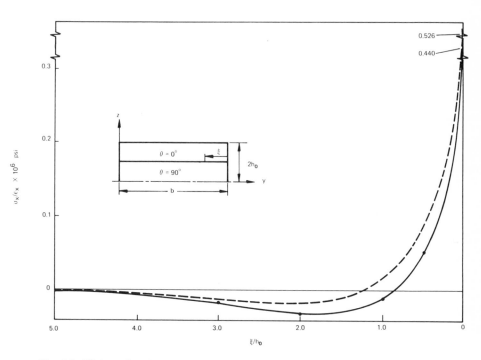

Fɪɢ. 24. Finite values for σ_z at the midplane. — — Converged solution; – – – – Fine mesh 0.0018 in.

It becomes clear that stacking sequences in selected orientations are important to minimize the interlaminar stresses. Also, it is evident that the prevention of large interlaminar normal stresses is desirable. It is noted that the normal stresses are both stacking sequence and load-sense dependent.

B. Calculations

Pipes (1972) shows that the in-plane shear stress τ_{xy} for each lamina and the interlaminar shear stress τ_{xy} between laminae are related by

$$\int \tau_{xy} \, dy \, dz = \int \tau_{zz} y \, dy \tag{24}$$

i.e., for a given laminate geometry τ_{xz} is a function of τ_{xy}. Pipes (1972) shows that the dependence of τ_{xy} on fiber orientation is given by

$$\tau_{xy} = \bar{Q}_{16}\epsilon_x + \bar{Q}_{26}\epsilon_y + \bar{Q}_{66}\gamma_{xy} \tag{25}$$

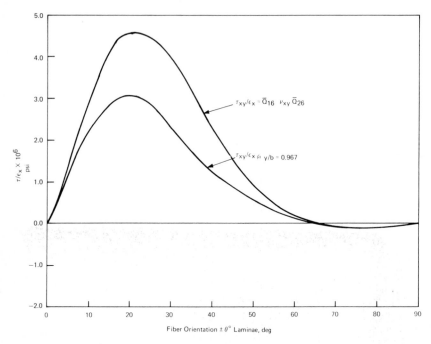

FIG. 25. Influence of fiber orientation on the shear stress components, τ_{xy} and τ_{xz}. $[0/+\theta/-\theta/-\theta/+\theta/0]$ graphite–epoxy; $b/h_0 = 15$.

where the $\bar{Q}_{ij}$ are the laminar reduced stiffness matrix items defined in Table III (Ashton *et al.*, 1969). For a balanced laminate exhibiting mid-plane symmetry which is subject to axial load, $\gamma_{xy} = 0$. Then normalizing Eq. (25) with the strain ϵ_x the relationship reduces to

$$\tau_{xy}/\epsilon_x = \bar{Q}_{16} - \nu_{xy}\bar{Q}_{26} \tag{26}$$

where ν_{xy} is the laminate Poisson's ratio.

The relationship of fiber orientation to the two shear stress components is shown in Fig. 25 for the previously mentioned graphite–epoxy system. Pipes (1972) also discusses the relationship of τ_{yz} and σ_y for each layer and shows it to be

$$\int \tau_{yz} \, dy = \int \sigma_y \, dz \tag{27}$$

Thus, for a given laminate configuration τ_{yz} is a function of σ_y, which may be predicted by lamination theory as

$$\sigma_y = \bar{Q}_{12}\epsilon_x + \bar{Q}_{22}\epsilon_y + \bar{Q}_{26}\gamma_{xy} \tag{28}$$

Again for a balanced, midplane symmetric laminate loaded axially the relationship σ_y may be simplified and normalized as before:

$$\sigma_y/\epsilon_x = \bar{Q}_{12} - \nu_{xy}\bar{Q}_{22} \tag{29}$$

Results are shown in Fig. 26 for the previously mentioned graphite–epoxy system. While Pipes (1972) did not develop the formula for the interlaminar normal stress σ_z, he shows that its relationship to τ_{yz} is

$$\frac{\partial \tau_{yz}}{\partial y} + \frac{\partial \sigma_z}{\partial z} = 0 \tag{30}$$

from which the formulation can be developed. He does point out that the maximum interlaminar normal stress occurs at $\theta = 30°$ in a $[0/\pm\theta]_s$ laminate, which corresponds to the orientation angle that gives the maximum values of σ_y and τ_{yz}. It can also be noted that while the maximum interlaminar shear stresses τ_{xz} and τ_{xy} occur at $\theta = 20°$, the values at 30° are still large. Reverse logic also shows that τ_{yz} (and σ_z) are still large at $\theta = 20°$. Thus it would seem logical to postulate that axially loaded in tension finite width $[0/\pm\theta]_s$ angleply laminates of graphite–epoxy with free edges

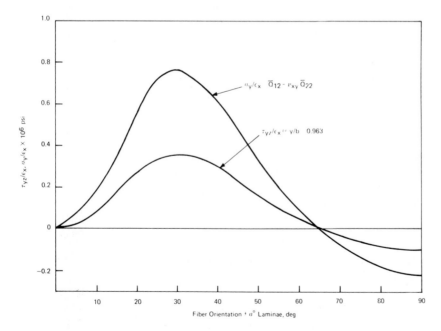

Fig. 26. Influence of fiber orientation on the stress components τ_{yz} and σ_y. $[0/+\theta/-\theta/-\theta/+\theta/0]$ graphite–epoxy; $b/h_0 = 15$.

may be subject to preultimate edge delamination if $10° \leq \theta \leq 40°$. The effect of restraints on the edges are not known; however, any such structure should be tested structurally to determine its effectiveness at preventing such problems.

Pipes (1972) also developed several average interlaminar stress formulas which predict interlaminar stresses in four-layer balanced symmetric laminates ($B_{ij} = 0$, $A_{16} = A_{26} = 0$) subjected to in-plane loads. For Mode I angleply laminates,

$$\tau_{xz} = \frac{h_0}{h}(\bar{Q}_{16} - \nu_{xy}\bar{Q}_{26})\epsilon_x \tag{31}$$

For Mode II the average interlaminar stresses are

$$\tau_{yz} = \frac{h_0}{h}(\bar{Q}_{12} - \nu_{xy}\bar{Q}_{22})\epsilon_x \tag{32}$$

and

$$\sigma_z = \left(\frac{h_0}{h}\right)^2(\bar{Q}_{12} - \nu_{xy}\bar{Q}_{22})\epsilon_x \tag{33}$$

where the $\bar{Q}_{ij}$ are the reduced stiffness matrix values given in Table III, h_0 is the layer thickness, h is the laminate thickness, ν_{xy} is the laminate Poisson's ratio, and ϵ_x is the applied axial strain. These average stresses are assumed to be uniformly distributed at the free edge over a distance equal to the laminate thickness, h. The thickness of the laminate is assumed to be small relative to its width. By using the above formulas, allowable values can be determined from free edge tensile specimen tests such that these formulas can be used in laminate stress analysis.

IV. Bonded Joints

This section will address the problem of adhesive bonded attachment of composite materials and structures to similar and dissimilar materials. Since adhesive bonding has become the preferred method of attachment for composite materials in most applications, it is the attachment area in which the most research and development has been done. While the necessity for adhesive bonding in metal-to-metal attachments is not as great as in composite-to-composite or composite-to-metal attachment, the usefulness of such joining in metals has been recognized. Most of the information presented herein is also applicable to all-metal joining. In fact, the analytical techniques simplify somewhat for isotropic materials, although there is usually more nonlinearity in metals than in the composite orientations that are normally used.

A. Efficiency and Cost Considerations

Material for this section is based on the survey work of Grimes (1971). It is emphasized that the purpose of this section is to delineate techniques for attachment efficiency and cost effectiveness in the design of structural joints in composite materials. Numerical data used in this section is for illustrative purposes only, and should not be considered valid for design; however, the test data given represents typical average values taken from the open literature for the materials treated.

1. Purpose, Scope, and Philosophy

The purpose of this section is to acquant the designer with elementary rule-of-thumb synthesis techniques and the experimental character of joints in composite material. Familiarity with the use of the various attachment concepts in specific design applications is necessary in order to select the most efficient one. A working knowledge of attachment design allowables criteria† and failure types will also be necessary for utilization of published data and/or for developing test programs for design allowables development. Once these aspects are mastered, the primary goal of efficient load transfer will be easier to attain.

In the creation of efficient joints, more than just the load transferral efficiency relative to that of the unjoined structure must be considered. Even the comparison of the weights of equal (planform) size segments of joined and unjoined structure does not provide the total picture of efficiency. One must look at the relative weight of various structural elements and components with and without joints over a wide range of sizes in order to select the most efficient size and configuration for use. To appreciate the importance of such analysis, one need only realize that the relative weight of the joint area of a panel compared to the weight of the panel without joints can range from 5% to well over 100%. This illustrates the necessity of considering all aspects of the attachment problem.

---

† This may be strongly influenced by the structural system design criteria.

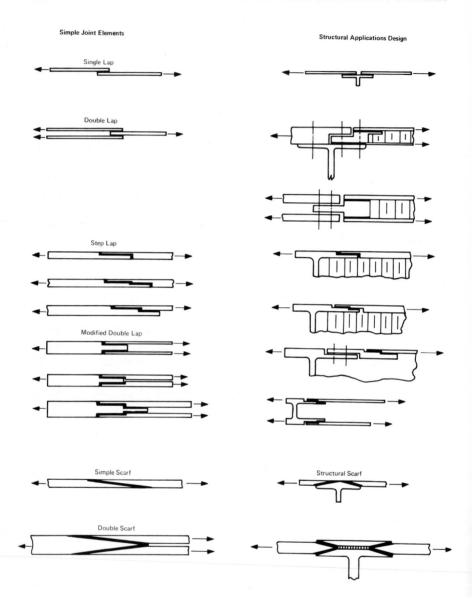

FIG. 27. Bonded joint concepts.

2. Concepts, Criteria, and Failure Types

This section covers conceptual design, allowables, criteria, and the study of failure types as related to the generation of design allowables and the study of joint efficiency.

(a) CONCEPTS. Since one approach to joint design is to use rule-of-thumb techniques followed by simple stress analysis, a knowledge of configuration, size, and proportion is necessary. Figure 27 presents several concepts showing a simple joint which might be tested and its structural counterpart. Size judgment must come from a knowledge of the part sizes to be joined, the allotted space for the joint, and a general idea of how much overlap †️ is required to carry the load. With such knowledge, "rough" estimate joint designs can be made with iterative analysis procedures used to refine them. Design allowables and criteria are now required to make the attachment both efficient and safe.

(b) CRITERIA. Joint design allowables criteria must necessarily be developed within the confines of the applicable structural criteria based on the knowledge of the following parameters: (1) purpose or function of joint, (2) type of load to be transferred, (3) magnitude of load(s), (4) strain compatibility of discrete elements of joint, (5) environment in which joint must function, (6) space requirements, (7) cost requirements, (8) weight efficiency needs, and (9) reliability.

The purpose or function of the joint is to transfer load from one structural member to another. The type of load to be transferred is related to the type of joint chosen, i.e., lap or butt joint; however, tension and shear loads of any magnitude are most efficiently transferred by a lap joint. Compression loads and/or bending moments may require a combination joint. The magnitude of loads to be transferred will affect the size, weight, and configuration of the joint as well as the type of adhesive to be used. Strain compatibility of the discrete elements of a joint means that they must all deform together or compatibly under loadings which stress them to a high percentage of their strength. Environmental considerations affect the choice of adherend and adhesive materials, cleaning and treatment processes, and postbonding protective coatings selection. Space requirements are concerned with designing a joint within the space available for it. In most cases the joint design and materials selection must reflect a minimum cost approach which still meets the strength and reliability requirements

---

†️ Pick a suitable L/t value, choose an average experimental τ_B (bondline shear strength) value, and calculate the overlap from $L = N/\tau_\mathrm{B}$, where N is lb/in. running load.

for the system. Weight efficiency may or may not be important to the structural system, but it will certainly affect the materials and process selection and the cost. Reliability is a difficult quantity to predict accurately short of performing a large number of substructural tests. However, it is a function of both manufacturing quality control and adequate design engineering for performance in the operational spectrum.

One of the key items in bonded joint criteria is the proper development of design allowables. Both "pure" adhesive mechanical properties and the "effective" ones obtained from simple lap joints are usually necessary. However, in many cases the latter are all that are available or can be developed, i.e., they must be used. While utilization of "pure" allowable properties with the appropriate analytical techniques and failure criterion (such as maximum stress) is universally applicable, the "effective" properties approach requires only a moderate number of simple lap joint tests to provide a straightforward empirical method. Such a method is only applicable for the materials and general configuration being studied, but it is short and simple for preliminary design use.

Preliminary design allowables can be developed using appropriate statistical reduction on simple bonded joint experimental data. An ultimate design factor of safety,† such as the 1.5 factor required for aircraft structures, should be used to increase the loads used in the design/analysis calculations, thereby providing operational safety. Another approach sometimes employed is to use mean experimental data as design allowable values. Such values are then modified, either prior to use or in the margin of safety calculation by a previously determined statistical prediction factor (see Section IV,C).

(c) Failure Types. Significant micromechanical damage leading to macromechanical damage and failure in the adherend part of the joints can define allowable strength levels to be used in the establishment of composite material application criteria, the prediction of failure modes, and the selection of ultimate load prediction techniques. Knowledge available on adherend laminate failure modes (Grimes et al., 1967, 1972) is useful in determining the critical damage threshold† and relating it to design allowables development and related criteria (Grimes, 1971). In adhesives, the problem has received some attention, although not in proportion to the amount of data available (Bodnar, 1966; Grimes et al., 1967, 1972; Douglas

---

† The actual factor and its application are a function of the structural system design criteria.

† See Section II, B.

Aircraft Co., 1969). Information on failure criteria has been found, primarily concerned with gross joint behavior.

Experimental microfailure and macrofailure analyses of lap and scarf-bonded joints with glass and boron–polymer composite adherends have resulted in delineation of several characteristic failure types, as observed and defined in Grimes *et al.* (1967, 1972) and Douglas Aircraft Co. (1969). These modes, shown in Fig. 28, are described as follows, where the parenthetical numerals are keyed to the figure:

I: (1) cohesive failure within the adhesive layer, (2) adherend matrix surface resin layer failure,

II: (3) adhesive–adherend interface failure on the surface of the resin,

III: (4) interlaminar resin layer failure,

IV: (5) transverse (parallel to the fiber) lamina failure (resin only), (6) transverse (parallel to the fiber) lamina failure (fiber-resin interface), (7) longitudinal (perpendicular to the fiber) lamina failure (fiber plus resin),

V: adherend tension failure.

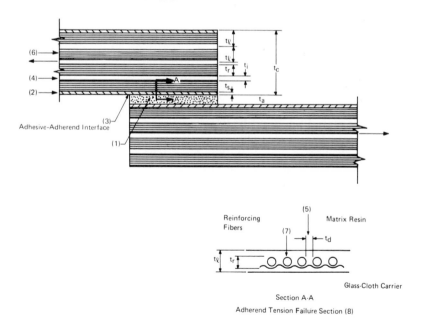

FIG. 28. Composite lap joint failure modes. Thickness legend: t_l—lamina; t_r—reinforcement layer; t_i—interlaminar resin layer; t_s—surface resin layer; t_a—adhesive layer; t_c—composite adherend; t_d—matrix between fibers.

Of these eight failure types, it will be noted that only the first seven are true joint failures. For purposes of categorization, these seven can be divided into four micro/macrofracture characteristic types: (I) cohesive, (II) interface, (III) interlaminar, (IV) lamina, and (V) laminate. Whether the adhesive–adherend interface failure actually occurs on a microscale is of no concern in design. The fact that this type of failure apparently does occur on a macroscale when processing or material quality are poor is enough justification for its consideration in quality control. It usually causes low failure loads below the elastic limit of both the adhesive and the adherend. Cohesive (within the adhesive) failure occurs by brittle fracture or by a rubbery tearing, depending on the type of adhesive used. While interlaminar failure (not related to edge effects) may be caused by poor processing, voids, delaminations, or thermal stresses, such failure causes should be considered on a gross scale in their effect on the resin layer tension–shear failures. The three types of lamina failures on a microscale can usually be considered as one type of layer failure on a macroscale.

Of the four types of failures generally categorized and defined as joint failure (I through IV), it is not generally considered acceptable in primary structure attachments for interface failure (II) to be the governing (weakest) mode. Therefore, the necessary quality control procedures should be used to prevent its occurrence.

3. *Design Allowables Development*

Design allowables development will be illustrated by using bonded joint data generated and analyzed by Grimes in Petit and Waddoups (1969) and Puppo and Evensen (1970), respectively.

Standard deviations were calculated on data utilizing polymer matrix composite primary adherends of nonwoven S-glass–epoxy (NGE) materials of several orientations and overlap lengths. These primary adherends were bonded to the same materials, aluminum (Al), titanium (Ti), and woven E-glass–epoxy (WGE) secondary adherends. Statistical data analysis was performed in order to study the data quality and provide a reduction factor for use in design allowables calculation using average test values. The data analysis effort has two primary objectives: a gross characterization of the "effective" strength properties of the adhesive material functioning as a lap joint constituent, and a meaningful estimate of the general test precision to establish statistical reliability guidelines and design allowables development. The procedure consists of two sequential steps: the generation of reliable precision estimates in order that confidence intervals might be established for the various mean failure stress measurements, and the subsequent use of these intervals to establish the "effective" material

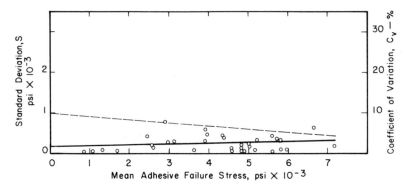

FIG. 29. Standard deviation and coefficient of variation *versus* mean adhesive failure stress. — — — Coefficient of variation; ——— Standard deviation.

properties as a function of the joint configuration. Data analysis work concentrated on adhesive and adherend failure stresses and on the running loads transferred in pounds per inch per ply.

Plots of standard deviation versus mean adhesive failure stress for these data are presented in Fig. 29. Included in this plot is a straight line fitted to the data points by linear regression techniques. The straight line is considered to be the best estimate of the overall test (or population) standard deviation (it can be seen by inspection that a straight line provides a good fit and that higher order regression would offer little improvement of fit). The advantage of the above approach is that a large number of degrees of freedom were utilized in the estimating procedure rather than the small number available in the three data points actually falling at a given level. This gives a more realistic calculation for confidence intervals and provides a means of looking at trends between test configurations and material types. Considering that the experimental parameters varied a great deal in these tests, that is, overlap length, orientation, and secondary adherend materials, a preliminary observation suggests that the general variance to be expected with different adherend and adhesive materials may well be about the same at any mean level.

In making the data analyses described above, the current practice of reporting variance in terms of the coefficient of variation† was examined. This is done in an attempt to compensate for the well-known tendency of the variance to increase with the mean, thereby providing the designer with a reasonable reduction factor. The analyses presented herein suggest that

† The coefficient of variation is obtained by dividing the sample standard deviation by the sample mean failure level.

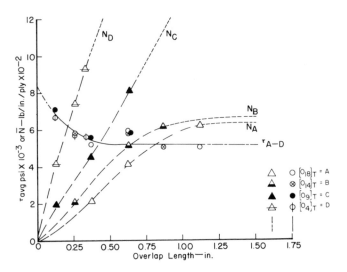

Fig. 30. NGE/NGE SwRI double lap/3M AF-126. Average test data, $n = 3$, material group A.

the rate of increase of variance with the mean may not be as great as with more standard materials and that the use of the coefficient of variation is an overcompensation. This can be seen in Fig. 29, which compares the sample coefficient of variance with the sample standard deviation for the Grimes *et al.* (1967) double-lap data. Here, it is apparent that a standard deviation estimate of 300 psi, for example, comes much closer to being descriptive of the variance over the whole range of failure stresses than does any value on the C_v line. It is not suggested that C_v numbers be disregarded in favor of S numbers for all data analysis; rather that variance be reported in terms of the mean for bonded joint data through the use of formulas of the form:

$$S = y + b \quad \text{(mean)}$$

where $y = $ const, and $b = $ slope, as would be derived from analyses of the type reported herein.

Calculation of the confidence intervals for the population mean adhesive failure stresses consists simply of using the regression line standard deviation estimate in the following formula:

$$\text{chosen confidence limits at } \bar{f}_s = \bar{f}_s \pm ts/n^{1/2} \quad (34)$$

where $\bar{f}_s$ is the average of experimentally determined mean adhesive failure stresses, n is the number of determinations, s is standard deviation, and

t is the deviate corresponding to the number of degrees of freedom involved in the regression line estimate of the standard deviation (not n) for the selected confidence level.

These limits establish the interval within which the mean of a very large number of tests would probably lie relative to the mean of the experimental data.

Design allowables are calculated as follows:

design allowables at chosen confidence level = lower confidence limit $- ts$

$$= \bar{f}_s - ts[1/n^{1/2} + 1] \quad (35)$$

where t and s have the same definitions as above. In this calculation, if the population mean $\bar{f}_s$ turns out to be at the lower confidence level, then about 5 of 100 specimens would fail at the design allowable stress level or lower, if 95% confidence limits were chosen. This is a conservative estimate; the real failure probabilities should be more favorable.

In the Grimes *et al.* (1967) data on double-lap composite adherend bonded joints, overlap lengths are varied; hence, it is possible to plot mean failure stress (or unit load) versus overlap lengths for various orientations and failure types. The mean experimental plots are presented in Figs. 30–32. Joint confidence limits (CL) and preliminary design allowables (PDA)

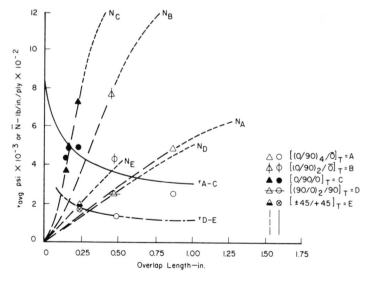

Fig. 31. NGE/AL and NGE/WGE SwRI double lap/3M AF-126. Average test data, $n = 3$, material group B.

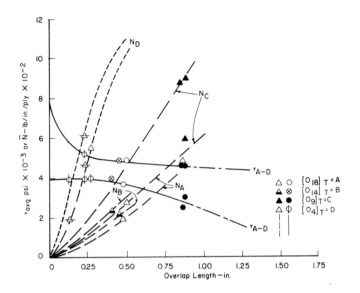

FIG. 32.   NGE/AL, NGE/WGE, and NGE/TI SwRI double lap/3M AF-126. Average test data, $n = 3$, material group B. *Note:* (1) Upper curve in each case represents cohesion or delamination failure. (2) Lower curve in each case represents adhesion failure.

can now be calculated from the following formulas using the data from these plots:

For double-lap joints, using 95% confidence limits

$$CL = \bar{f}_s \pm (187 + 0.0171\bar{f}_s) \text{ psi}$$

or

$$CL = \bar{N} \pm (9.25 + 0.0496\bar{N}) \text{ lb/in./ply} \tag{36}$$

$$PDA = \bar{f}_s - (324 + 0.0296\bar{f}_s)(1/n^{1/2} + 1) = 0.9533\bar{f}_s - 511 \text{ psi}$$

or

$$PDA = \bar{N} - (16 + 0.086\bar{N})(1/n^{1/2} + 1) = 0.8645\bar{N} - 25 \text{ lb/in./ply} \tag{37}$$

where $\bar{N} = $ lb/in./ply running load per ply transferred in the composite adherend.

Figure 32 shows that a weak interface is detrimental to composite adherend bonded joints. The cause of this could be adhesive viscosity† (at cure temperature) or cleaning.

† This is a function of the time/temperature/pressure cycle.

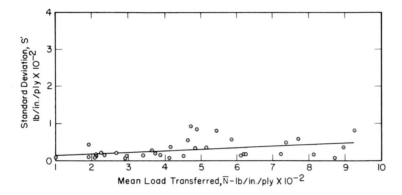

Fig. 33. Standard deviation *versus* mean load transferred.

The regression line standard deviation analyses performed on the composite adherend data on the unit running loads transferred per ply are essentially a reiteration of those described above for adhesive failure stresses. Figure 33 presents the plot of standard deviation versus mean running load transferred in pounds per inch per ply. Because the adhesive failure stress and the running load are both calculated at the failure point and thus have a proportional relationship, it was expected that the linear regressions would look much alike. That this was indeed the case can be seen in Fig. 34, which presents comparisons of the two corresponding standard deviation estimates.

In the analysis of the adhesive shear stresses, mean failure strengths are presented on plots of failure stress versus overlap length. Confidence inter-

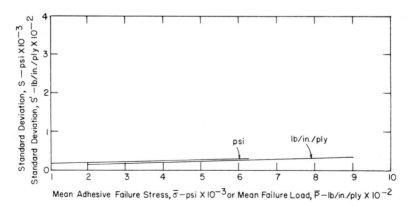

Fig. 34. Comparison of standard deviations.

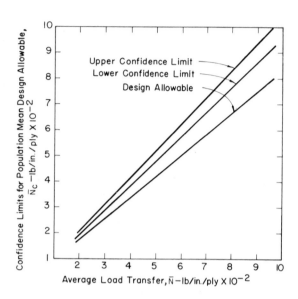

Fig. 35. Unit load transfer confidence limits and design allowance.

vals and design allowables for mean loads transferred are shown by the use of the plots contained in Fig. 35. The values for these plots were obtained in the same manner as were the mean adhesive failure stress statistics [see Eqs. (34) and (35)].

4. *Application Studies*

This section covers the design and analysis of a hypothetical S-glass–epoxy panel with joints, and studies the total weight picture of joints relative to panel weight. It covers a typical sandwich panel and joint design with a high axial loading possible in either direction, utilizing S-glass–epoxy bidirectional [0/90]c composite skins, titanium edge members, and aluminum honeycomb core.

Although experimentally developed design allowables and extensive failure mode analyses will be required in an actual structure, this section will deal only with one condition, where a design load of variable magnitude has a corresponding allowable for a specific set of materials. The actual magnitude of the allowable will only vary with the overlap length and number of laminate plies.

The overlap length variable is a familiar one in which the strength increases as this dimension increases, but at a diminishing rate of increase. [See Figs. 36–38 (Grimes *et al.*, 1967).] Whatever structural configuration

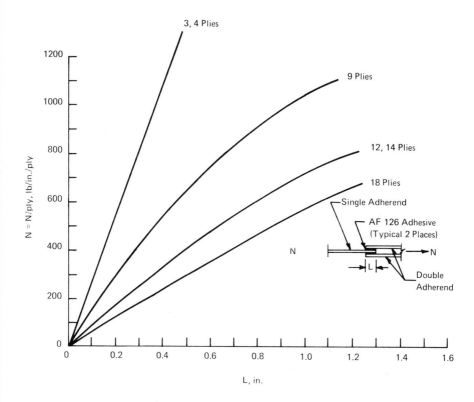

FIG. 36. Load transmission capability of joint. Single adherend material: Scotchply XP 2515 Unit and crossply. Double adherend material: (1) Same as single adherend material; (2) 7075-T6 aluminum (clad); (3) Cordo-preg E-293 75 D81 1-550.

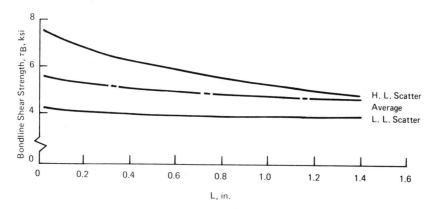

FIG. 37. Bondline shear strength of joint. See Fig. 36 for legend.

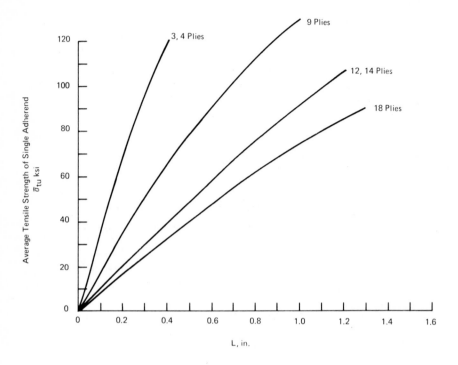

Fɪɢ. 38. Tensile strength of joint. See Fig. 36 for legend.

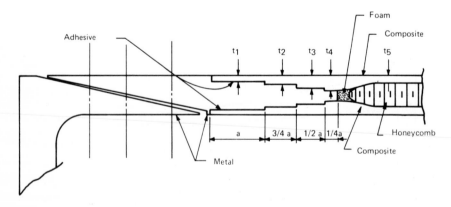

Fɪɢ. 39. Composite structural joint concept.

is used, two rules-of-thumb will help. First, use stepped lap joints to reduce the effective laminate thickness and overlap length. Second, use a variable overlap length in the stepped laps for more efficient load transfer. Thinner laminate sections can use larger overlaps, while thicker ones can use shorter overlaps, thereby taking advantage of the joint's most efficient load transmission characteristics. Figure 39 illustrates such a configuration. Tables VI and VII show a strength analysis for two overlap lengths. In Table VI, the assumed unit load capability per ply gives gross adhesive stresses that are too high compared to Fig. 37. The total overlap length is 1.28 in., including necessary clearances. In Table VIII a second iteration is made using approximately twice the overlap length (2.28 in. overall). The adhesive stresses are well within the adhesive capability, while carrying about the same load (and stresses) in the adherend. Part C of Tables VI and VII gives the assumed effective thicknesses and stresses in the joint.

The efficiency of this joint may be calculated as follows.

1. The *joint efficiency* is defined as the ratio of the load-carrying capabilities of the joined structure to that of a continuous structure of the same size:

$$\text{joint eff } (\%) = \frac{\text{joint strength}}{\text{continuous structure strength}} \times 100 \qquad (36)$$

Efficiencies in excess of 100% imply excess weight.

2. The *weight efficiency* is defined as the ratio of the weight of a unit width of continuous structure to that of a unit width of the joint, where the length of the continuous structure used for comparison is equal to the total length of the joint and reinforced areas (measured normal to the joint):

$$\text{wt eff } (\%) = \frac{\text{wt of continuous strip}}{\text{wt of joint}} \times 100 \qquad (37)$$

3. The *overall efficiency* is defined as the product of the weight efficiency and the joint efficiency:

$$\text{overall eff } (\%) = \frac{\text{wt eff}}{100} \times \frac{\text{joint eff}}{100} \times 100 \qquad (38)$$

Since no test data on the joint configuration of Tables VI and VII and Fig. 39 are available, it will be assumed that they are 100% efficient in the load transmission of 5884 and 5600 lb/in./face, respectively. The sandwich panel thickness is assumed to be 0.750 in., and the 5052 H-39 aluminum core density is 8.1 lb/ft³ ($\frac{1}{8}$ in. cell size).

TABLE VI

STRUCTURAL JOINT STRENGTH ANALYSIS. I

A. Load transfer and adhesive stress

Dim.		Overlap (in.)	$N/2$ (lb/in./ply)		No. of plies		Load transferred (lb/in. force)	Gross adhesive stress, τ_B—psi
a	$=$	0.4	538	$\times$	4	$=$	2150	5380
$\frac{3}{4}a$	$=$	0.3	212	$\times$	9	$=$	1908	6380
$\frac{1}{2}a$	$=$	0.2	88	$\times$	14	$=$	1232	5750
$\frac{1}{4}a$	$=$	0.1	33	$\times$	18	$=$	594	5940
		1.0 + clearance					5884	

B. Actual adherend thicknesses and stresses

Actual dim.	Actual no. of plies		Ply thickness (in.)		Actual thickness (in.)	Gross adherend stress, σ_A—psi
t_5	14	$\times$	0.0076	$=$	0.1064	55,000
t_4	18	$\times$	0.0076	$=$	0.1368	42,800
t_4	18	$\times$	0.0076	$=$	0.1368	4330
t_3	14	$\times$	0.0076	$=$	0.1064	11,550
t_2	9	$\times$	0.0076	$=$	0.0684	27,900
t_1	4	$\times$	0.0076	$=$	0.0304	70,800

C. Effective thicknesses and stresses

Effective dim.		Effective no. of plies		Ply thickness (in.)		Effective thickness (in.)	Net adherend stress, σ_A—psi
t_5	$=$	14	$\times$	0.0076	$=$	0.1064	55,000
t_4	$=$	18	$\times$	0.0076	$=$	0.1368	42,800
$t_4 - t_3$	$=$	4	$\times$	0.0076	$=$	0.0304	19,600
$t_3 - t_2$	$=$	5	$\times$	0.0076	$=$	0.0380	32,400
$t_2 - t_1$	$=$	5	$\times$	0.0076	$=$	0.0380	50,200
t_1	$=$	4	$\times$	0.0076	$=$	0.0304	70,800

TABLE VII

A. Load transfer and adhesive stress

Dim.		Overlap (in.)	$N/2$ (lb/in./ply)	No. of plies		Load transferred (lb/in. force)	Gross adhesive stress, τ_B—psi
a	=	0.8	543 ×	4	=	2172	2720
$\frac{3}{4}a$	=	0.6	187 ×	9	=	1676	2790
$\frac{1}{2}a$	=	0.4	84 ×	14	=	1176	2940
$\frac{1}{4}a$	=	0.2	32 ×	18	=	676	2880
		2.0 + clearance				5600	

B. Actual adherend thicknesses and stresses

Actual dim.	Actual no. of plies		Ply thicknesses (in.)		Actual thickness (in.)	Gross adherend stress, σ_A—psi
t_5	14	×	0.0076	=	0.1064	52,500
t_4	18	×	0.0076	=	0.1368	41,000
t_4	18	×	0.0076	=	0.1368	4200
t_3	14	×	0.0076	=	0.1064	11,000
t_2	9	×	0.0076	=	0.0684	24,500
t_1	4	×	0.0076	=	0.0304	71,700

C. Effective thicknesses and stresses

Effective dim.		Effective no. of plies		Ply thicknesses (in.)		Effective thickness (in.)	Net adherend stress, σ_A—psi
t_5	=	14	×	0.0076	=	0.1084	52,500
t_4	=	18	×	0.0076	=	0.1368	41,000
$t_4 - t_3$	=	4	×	0.0076	=	0.0304	18,900
$t_3 - t_2$	=	5	×	0.0076	=	0.0380	31,000
$t_2 - t_1$	=	5	×	0.0076	=	0.0380	44,200
t_1	=	4	×	0.0076	=	0.0304	71,700

TABLE VIII

PANEL/JOINT WEIGHT AND EFFICIENCY SUMMARY

Item	Detail part[a]	Weight in lb/in. of width			
		I	IA[b]	I	IIA[b]
Joint	Composite	0.007014	0.007014	0.011319	0.011319
	Foam	0.000140	0.000140	0.000140	0.000140
	Titanium	0.050240	0.023120	0.033688	0.040344
	Adhesive	0.000361	0.000381	0.000785	0.000785
		0.057765	0.032636	0.110932	0.051588
Panel	Composite	0.00957		0.01785	
	Adhesive	0.00044		0.00081	
	Honeycomb	0.00161		0.00390	
		0.01162 lb/in. (for 1.28 in. length)		0.02076 lb/in. (for 2.28 in. length)	
Weight efficiency (%)		20.1	35.6	18.7	33.8

[a] See Fig. 40.

[b] Hollow extrusion weight of titanium in IA and IIA designs assumed to be one-half the weight of solid edge member.

If the titanium unit weight is 0.16 lb/in.^{3} and the S-glass–epoxy composite unit weight is 0.07 lb/in.^{3}, the joint weight efficiency can be calculated as shown in Table VIII from Fig. 40 dimensions. From this table it can be seen that the most efficient length for these load transmission requirements is somewhere between these extremes. The calculations indicate that unit joint weight for such a load transfer magnitude will be approximately 2.5 to 5 times the unit weight of the panel outside the joint. These efficiencies are competitive with metal-bonded sandwich panels using solid metal edge members in a similar fashion. As can be seen from Table VIII, the joint could be made even more efficient by making the titanium of a tubular box construction; i.e., approximately doubling the weight efficiency.

While the preceding is a conceptual design/analysis, values used were derived experimentally. Strain compatibility analysis should be made in this case even though the maximum gross laminate stress of 71,700 psi is substantially below the average [0/90]c laminate strength of 113,830 psi in tension. This is because the laminate proportional limit is 29,770 psi and the Poisson ratio is about 0.08. While the stresses in the titanium are low,

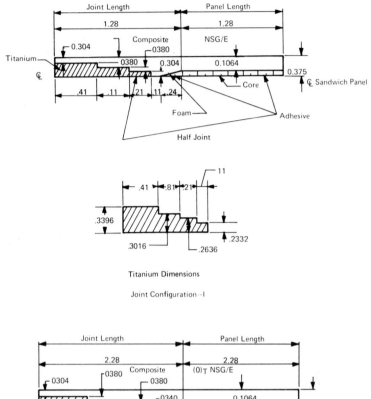

Joint Configuration—I

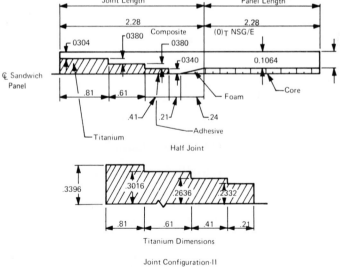

Joint Configuration-II

FIG. 40. Joint configurations I and II—panel/joint weight efficiency study.

its Poisson ratio is relatively high compared to the composite. This provides another reason for checking strain compatibility. The interlaminar shear strength of 7000 psi is substantially above the adhesive shear stress of 2940; therefore, the interlaminar shear stress is not likely to be critical.

This conceptual design/analysis was presented as an example of how to use experimental data in empirical design. Further study of the efficiency of such panel joints should consider sizes and aspect ratios. The following formulas compare panel weight (not including joint weight) with joint weight only:

$$\text{joint wt} = 2(a + b)J$$

$$\text{panel wt} = ab \cdot w \tag{39a}$$

$$a/b = k \qquad \text{(aspect ratio)}$$

$$a = kb$$

i.e.,

$$\text{joint wt} = 2(kb + b)J = 2b(k + 1)J$$

$$\text{panel wt} = kb^2w$$

$$\frac{\text{joint wt}}{\text{panel wt}} = \frac{2b(k + 1)J}{kb^2w} = \frac{2(k + 1)J}{kwb} \tag{39b}$$

where w is the panel unit weight in psi, k the aspect ratio of panel, J the unit joint weight in lb/in. length, a the panel length in in., and b the panel width in in.

The panel and joint weights are

$$\text{panel wt} = 0.0182 \text{ psi}$$

$$\text{joint wt} = \begin{cases} 0.1156 \text{ lb/in.—Panel I} \\ 0.652 \text{ lb/in.—Panel IA} \\ 0.2218 \text{ lb/in.—Panel II} \\ 0.1232 \text{ lb/in.—Panel IIA} \end{cases}$$

In the joint load transmission, Panel I will transmit 11,768 lb/in., and Panel II will transmit 11,200 lb/in.

Calculation of the panel weights and the joint weights is performed for four panel widths (b) ranging from 5 to 20 in. and four aspect ratios ranging from 1 to 4.

These calculations are plotted for four joint unit weights in Figs. 41 and 42 and show how the joint weight compares with the panel weight (not

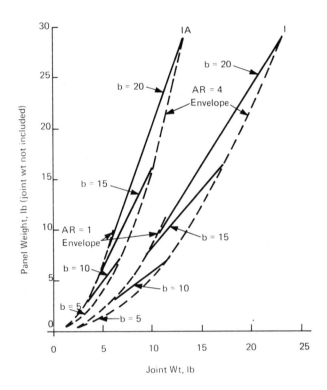

FIG. 41. Panel/joint weight relationship configurations I and IA.

including joint) for various panel sizes and aspect ratios. Designs I and II are the same as those given in Fig. 40 and Table VIII, whereas Designs IA and IIA are the same as I and II except that the titanium edge member is a hollow extrusion. For the highly loaded design studied, the most efficient joints have weights ranging from 20 to 100% of the panel weight for Design I and from 25 to 150% of the panel weight for Design II.

5. *Cost Effectiveness Methods*

This section is a summary of a cost effectiveness study performed previously by the Southwest Research Institute for an earlier edition of the Design Guide. It is emphasized that the following discussion is intended only to exemplify cost effectiveness techniques, and that numerical cost and rate data used in this study are purely for illustrative purposes. Cost effectiveness data, per se, such as the labor cost of a specific fabrication process, are of course a specific function of the local labor market and other

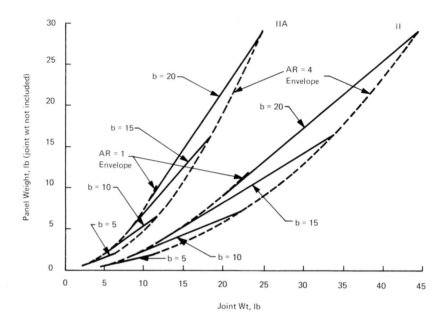

Fig. 42. Panel/joint weight relationship configurations II and IIA.

circumstances within each particular organization. Such data will have to be generated and maintained by each user.

While there is no way to break out the attachment cost portion of these figures from the total, the assembly installation costs of the boron–epoxy panels into a completed structure are estimated to be 1.9 times more expensive than for the conventional aluminum panels. Since these assembly techniques are of the mechanical type, the 1.9 factor may be useful in making preliminary estimates of the cost of using mechanical attachments in fibrous composites compared with the costs of similar attachments in aluminum structures.

Using two $\frac{1}{2}$-in. overlap lengths, it can be seen that for a joint width of 20 in., an adhesive joint area of 20 in.^{2} will result with 40 in.^{2} of surface preparation needed. The necessary tooling for bonding will also be required as well as an approximately 2 hr bonding process followed by nondestructive inspection. While the manhours required for this complete process could be as low as 2 and as high as 6, an average figure of 4 manhours will be used along with $1 in material costs. Tooling costs will be approximately $100. Capital equipment costs (for the press or autoclave and the inspection equipment) will not be considered. The direct cost for this joint will be

$4 \times \$3.50/\text{hr}$ (average skilled labor direct cost) $= \$14$ with a tooling cost of $100. These figures would have to be incorporated into each company's cost estimating structure covering overhead, vacation and sick leave, general and administrative, and profit costs to arrive at the total cost. The $14 results in a direct cost of $0.70/in. width of double-lap bonded joint with a material cost of $0.05/in. width and a tooling cost of $5/in. width. As pointed out previously, this joint results in a weight increment (penalty) of 0.044 lb/in. Then the load/weight index I_1 is:

$$I_1 = N/\Delta w = \frac{0.000 \text{ lb/in. (load)}}{0.044 \text{ lb/in. (wt increment)}} = 136{,}000 \qquad (40a)$$

For the bolted joint, a thickness of 0.282 in. is required with 17 bolts to be installed. Estimates on hand installation, materials, and tooling are about the same as for bonded joints; however, automatic drilling and rivet or bolt installation machines are in widespread use now, so 1 manhour should be sufficient for the total installation and inspection. Then $1 \times \$3.50 = \$3.50$ or $0.175/in. direct cost with a total fastener cost of $1 or $0.05/in. and a tooling cost of $100 or $5/in. Capital equipment costs (for the automatic drilling and riveting machines) are not considered. As determined earlier for a 6000 lb/in. load-carrying capability, the weight increment (penalty) for a bolted joint is 0.100 lb/in., so the load/weight index is

$$I_2 = \frac{N}{\Delta W} = \frac{6000 \text{ lb/in. (load)}}{0.100 \text{ lb/in. (wt increment)}} = 60{,}000 \qquad (40b)$$

Using hypothetical rates to establish gross costs, a vacation and sick leave (V&SL) rate of 20% of direct cost, an overhead (OVH) rate of 150% (of direct cost plus V&SL), a general and administrative (G&A) rate of 50% (on the total of direct, V&SL, and OVH), and a profit of 10% (on the total direct, V&SL, OVH, G&A, material and tooling) gives $9.03/in. for the bonded joints and $6.42/in. for the mechanically attached joints. This is a cost factor ratio (C_1/C_2) of 1.40 (bonded joint cost/mechanical joint cost). The same type of ratio of their load/weight indexes (I_2/I_1) gives 0.44, indicating the mechanical joint is only 44% as efficient as the bonded joint. A cost effectiveness factor might be

$$F_{\text{CE}} = \frac{C_1}{C_2} \times \frac{I_2}{I_1} = 1.40 \times 0.44 = 0.615 \qquad (41)$$

with 1.0 being the standard, above 1.0 less cost effective, and below 1.0 more cost effective than mechanically fastened composite joints. Therefore, for this example, adhesive-bonded joints are shown to be more cost effective.

TABLE IX

COMPARISON OF ANALYSIS TYPES ON BONDED JOINTS

Investigator	Material nonlinearities		Inter-laminar shear	Temp. effects	Analysis type[a]	Joint types	Predictive capabilities	
	Adherends	Adhesive					Stress	Ultimate load
Grimes et al. (1972)	yes	yes	no	no	D.E.	single, double, step	yes	yes
Grimes et al. (1972)	yes	yes	yes	no	F.E.	single, double, step	yes	no
Haddock (1972)	no	yes	no	yes	D.E.	single, step	yes	yes
Hart–Smith (1972)	no	yes	yes	yes	D.E.	single, double, step, scarf	yes	yes
Fehrle (1972)	no	yes	yes	yes	D.E.	single, double	yes	no

[a] D.E. is differential equation with adherends as plates. F.E. is finite-element two-dimensional analysis.

B. Analytical Methods Development

Bonded joints have been analyzed by two basic techniques—the differential equation and the finite-element approach. The approaches used by investigators differ primarily in the different assumptions relating to the material and deformation characteristics of the joint. Table IX indicates the basis for some of the more well-known bonded joint analyses. In general, all the differential equation approaches idealize the adherends as a plate member and the adhesive as a thin biaxially stressed region. The finite-element approaches generally use a two-dimensional plane stress (or strain) idealization.

In Section IV,B,1 the differential equation and finite-element approaches as developed by Grimes *et al.* (1972) will be outlined briefly. The other approaches listed in Table IX are well documented in their respective references. Test results indicate discrepancies in all theories and the "best" approach is still a matter of debate. The first approach by Grimes *et al.* (1972) has two main advantages: (1) it has been empirically corrected by experimental results and (2) it has an ultimate load predictive capability.

1. Differential Equation Approach

This section contains a summary of nonlinear analysis methods by the differential equation approach for bonded single-lap joints subjected to static loads. Double- and step-lap joints are discussed in Grimes *et al.* (1972). These three joints are shown in Fig. 43, along with the coordinate systems, dimensions, and applied loads which will be utilized in the following developments. The joints are assumed to be sufficiently wide in the y direction (perpendicular to the plane of the paper) such that the material under load is in a state of plane strain; i.e., the transverse extensional strain ϵ_y and the shear strains γ_{xy} and γ_{yz} are assumed to be zero. In general, the adherends may be either orthotropic (laminates) or isotropic, and may have different thicknesses which are constant for each adherened. The adhesive is assumed to be isotropic and of a constant thickness which is much smaller than the adherend thickness. The adherends are assumed to be flat plates in bending; i.e., normal stresses through the thicknesses (σ_z) are neglected. Interlaminar shear stresses (τ_{xz}, τ_{yz}) are neglected. Laminates are assumed to be symmetrical about their middle surface.

(a) EQUILIBRIUM EQUATIONS. The differential equations of equilibrium governing the behavior of a segment of a bonded single-lap joint can be developed from the free bodies in Fig. 44. (The joint is assumed to have a unit width in the y direction.) Summing forces in the x and z directions and

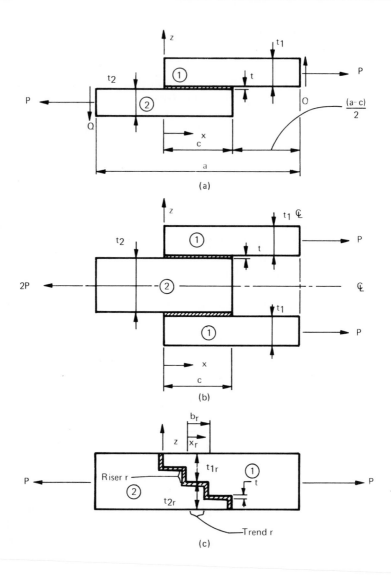

Fɪɢ. 43. Dimensions and coordinate system. (a) Single lap; (b) double lap; (c) step lap, typical for step r—R steps in general (3 shown).

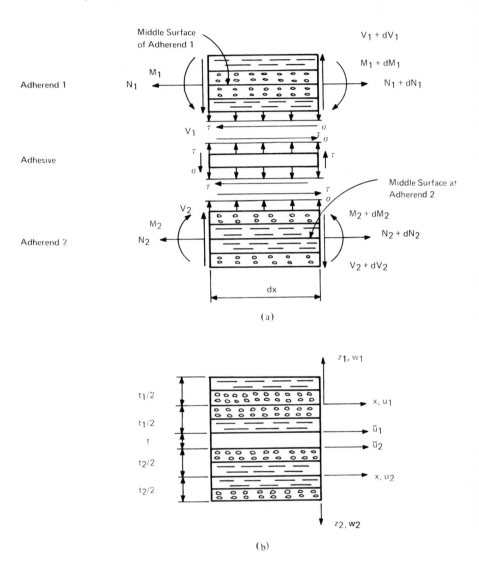

FIG. 44. Forces and displacements for an element of infinitesimal length of a single-lap bonded joint. (a) Free-body diagram; (b) displacements.

moments in the x, z plane for adherends 1 and 2 gives

$$\frac{dN_1}{dx} - \tau = 0, \qquad\qquad \frac{dN_2}{dx} + \tau = 0 \qquad (42a)$$

$$\frac{dV_1}{dx} - \sigma = 0, \qquad\qquad \frac{dV_2}{dx} - \sigma = 0 \qquad (42b)$$

$$\frac{dM_1}{dx} - V_1 + \tau\frac{t_1}{2} = 0, \qquad \frac{dM_2}{dx} - V_2 - \tau\frac{t_2}{2} = 0 \qquad (42c)$$

where σ and τ are the normal stress and shear stress in the adhesive, respectively, which are assumed constant through the thickness of the adhesive, and N_i, V_i, and M_i are the stress resultants for adherend i.

By introducing stress function φ and θ, the stresses which satisfy the equilibrium equations (42) can be written as

$$\tau = \varphi'/2, \qquad\qquad\qquad \sigma = \theta''/2$$

$$N_1 = (P + \varphi)/2, \qquad\qquad N_2 = (P - \varphi)/2 \qquad (43)$$

$$M_1 = \frac{1}{2}\left[\theta + \frac{P\bar{t}}{a}\left(x - \frac{c}{2}\right) - \frac{t_1}{2}\varphi\right], \qquad M_2 = \frac{1}{2}\left[\theta - \frac{P\bar{t}}{a}\left(x - \frac{c}{2}\right) + \frac{t_2}{2}\varphi\right]$$

$$V_1 = \frac{1}{2}\left(\theta' + \frac{P\bar{t}}{a}\right), \qquad\qquad V_2 = \frac{1}{2}\left(\theta' - \frac{P\bar{t}}{a}\right)$$

where the prime denotes differentiation with respect to x and $\bar{t} = (t_1 + t_2)/2$.

(b) COMPATIBILITY EQUATIONS. Another set of equations, namely the compatibility equations, must be brought into play. The shear strain γ and normal strain ϵ which are assumed constant through the adhesive are given by

$$\gamma = (\bar{u}_1 - \bar{u}_2)/t$$
$$\epsilon = (w_1 + w_2)/t \qquad (44)$$

where $\bar{u}_1$ and $\bar{u}_2$ are the x displacements of the upper adherend lower face and the lower adherend upper face, respectively (Fig. 42b):

$$\bar{u}_1 = u_1 + \frac{t_1}{2}w_1'$$
$$\bar{u}_2 = u_2 + \frac{t_2}{2}w_2' \qquad (45)$$

The quantities u_i and w_i are the axial and lateral displacements of the mid-plane of adherend i, respectively, as shown in Fig. 42b.

(c) CONSTITUTIVE EQUATIONS. Constitutive equations must now be introduced to relate material deformations to stresses. The bonded joints are composed of both isotropic and orthotropic materials: isotropic and/or orthotropic adherends and an isotropic adhesive.

(d) ISOTROPIC ADHEREND. The adherends are assumed to be in a state of plane stress in the x, y plane (Fig. 43), i.e., $\sigma_z = \tau_{xz} = \tau_{yz} = 0$. (The additional assumption of plane strain in the x, z plane, i.e., $\epsilon_y = \gamma_{xy} = \gamma_{yz} = 0$, will be introduced later.) By the deformation theory of plasticity for an isotropic material in plane stress, the relationship between stresses and strains in the inelastic regime can be stated as (Grimes *et al.*, 1972)

$$\begin{Bmatrix} \sigma_x \\ \sigma_y \\ \tau_{xy} \end{Bmatrix} = \frac{E_s}{(1 - \nu_p^2)} \begin{bmatrix} 1 & \nu_p & 0 \\ \nu_p & 1 & 0 \\ 0 & 0 & \dfrac{1-\nu_p}{2} \end{bmatrix} \begin{Bmatrix} \epsilon_x \\ \epsilon_y \\ \gamma_{xy} \end{Bmatrix} \tag{46}$$

in which E_s, the secant modulus, is

$$E_s = \bar{\sigma}/\bar{\epsilon} \tag{47}$$

ν_p is the plastic Poisson ratio and $\bar{\sigma}$ is the effective stress

$$\bar{\sigma} = (\sigma_x^2 - \sigma_x\sigma_y + \sigma_y^2 + 3\tau_{xy}^2)^{1/2} \tag{48}$$

If the Ramberg–Osgood (1943) approximation to the stress–strain curve is used, the relationship between $\bar{\sigma}$ and $\bar{\epsilon}$ can be expressed by

$$\bar{\epsilon} = \frac{\bar{\sigma}}{E} + \frac{3}{7}\frac{\sigma_0}{E}\left(\frac{\bar{\sigma}}{\sigma_0}\right)^n \tag{49}$$

where σ_0 and n are material constants selected such that Eq. (49) fits the nonlinear portion of the uniaxial stress–strain curve.

The additional assumption of zero strain in the y direction can now be conveniently introduced ($\epsilon_y = \gamma_{xy} = 0$). One can then proceed to develop the relationships between the adherend stress resultants N and M and the middle surface strain, e and κ, by appropriate integration through the plate thickness:

$$N = Ae - N_p$$
$$M = D\kappa - M_p \tag{50}$$

where A and D are the plate elastic membrane and bending stiffnesses and N_p and M_p are the plastic components at the stress resultants.

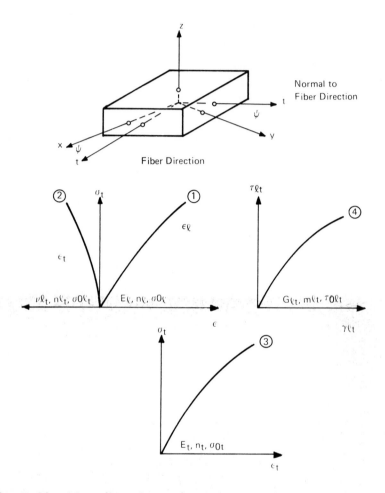

FIG. 45. Material coordinates l, t, y and stress–strain curves from uniaxial stress tests in principal directions.

(e) ORTHOTROPIC ADHEREND. By details outlined in Grimes *et al.* (1972) the deformation theory of plasticity for orthotropic materials leads to the following relationship between stresses and strains in the principal material directions (Fig. 45):

$$\left\{ \begin{array}{c} \sigma_l \\ \sigma_t \\ \tau_{lt} \end{array} \right\} = \left[\begin{array}{ccc} Q_{11s} & Q_{12s} & 0 \\ Q_{12s} & Q_{22s} & 0 \\ 0 & 0 & Q_{66s} \end{array} \right] \left\{ \begin{array}{c} \epsilon_l \\ \epsilon_t \\ \gamma_{lt} \end{array} \right\} \qquad (51)$$

where the Q_{ijs} are secant stiffness elements. The values of these elements are determined such that Eq. (51) is satisfied for the conditions of uniaxial stress with the following definition of effective stress:

$$\bar{\sigma} = \left[\alpha_{11}\sigma_l{}^2 - \alpha_{12}\sigma_l\sigma_t + \alpha_{22}\sigma_t{}^2 + \alpha_{66}\tau_{lt}^2 \right]^{1/2} \tag{52}$$

A Ramberg–Osgood law, similar to Eq. (49), is used to approximate each of the four uniaxial curves shown in Fig. 45, which are obtained by uniaxial tests of a typical lamina.

In a manner similar to that used for isotropic adherends, the previous equations along with a transformation equation are used to obtain the constitutive equations for a laminated plate composed of different layers of an orthotropic material.

(f) ISOTROPIC ADHESIVE. The adhesive is assumed to be an isotropic material and the constitutive equations of Grimes et al. (1972) are utilized. The relations for the three-dimensional stress state will now be specialized for the adhesive. The normal stress in the x direction is neglected; $\sigma_x = 0$. Since the joint is assumed to be in a state of plane strain in the x, z plane, one has $\gamma_{xy} = \gamma_{yz} = 0$. Hence, the equations of Grimes et al. (1972) apply to the adhesive in the following form (after separation of inelastic and

TABLE X

MATERIAL CONSTANTS FOR RAMBERG–OSGOOD APPROXIMATION

Curve	Adhesive (AF-126-2)		
	G (ksi)	τ_0 (ksi)	n
τ vs γ	175	3.32	2.684
	Adherend (Narmco 5505) (unidirectional)		
	E_i (ksi)	σ_{0i} (ksi)	n_i
σ_l vs ϵ_l	29,600	312.7	4.463
σ_l vs ϵ_l (ϵ_x)$_z$	$-130,000$	285.5	5.129
σ_t (σ_z) vs ϵ_l	$-130,000$	285.5	5.129
σ_t (σ_z) vs ϵ_t (ϵ_z)	2750	11.91	2.541
σ_t (σ_z) vs ϵ_z (ϵ_t)	-8870	10.52	3.350
τ_{lt} (τ_{lz}) vs γ_{lt} (γ_{lz})	933	7.95	2.991
τ_{tz} vs γ_z	191	68.44	2.031

elastic portions and introduction of the plane strain assumption):

$$\sigma = \frac{E\epsilon}{1 - \nu^2} - \sigma_p$$

$$\tau = G\gamma - \tau_p \tag{53}$$

in which the subscripts on the adhesive stresses and strains have been removed.

(g) GOVERNING DIFFERENTIAL EQUATIONS. The equilibrium, compatibility, and constitutive equations are combined to develop the governing differential equations for the single-lap joint in the following form:

$$\theta^{(\mathrm{IV})} + p_1\theta - p_2\varphi = q_1 + q_2''$$

$$\varphi'' - p_3\varphi + p_4\theta = q_3 + q_4' \tag{54}$$

where

$$p_1 = \frac{E}{t(1 - \nu^2)}\left(\frac{1}{D_1} + \frac{1}{D_2}\right)$$

$$p_2 = \frac{E}{2t(1 - \nu^2)}\left(\frac{t_1}{D_1} - \frac{t_2}{D_2}\right)$$

$$p_3 = \frac{G}{t}\left(\frac{1}{A_1} + \frac{1}{A_2} + \frac{t_1^2}{4D_1} + \frac{t_2^2}{4D_2}\right)$$

$$p_4 = \frac{G}{2t}\left(\frac{t_1}{D_1} - \frac{t_2}{D_2}\right) \tag{55}$$

$$q_1 = -\frac{PE\bar{t}}{at(1 - \nu^2)}\left(\frac{1}{D_1} - \frac{1}{D_2}\right)\left(x - \frac{c}{2}\right) - \frac{2E}{t(1 - \nu^2)}\left(\frac{M_{1p}}{D_1} + \frac{M_{2p}}{D_2}\right)$$

$$q_2 = -2\sigma_p$$

$$q_3 = \frac{PG}{t}\left[\frac{1}{A_1} - \frac{1}{A_2} + \frac{\bar{t}}{2a}\left(\frac{t_1}{D_1} + \frac{t_2}{D_2}\right)\left(\frac{c}{2} - x\right)\right]$$

$$+ \frac{G}{t}\left[\frac{2N_{1p}}{A_1} - \frac{2N_{2p}}{A_2} - \frac{t_1 M_{1p}}{D_1} + \frac{t_2 M_{2p}}{D_2}\right]$$

$$q_4 = -2\tau_p$$

Equations (54) represent the governing differential equations for the single-lap joint. It will be noted that they are nonlinear equations since the plastic quantities N_{ip}, M_{ip}, σ_p, and τ_p are nonlinear functions of the displacements. However, as the equations are written, the portions on the left are linear differential equations with constant coefficients (p_i are constants). The portions on the right (q_i) which contain the plastic portions are nonlinear. Equations (54) are, thus, in proper form for an iterative solution.

From Fig. 43a the boundary conditions for the single-lap joint are developed by requiring that the stress resultants in the upper adherend be zero at $x = 0$ and the stress resultants in the lower adherend be zero at $x = c$:

$$
\begin{array}{cc}
\underline{x = 0} & \underline{x = c} \\[4pt]
\varphi_0 = -P & \varphi_c = P \\[8pt]
\theta_0 = \dfrac{P}{2}\left(\dfrac{c\bar{t}}{a} - t_1\right) & \theta_c = \dfrac{P}{2}\left(\dfrac{c\bar{t}}{a} - t_2\right) \\[16pt]
\theta_0' = -\dfrac{P\bar{t}}{a} & \theta_c' = \dfrac{P\bar{t}}{a}
\end{array}
\tag{56}
$$

These boundary conditions, along with Eqs. (54) and the constitutive equations, are the governing equations for the bonded single-lap joint. The basic form of Eqs. (54) also applies to double- and step-lap joints as described in Grimes *et al.* (1972).

2. *Discrete-Element Approach*

In Grimes *et al.* (1972), the complete details of the finite-element solution are outlined. The solution is based on the well-documented finite-element theory. The joint is again assumed to be in a state of plane strain in the x, z plane. A typical finite element is a constant strain triangle. Deformation plasticity theory is used (similar to the differential equation approach except all three dimensions must be retained here). Since no classical plate assumptions are made, shear and normal stress deformations of the adherends are included. The composite material is assumed to be orthotropic with transverse isotropy, i.e., isotropic in a plane perpendicular to the fibers.

3. *Comparison of Theoretical and Discrete-Element Results*

In order to compare the theoretical and discrete-element analysis methods, the three particular joint configurations shown in Fig. 46, i.e., single lap, double lap, and step lap, are analyzed by both methods.

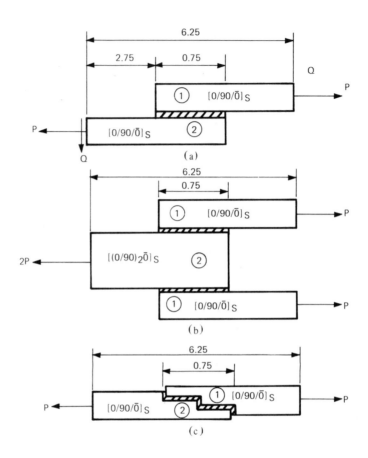

Fig. 46. Joint configurations for comparison of analysis methods. (a) Single lap; (b) double lap; (c) step lap.

The material properties used in the Ramberg–Osgood approximation of the adhesive shear stress–strain curve are shown in Table X. Poisson's ratio of the adhesive is taken as 0.3. The material constants for the characterization of a typical lamina of an adherend are also given in Table X. They represent the Ramberg–Osgood constants for the various uniaxial stress–strain curves. The finite-element idealization of the single-, double-, and step-lap joint are shown in Figs. 47, 48, and 49, respectively. Joint boundary conditions are illustrated schematically in these figures.

Results from the discrete-element analysis for the shear and normal stress in the adhesive are presented as circled points in Figs. 50–52 for the single-, double-, and step-lap joints, respectively. The theoretical analysis tech-

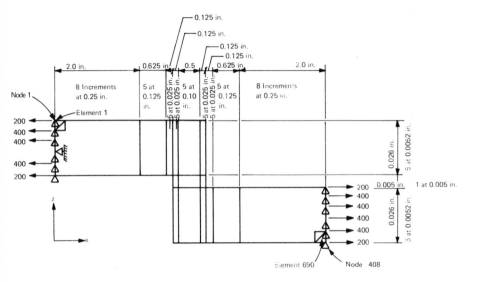

Fig. 47. Discrete-element layout for single-lap joint.

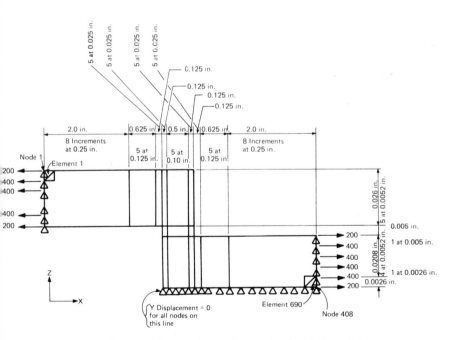

Fig. 48. Discrete-element layout for double-lap joint.

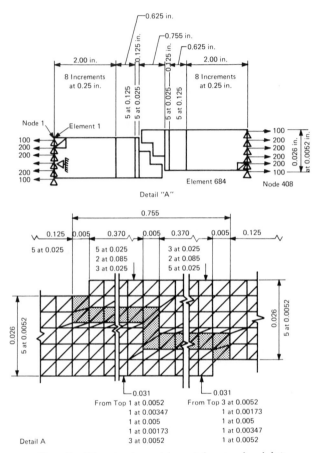

FIG. 49. Discrete-element layout for step-lap joint.

nique outlined previously and programmed in Fortran IV is also used to analyze the joints. The results of the theoretical analysis are presented as the curves in Figs. 50–52 for the three joints.

Despite the different assumptions involved in the finite-element method and the analytical method, e.g., three-dimensional stresses in the finite-element method *versus* negligible shear deformation in the adherends for the analytical method, the comparison of the results in Figs. 50 and 51 is quite good for the adhesive shear stress in the single- and double-lap joint. The difference in the two methods for the step-lap joint adhesive shear (Fig. 52) is probably due to both of the following two causes: (1) Shear deformation is neglected in the adherends for the theoretical method. For the step, the adhesive is attached to the 90° oriented layers. The shear modulus of

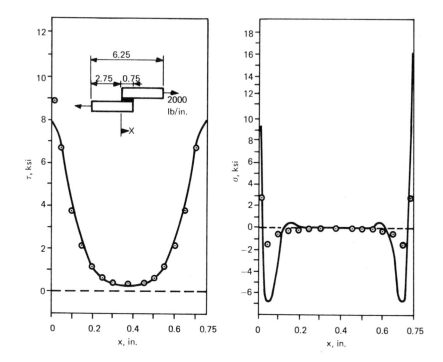

FIG. 50. Adhesive stress, single-lap joint. — Theoretical; ⊙ Discrete element.

these layers in the plane of the joint is only 191 ksi (see Table X), which is about equal to that of the adhesive itself. (2) Transmission of force through the step risers is neglected in the theoretical method. Hence, the total force is transmitted by shear along the treads. Thus, the average shear stress for the theoretical method is about 1000/0.75 or 1333 psi, whereas it is lower for the discrete-element method since some force is transmitted through the risers.

4. *Theoretical/Experimental Behavior Comparisons and "Effective" Properties*

(a) GENERAL. The purpose of this section is to show the correlation between the theoretically predicted joint behavior (including failure loads) and the experimental results on both small simple specimens and larger complex assemblies.

(b) ADDITION OF EFFECTIVE BENDING. The theory outlined in Section IV,B,2 was used to predict the failure loads of several of the experimental

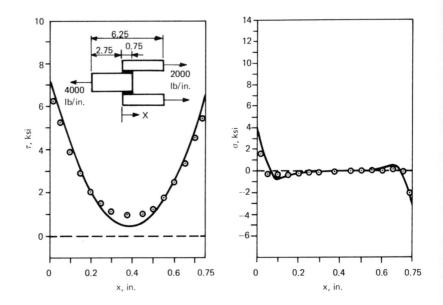

Fig. 51. Adhesive stress, double-lap joint. — Theoretical; ⊙ Discrete element.

TABLE XI

Average Adhesive Mechanical Properties

	Material	
Property	AF 126-2 (LSHE)	MB-329 (HSLE)
σu	5513 psi	7300 psi
E^a	0.22568×10^6 psi	0.96847×10^6 psi
ν^a	0.40	0.4284
τ_u	7170 psi	8970 psi
G	0.0806×10^6 psi	0.399×10^6 psi

[a] These values are calculated. Such calculations are based on experimentally measured G and E (constrained) values assuming an isotropic-elastic relationship among E, G, and ν. See Grimes et al. (1972).

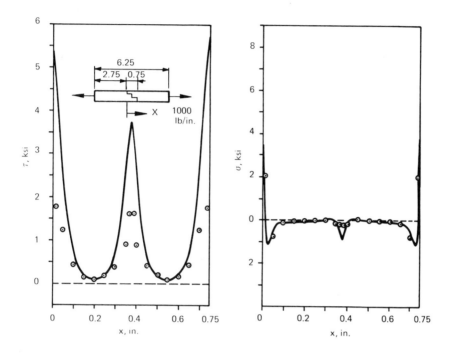

FIG. 52. Adhesive stress, step-lap joint. — Theoretical; ⊙ Discrete element.

joint configurations. Maximum stress theory was used for the adhesive and isotropic adherends. Maximum strain theory was used for the composite adherends. These theories were incorporated into the computer program.

Early investigation indicated that the theory as presented predicted excessively low failure loads. Comparison of analytical and experimental strains indicated the theory predicted excessively high bending strains. For example, the theory predicted compressive strains in adherend 2 of the single lap at $x = 0$, $z_2 = t_2/2$ (refer to Fig. 44). This was never observed in the experimental data. Similar inconsistencies arose in the double and step lap. The primary cause of the high predicted bending stresses is the small deflection assumption for the derivation of the equilibrium equations. As the axial load is increased, the eccentricity of the joint is reduced and, therefore, the bending due to the axial load is also reduced. (The reverse occurs in the familiar beam-column problem.) Thus, the moment in adherend 2 of the single lap at $x = 0$ is significantly less than predicted. This is in part is due to the plane sections remain plane assumption, which exaggerates the bending contribution since, in the vicinity of the adherend–adhesive interface, shear deformations are significant.

In order to remedy this situation without revising the entire theory, an effective bending factor, k_e, is introduced. This factor reduces all the computed bending moments in the joint by k_e. The quantity k_e is introduced into the equations of Section IV,B,2 in the following form:

$$M_1 = \frac{1}{2}\left[\theta + \frac{P\bar{l}}{a}\left(x - \frac{c}{2}\right) - \frac{t_1}{2}\varphi\right]k_e$$

$$M_2 = \frac{1}{2}\left[\theta - \frac{P\bar{l}}{a}\left(x - \frac{c}{2}\right) + \frac{t_2}{2}\varphi\right]k_e \tag{43M}$$

$$p_1 = \frac{E}{t(1 - \nu^2)}\left(\frac{1}{D_1} + \frac{1}{D_2}\right)k_e$$

$$p_2 = \frac{E}{2t(1 - \nu^2)}\left(\frac{t_1}{D_1} - \frac{t_2}{D_2}\right)k_e$$

$$p_3 = \frac{G}{t}\left(\frac{1}{A_1} + \frac{1}{A_2} + \frac{t_1^2 k_e}{4D_1} + \frac{t_2^2 k_e}{4D_2}\right)$$

$$p_4 = \frac{G}{2t}\left(\frac{t_1}{D_1} - \frac{t_2}{D_2}\right)k_e \tag{55M}$$

$$q_1 = -\frac{PE\bar{l}k_e}{at(1 - \nu^2)}\left(\frac{1}{D_1} - \frac{1}{D_2}\right)\left(x - \frac{c}{2}\right) - \frac{2E}{t(1 - \nu^2)}\left(\frac{M_{1p}}{D_1} + \frac{M_{2p}}{D_2}\right)$$

$$q_3 = \frac{PG}{t}\left[\frac{1}{A_1} - \frac{1}{A_2} + \frac{k_e t}{2a}\left(\frac{t_1}{D_1} + \frac{t_2}{D_2}\right)\left(\frac{c}{2} - x\right)\right]$$

$$+ \frac{G}{t}\left[\frac{2N_{1p}}{A_1} - \frac{2N_{2p}}{A_2} - \frac{t_1 M_{1p}}{D_1} + \frac{t_2 M_{2p}}{D_2}\right]$$

Similar expressions for the double and step lap are developed in Grimes *et al.* (1972).

(c) ANALYTICAL EXPERIMENTAL BEHAVIOR COMPARISON. For correlation purposes the averaged results from 16 lap shear assemblies[†] were chosen as representative samples of the 67[‡] investigated in Grimes *et al.* (1972).

---

† Each assembly represents 3 or 4 specimens.
‡ Totaling 203 individual specimens.

TABLE XII

Variable Bending Factor
Selections: BF/JT[a]

Joint type	Bending factor
Single lap	0.01
Double lap	0.02
Step lap	0.10

[a] Based on joint type only.

Seven single-lap (S.L.), seven double-lap (D.L.), and two step-lap (St.L.) joints were chosen, covering adhesive systems and adherend combinations, selectively. Adherend properties were obtained from Grimes *et al.* (1972) and the literature for use in the computer prediction program. Adhesive properties, taken from the literature, are presented in Table XI.

The nonlinear joint behavior equations are programmed for failure by (1) cohesive fracture of the adhesive by the maximum stress theory, (2) tensile failure of the composite adherend by maximum strain theory, and (3) tensile failure of the titanium adherend by maximum stress theory.

TABLE XIII

Best Bending Factor Selections: BF/JT–AT–FT[a]

Joint type	Adhesive type	Primary failure type	Bending factor
S.L.	LSHE or HSLE	AT or CF	0.01
D.L.	LSHE	CF	0.20
D.L.	LSHE	AT	0.02
D.L.	HSLE	CF	0.02
2 St.L.	LSHE	AT	0.10
3 St.L.	LSHE	CF	0.01

[a] (Based on joint type, adhesive type, and failure type). S. L. is single lap, D.L. is double lap, St.L. is step lap, LSHE is low stiffness/high elongation (AF-126-2), HSLE is high stiffness/low elongation (MB-329), AT is adherend tension, and CF is cohesive fracture (bondline or composite surface resin).

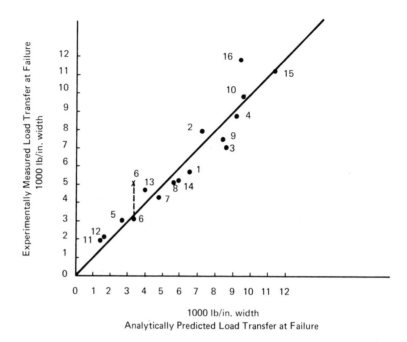

1000 lb/in. width
Analytically Predicted Load Transfer at Failure

FIG. 53. Correlation curve on bonded joints for BF/JT: bending factor chosen by joint type only. *Note:* Point 6 failure was taken as the proportional limit knee on the extensometer load/deflection curve. Actual ultimate is shown by the x point. Joint variables covered: Adherend combinations—B/B and B/T; adherend orientations −0,0/90,0/±45; adhesive types—LSHE (AF-126-2) and HSLE (MB-329). Joint types: S.L., D.L., and St.L. Failure types: A. Cohesive fracture (CF) of bondline or composite surface resin; B. Adherend tension (AT).

Values of the bending factor were selected for reasonable correlation with each joint type (BF/JT) and are listed in Table XII. Figure 53 shows the experimental/analytical correlation with these bending factors by joint type. A limited amount of effort devoted to further refining the values of the bending factor for various adhesive types and failure types within the joint types (BF/JT, AT, FT) resulted in the values shown in Table XIII with the corresponding correlation shown in Fig. 54. These approaches could be extended to other joint configurations, as the refinement of the bending factor is limited only by the experimental data available.

Figure 55 shows the plots of the predicted surface strains in the overlap area of specimen LSA-20-1 at one load level with the experimentally measured values superimposed. Figure 56 presents the predicted surface strains in the overlap area of specimen LSA-62-1 at one load level with the experimental points superimposed. Correlation is good. Note that the experimentally measured longitudinal surface strain values correlate very closely to those predicted for both composite and titanium adherends. The experimentally measured transverse strains on the composite are also shown. Since the plane strain assumption is used in the program, the predicted transverse strains are zero. The computer predicted shear and normal stress distribution at predicted failure loads are shown in Fig. 57 for single-lap joints (LSA-20) and in Fig. 58 for double-lap joints (LSA-62). Since both the ultimate load and surface strain predictions check out experimentally, the shear and normal stress plots should be reasonably accurate. Actually it is postulated that the shear stress near the end of the joint reaches a maximum about one bondline thickness in from each end because it must go to zero at these ends. Since the equations have been modified empirically, this discrepancy is not considered a serious drawback in its design application.

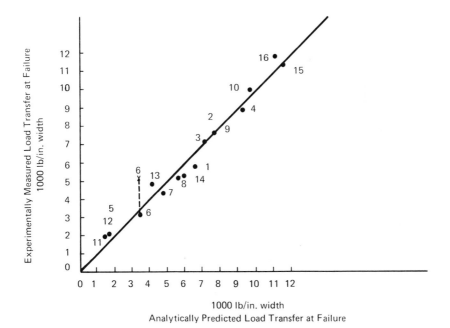

FIG. 54. Correlation curve on bonded joints for BF/JT–AT–FT: bending factor chosen by joint type, adhesive type, and failure type. See Fig. 53 for Note and variables and types covered.

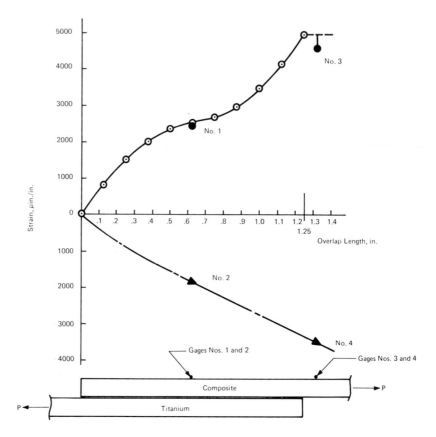

FIG. 55. Theoretical/experimental correlation of single-lap joint surface strains. Type bending factor: BF/JT; bending factor, k_e = 0.010. Specimen LSA-20-1; single lap; P = 4400 lb at failure. ⊙ Theoretically predicted longitudinal strain; ● Experimentally measured longitudinal strain; ▲ Experimentally measured transverse strain.

C. Design/Analysis Application

1. Discussion of Approach

Design oriented experimental data curves for composite adherend joints can be generated by plotting failure loads versus the geometric parameter L/t. For each composite orientation a plot of running load/ply versus L/t is recommended. The running loads at joint failure in pounds per inch are divided by the number of plies to get the running load/ply ($\bar{N}$) in pounds per inch per ply. The L/t parameter may be obtained by dividing the bondline overlap length by the adherend thickness. Always use the smaller of the two adherend thicknesses.

For this project, data from selected, representative joints were picked from Grimes *et al.* (1972) for use in design oriented experimental data curve generation. The predicted failure load values and the use of $\bar{N} = 0$ when $L/t = 0$ define these curves (or lines) up to laminate failure. Laminate failure then becomes a cutoff at $\bar{N}$ = laminate failure load (constant). This cutoff value may be predicted or plugged in from experimental data on laminates. While the cutoff shown here is based on laminate adherend failure it could just as easily be based on metal adherend failure (for composite–metal joints) where this is critical.

2. Design Curves

The design oriented average experimental data curves generated fall on or very close to the nonlinear analytically predicted joint failure load

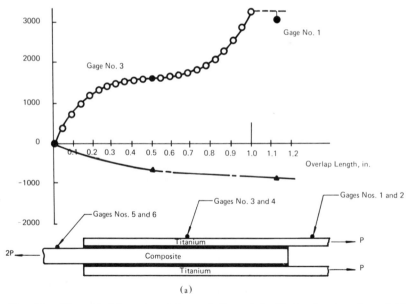

(a)

Fig. 56. Theoretical/experimental correlation of double-lap joint surface strains. (a) Titanium adherend; (b) composite adherend. Type bending factor, BF/JT, $k_e = 0.020$. Specimen LSA 62-1, double lap, $P = 2535$ lb at failure. ○ Theoretically predicted longitudinal strain; ● Experimentally measured longitudinal strain; ▲ Experimentally measured transverse strain.

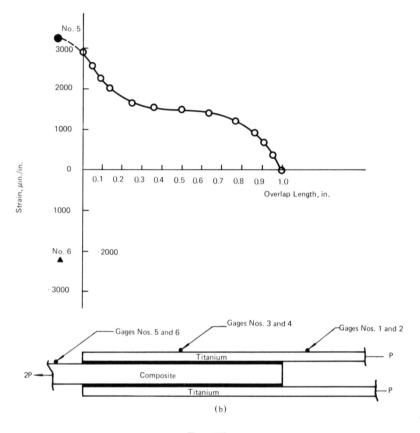

FIG. 56b.

values as shown in Fig. 59. All predicted and actual failure modes correspond except one, that being No. 36. Actual failure of this joint was by
laminate adherend tension, while its predicted failure was by cohesive
fracture of the adhesive.[†] Experimentally measured boron–epoxy laminate
tensile ultimate strength is used as the horizontal cutoffs for these curves
with the points 31, 33, and 36 used for correlation.

Use of such design oriented experimental data curves which allow prediction of average test values for any L/t (or vice versa) is one method of
allowables determination. Statistically based formulas can be applied with
such data to obtain reduced values for use as design allowables. Such
formulas were developed in Section IV,A. The 95% confidence design ulti-

---

[†] Changing the bending factor k_3 from 0.02 to 0.05 predicts adherend tension failure
mode but at a somewhat lower failing load.

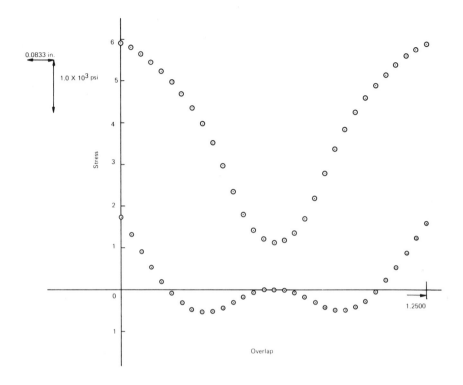

Fɪɢ. 57. Predicted bondline shear and normal stress distribution at predicted failure load—S.L. Specimen LSA 20, single lap. ⊙ Tau, ⊙ sigma, $P_u = 4677$.

mate allowables may be calculated using the general formula [given by Eq. (35)] in which the average (mean) value can be taken from the Fig. 59 curves. The other parameters are known or can be determined from the detailed data tabulation of Grimes *et al.* (1972).

Once the nonlinear analytical formulas have been checked out with simple lap joint tests utilizing the joint configuration and material combination desired, they can be used to generate a family of curves for design allowables purposes as was done herein. Alternatively, the computerized formulas could be modeled as single, double, or step lap. If it is desired to use the type of allowable curve generated above directly in design, it will be necessary to use a design factor K which would be

$$K = \frac{DA}{\bar{f}_s} = \frac{\bar{N}_D}{N_f'} \tag{57}$$

where DA = design allowables value, $\bar{N}_D$ is in lb/in./ply [use Eq. (35)],

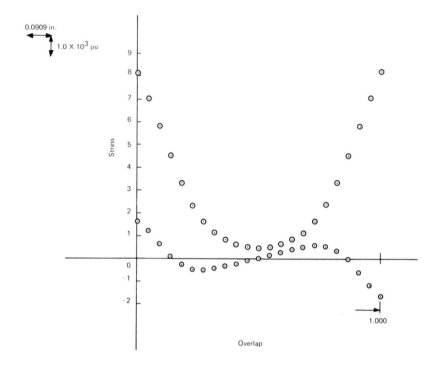

FIG. 58. Predicted bondline shear and normal stress distribution at predicted failure load—D.L. Specimen LSA 62, double lap. ⊙ Tau, ⊙ sigma, P_u = 2896 ×2.

$\bar{f}_s$ = mean value of strength, and $\bar{N}_f$ is in lb/in./ply. To use the curve in this fashion the design load in pounds per inch per ply would be input on the ordinate to curve intersection and the L/t value read on the abscissa at that point. This L/t value would then have to be adjusted as follows:

$$(L/t)_D = \frac{1}{K}(L/t)_f = \frac{\bar{N}_f}{\bar{N}_D}(L/t)_f$$

where $(L/t)_D$ = design value and $(L/t)_f$ = mean value read from curve. If the input load is above the horizontal cutoff line (as in Fig. 58), a stronger orientation or composite material must be used.

When using the design predictive formulas or computer programs, the distance between assumed zero bending moments points on the adherend on each side of the joint (quantity a) must be known or very large† as

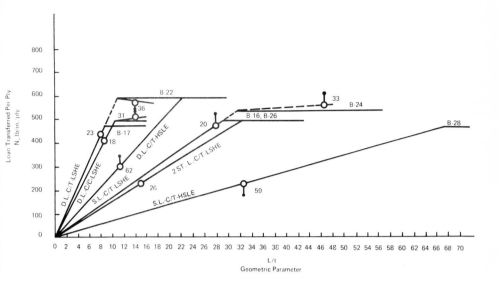

FIG. 59. Design curves for single-, double-, and step-lap joints. 0.50 F.V. B/E composite adherend $-[0/\pm45]c/6A1$-4V annealed Ti adherend. Adhesives: LSHE = AF-126-2 and HSLE = MB-329. B-XX = ultimate tensile strength of panel B-XX; S.L. = single lap, D.L. = double lap, 2St.L. = two-step lap. ○ Experimental point; ● Analytically predicted point.

compared to the overlap length c. That is, the ratio c/a must be known or small† (in the latter case it can be assumed to be zero).

Design ultimate allowables can be calculated based on the nonlinear design/analysis formula prediction values. These values are used as mean strength values and can be applied to most any joint design which is or can be broken into single-, double-, or step-lap configurations. If the users then have a large backlog of lap joint test data, typical experimentally based statistical parameters will also be available. These can be used with the predicted mean strength to calculate bonded joint design ultimate allowables for most any adherend–adhesive and configuration combination.

Where insufficient basic adherend or adhesive material properties are known, the use of these formulas will be advantageous. This can be done by using assumed "effective" properties,‡ chosen on a trial-and-error basis to

† The ratio c/a should be 1/50 or smaller.
‡ In the form of the Ramberg–Osgood three-parameter stress–strain curve values for the adherend orthotropic lamina or isotropic material and the adhesive.

predict failure loads and correlate them with the results from a few simple lap joint tests. Such a procedure will provide a powerful technique for mean joint strength prediction. However, such "effective" properties may be substantially different from the real ones as shown in Grimes (1971).

Since the predicted mean strength and type of failure of the wide (complex) joints of Grimes *et al.* (1972) were also reasonably accurate when compared with experimental results, design allowables calculated from such mean strength predictions should also be accurate. Therefore, the use of the standard 1.5 factor of safety on design limit loads to obtain design ultimate loads should be sufficient to provide ample operational safety for static load conditions at room temperature.

V. Mechanically Fastened Joints

Attachment between two composites or between a composite and a metal via mechanical means is a problem if standard attachment procedures and design technology are used. These problems are caused by the material's low bearing and compression strength (glass and graphite reinforcements) and its naturally weak interlaminar zone (reflecting the polymer resin strength, only). In addition most composites have low in-plane shear strength which is detrimental to mechanical fastening. Edge effects at holes or other discontinuities not only can cause local interlaminar failures but the effective stress concentration factors can range from below to well above those occurring in a similar metal piece, depending primarily on the laminate's fiber orientation relative to the load directive. With all these disadvantages, should mechanically fastened joints be used at all? The answer is yes if the applications are properly chosen and the joint properly designed. The latter is a difficult task with so little known about mechanically fastened joints.

Basically standard mechanical fastening techniques such as rivets, bolts, pins, screws, etc., should not be used in critical and/or primary structural applications if they can be avoided. However, for secondary and noncritical applications these types of joints not only function well, but are the most cost effective attachment means. It should be emphasized that proper fabrication and installation procedures are necessary for such joints to perform properly. For instance, close tolerance, burr-free holes with no crazing or delamination are required for proper function. Bolts and pins should be close tolerance, fitted to these holes, because sloppy fits and tolerances can be a disaster in these materials. Bucked rivets which swell in diameter should not be used unless special bushed, reinforced, or shim joints are used and then only with caution.

For nonstandard mechanical fastening there are possibilities for use in primary structure, once the engineer understands how the material functions micromechanically and macromechanically under load. This is an area where little published research is available and much new work needs to be done.

Section V,A covers standard mechanical fastening, whereas Section V,B presents some information on nonstandard mechanical fastening.

A. Standard Mechanical Fastening

This section covers the basic behavior (empirically derived) of simple bolted and bolted–bonded joints subjected to a static tensile loading. The experimental data are taken from those published in MIL-HDBK-17 (Dept. of Defense, 1971) which is based on the research performed by Hawley *et al.* (1969).

When a double-lap joint with a single 0.190 in. diameter bolt is used with the single member being composite and the double member being 7075 T-6 aluminum, the results shown in Fig. 60 can be obtained from the Dept. of Defense (1971). Note the weak shear strength of the boron–epoxy (B/E) and the glass–epoxy (G/E) materials as evidenced by the large e/d (7) required to get out of the double shear-out range for two different lamination sequences. Above $e/d = 7$ net section tension through the bolt hold takes over as the predominant failure mode. Note that the ordinate stress is that occurring away from the hole area and that it represents only 24% of the boron–epoxy tensile specimen strength (assumed to be 120 ksi)† and 30% of the nonwoven S-glass–epoxy tensile specimen strength (assumed to be 70 ksi).† Such strength reductions at these loaded bolt holes indicate stress concentration factors (SCF) of the magnitude discussed in Section II,A on discontinuities. The critical parameters here are the e/d and S/d ratios. At the S/d value of 4 and larger (with e/d value of 7 or larger), one can expect some increase in strength with the failure mode going to a combined one of net section tension on one side of the hole and single shear-out between the hole and edge.

Standard strength of materials formulas (P/A) are used in the data analysis. As long as the actual anticipated loads are multiplied by the appropriate fitting and safety factors, these same methods of analysis can be

† For [0/±45/0]c orientations, only.

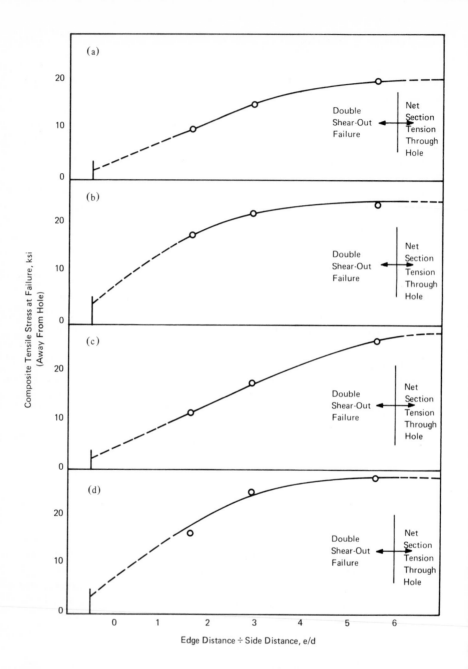

Fig. 60. Tensile stress *versus* e/d at failure, single bolt—double lap. $d/t = 1.58$, $S/d = 2.63$, $t = 0.120$ in. (a) G/E—aluminum joint, $[\pm 45/0_4]_S$, $t_p = 0.010$ in.; (b) G/E —aluminum joint, $[0/\pm 45/0]_{3S}$, $t_s = 0.010$ in.; (c) B/E—aluminum joint, $[\pm 45/0_4]_{2S}$, $t_p = 0.005$ in.; (d) B/E—aluminum joint, $[0/\pm 45/0]_{3S}$, $t_p = 0.005$ in.

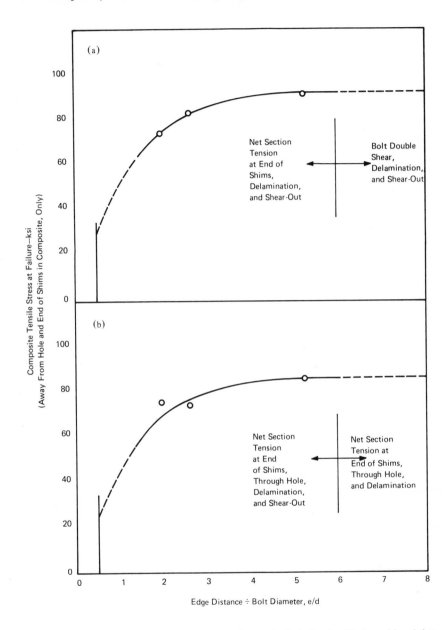

Fig. 61. Tensile stress *versus* e/d at failure, single-bolt, double-lap shim joint. $d/t = 0.98$, $S/d = 1.98$, $t = 0.192$. (a) B/E shim reinforced steel joint; $[\pm 45/0_4]_{2S}$ + shims; $t_p = 0.005$ in., $t_s = 0.003$ in. 17-7PH S.S. (b) B/E shim reinforced steel joint; $[0/\pm 45/0]_{3S}$ + shims; $t_p = 0.005$ in., $t_s = 0.003$ in. 17-7PH S.S.

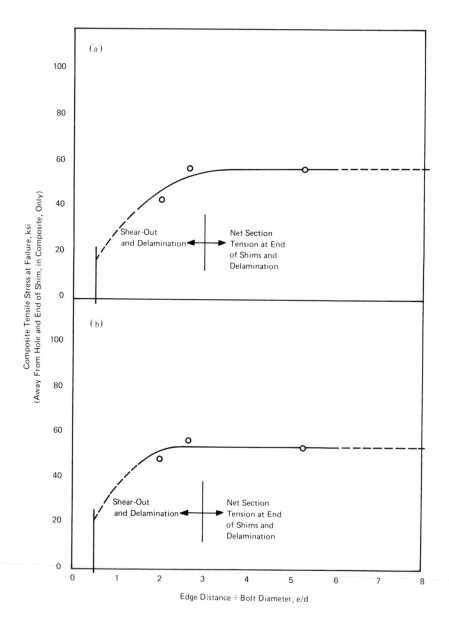

F_IG_. 62. Tensile stress *versus* e/d at failure, single-bolt, double-lap shim joint. $d/t = 0.98$, $S/d = 1.98$, $t = 0.192$. (a) Glass–epoxy shim reinforced steel joint; $[\pm45/0_4]_S$ + shims; $t_p = 0.010$ in., $t_s = 0.003$ in. 17-7PH S.S. (b) Glass–epoxy shim reinforced steel joint; $[0/\pm45/0]_{3T}$ + shims; $t_p = 0.010$ in., $t_s = 0.003$ in. 17-7PH S.S.

used in design. Allowable values should be based on experimental data which have been statistically reduced.

According to the Dept. of Defense (1971) the use of bushed holes did not increase the static strength of these joints, but the use of two 0.036 in. 17-7 PH steel shims located evenly through the laminate thickness in the hole area did. Figures 61 and 62 show these improvements for boron–epoxy and S-glass–epoxy composite double-lap joints. Note that an e/d of 6 is still required to prevent some shear-out. Above this e/d net section tension of the composite at the end of the shims is the cause of failure in all but the $[\pm45/0_4]2_\text{S}$ + shims boron–epoxy laminate, which failed the 0.190 steel bolt in double shear. These joints failed at 71% of the boron–epoxy† tensile strength and 79% of the glass–epoxy† tensile strength, i.e., a big improvement over the standard joint but at some weight penalty.

The effects of lamination sequence, lap joint type, and material on joint strength are shown in Fig. 63 for one set of geometric parameters. Note that the shear-out mode of failure provides the lowest joint strength, while the bolted, bonded joint provides the highest static strength short of an all

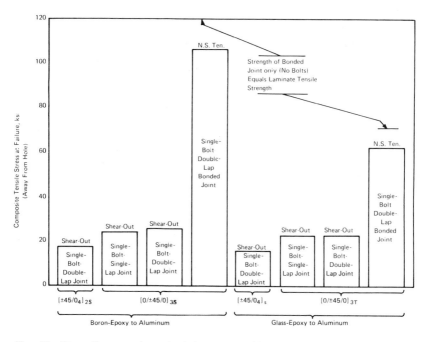

FIG. 63. Strength comparisons for joint types. $e/d = 3.95$, $S/d = 2.63$, $d/t = 1.58$, $1/t = 12.5$.

bonded joint. Increasing e/d would change shear-out failures to the net section tension and increase strength somewhat (not shown in Fig. 63). Also the shim joint strength (not shown) would fall somewhat below the bolted–bonded configuration but would be better than standard mechanical fastening.

There is some evidence that the bolted–bonded concept can be superior to bonded joints in fatigue. This is achieved by designing the mechanical fastening to aleviate the large normal tensile stresses that occur in all bonded joints under axial tension load near the joint ends.

Key advice in designing standard mechanical joints is to perform tests on joints similar to the operational ones and under similar environments and loadings. Then use standard strength of materials joint design technology with appropriate empirical modification.

B. Nonstandard Mechanical Fastening

Little information is available in this area; however, some insight can be provided. Friction wedge joints developed by Vertol Div. of Boeing for attachment of composite material blade structure to metal root attachments have been developed and tested. These joints are also bonded for redundancy, but they will carry the load even if the bondline fails. The idea is to flair the end of the composite (female) member in a wedge shape and design an external (male) reverse wedge that mechanically fits over it and clamps it. Thus the load is transferred by a combination of friction and normal bearing into tension in the composite.

In another case, Bell Helicopter studied the same application but tried using fibers which came in from the composite part and wrapped around a metal insert and went back into the part. This approach makes the joint an integral part of the composite. The concept is good but it needs more development work, especially in the area of fabrication and quality control.

List of Symbols

Fiber orientations relative to principal axis

$[0/90]_c$	Of the general 0/90 orientation, any no. of plies, usually symmetric	$[+45]_c$	of plies, usually symmetric Of the general ± 45 orientation, any no. of plies, usually symmetric
$[0/\pm 45]_c$	Of the general $0/\pm 45$ orientation, any no.	$[0/\pm 45]_{2s}$	$(0/+45/-45/-45/$ $+45/0) \times 2$

$[0/90]_S$	$(0/90/90/0)$		material constant
$[90/0]_S$	$(90/0/0/90)$	p_i, q_i	Parameters in joint
$[+45/0]_S$	$(45/0/0/-45)$		differential equation
$[\pm 45]_S$	$(45/-45/-45/45)$	r	Radius of hole type
$[\pm 15]_S$	$(15/-15/-15/15)$		discontinuity (see Fig. 2)
$[\pm 55]_S$	$(55/-55/-55/55)$	s	Side distance
$[\pm 60]_S$	$(60/-60/-60/60)$	t	Perpendicular to principal
$[\pm 15/\pm 45]_S$	$(15/-15/45/-45/$		lamina axis (transverse
	$-45/+45/-15/15)$		fiber distance), laminate
$[\pm 45/\pm 15]_S$	$(45/-45/15/-15/$		thickness, adhesive
	$-15/15/-45/45)$		thickness
$[45/\mp 15/-45]_S$	$(45/-15/15/-45/$	t_i	Adherend thickness
	$-45/15/-15/45)$	$\bar{t}$	$(t_1 + t_2)/2$
$[15/\pm 45/-15]_S$	$(15/45/-45/-15/$	u, v, w	Displacements in the x, y, z
	$-15/-45/45/15)$		coordinate directions
		w	Unit panel weight
a	Characteristic dimension of	x, y, z	x, y, z coordinate directions
	the intense energy region		
	(Fig. 2), lap length	A	Plate membrane stiffness
	(Fig. 39), panel length	A_{ij}	Extensional stiffness matrix
	dimension		coefficients for laminate
b	Semiwidth of laminate		subject to in-plane
	specimen, panel width		loading
	dimension	C_v	Coefficient of variation
c	Bonded joint overlap	$C_1 L_1$	Confidence limit
	length	C_1, C_2	Bonded and mechanical
d	Fiber diameter or bolt		joint cost factors,
	diameter		respectively
e	Edge distance, in plane	D	Plate bending stiffness
	plate strain	E	Modulus of elasticity of
f_s	Mean bondline shear		material
	strength	E_s	Secant modulus
f_{xz}	Average interlaminar shear	$E_x, E_y,$	Elastic constants for
	stress in x, z plane	G_{xy}, ν_{xy}	laminate in x and y
f_{yz}	Average interlaminar shear		directions
	stress in y, z plane	E_f, ν_f	Elastic properties of
f_z	Average interlaminar		reinforcing fiber
	tension in z direction	E_m, E_r, ν_r	Elastic properties of resin
g	Energy available for crack		matrix
	extension	E_{ij}, G_{ij}, ν_{ij}	Lamina elastic constants
h	Laminatec thikness	F_L, F_T, F_{LT}	Allowable axial stress in
h_k, h_k^{-1}	Thickness of kth ply		L, T direction and shear
k	Aspect ratio (AR)		stress in LT direction
k_e	Effective bending factor	F.V.	Fiber volume, usually in %
l	Principal lamina axis	F_{CE}	Cost effectiveness factor
	(longitudinal fiber	G	Shear modulus
	direction)	I_1, I_2	Load weight indices
n	Number of specimens or	J	Joint unit weight in psi
	data points in a sample,	K	Design factor
	a Ramberg–Osgood	K_I	Stress intensity factor

K_T	Stress concentration factor (SCF)	γ	Shear strain, linear for small angles
L, T, l, t	Primary lamina reinforcement axis	$\gamma_{xy}, \gamma_{yz}, \gamma_{zx}$	Shear strain, linear for small angles in xy, yz, zx direction of laminate
L	Joint bondline overlap length	Δ	Increment or decrement
M_i, N_i, V_i	Adherend moment normal and shear stress resultants	ϵ	Axial strain
		$\epsilon_z, \epsilon_y, \epsilon_z$	Axial strain in x, y, and z directions
M_p, N_p	Plastic stress resultants	$\epsilon_z{}^0, \epsilon_y{}^0, \gamma_z{}^0$	Average lamina strains
N	Mean running load/ply (lb/in./ply)	ϵ, γ	Adhesive normal and shear strains
N_z, N_y, N_z	Laminate unit (or running) axial and edgewise shear loads (lb/in.)	$\bar{\epsilon}$	Effective strain
		θ	Acute angle measured from x to y axis, counterclockwise
P	Applied joint load		
PDA	Preliminary design allowables	θ, φ	Stress functions
Q_{ij}	Stiffness matrix coefficients for a generally orthotropic lamina; Q_{ij} is for specially orthotropic lamina, i.e., along principal axes, only	κ	Local curvature
		ν	Elastic Poisson ratio
		ν_p	Plastic Poisson ratio
		σ	Applied axial stress, psi or ksi; σ—axial failure stress
Q_{ij}^*	Stiffness matrix coefficients for a laminate	σ_0	Critical stress
		σ_{max}	Maximum stress
Q_{ijs}	Orthotropic secant stiffness elements	σ_O	Average stress in specimen away from hole or with no hole, Hamberg–Osgood material constants
SCF$_f$	Stress concentration factor in fibers		
SCF$_m$	Stress concentration factor in matrix	$\sigma_x, \sigma_y, \tau_{xy}$	Axial stress in x, y directions and shear stress in xy direction
S_{ij}	Compliance matrix coefficients for a homogeneous anisotropic lamina	σ_θ	Tangential stress at edge of hole at angle θ from x axis
S	Standard deviation	σ_α	Stress on lamina or unidirectional laminate at angle α to the reinforcement
U_i	Invariants which are a function of Q_{ij}		
$U(y, z)$	Displacements causing experimental moiré surface strains	$\bar{\sigma}_f$	Fiber failure stress
		$\bar{\sigma}_0$	Laminate failure stress
V_f	Fiber volume fraction (decimal)	$\sigma_0{}^*, \tau_0{}^*$	Maximum strain criterion limit stresses
V. V.	Void volume (%)	σ_z	Tensile stress normal to plane of laminate, i.e., interlaminar normal tensile stress
ΔW	Weight increment		
α	Angle of reinforcement relative to principal axis	$\bar{\sigma}$	Mean failure stress, effective stress
α_i	Orthotropic constants		

$\bar{\sigma}_{tu}$	Adherend tensile ultimate strength	τ	Shear stress, τ–failure shear stress
σ_A	Adherend stress	τ_{xz}	Interlaminar shear stress in x, z plane
σ, τ	Adhesive shear and normal stress	τ_{xy}	Edgewise shear stress in x, y plane
σ_l, σ_t, σ_z, τ_{lt}, τ_{lz}, τ_{tz}	Lamina stresses in principal directions	τ_{yz}	Interlaminar shear stress in y, z plane
ϵ_l, ϵ_t, ϵ_z, γ_{lt}, γ_{lz}, γ_{tz}	Lamina strains in principal directions	τ_B	Average bondline shear strength or stress
σ_p, τ_p	Adhesive plastic stresses		

References

Ashton, J. E., Halpin, J. C., and Petit, P. H. (1969). "Primer on Composite Materials: Analysis." Technomic, Westport, Connecticut.

Barker, R. M., and MacLaughlin, T. F. (1971). *J. Compos. Mater.* **5**, 492.

Bodnar, M. J. (1966). "Structural Adhesives Bonding." Wiley (Interscience), New York.

Bowie, O. L. (1956). *J. Math. Phys.* **35**, 70.

Chamis, C. C., Hanson, M. P., and Serafini, T. T. (1973). Criteria for Selecting Resin Matrices for Improved Composite Strength. *Modern Plastics*, May.

Daniel, I. M., and Rowlands, R. E. (1971). *J. Compos. Mater.* **5**, 250.

Dept. of Defense (1971). Plastics for Aerospace Vehicles, Part 1. Reinforced Plastics, MIL-HDBK-17A. Washington, D.C.

Douglas Aircraft Co./McDonnell Douglas Corp. (1969). Investigation of Joints and Cutouts in Advanced Fibrous Composites for Aircraft Structures—Joint and Attachment Investigation, Vol. I, Technical Discussion and Summary, AFFDL-TR-69-43, Contract F33615-67-C-1582.

Ferhrle, A. C. (1972). Fatigue Phenomena of Joints in Advanced Composites. *Proc. Conf. Fibrous Compos. Vehicle Design*, AFFDL-TR-72-130, pp. 857–890.

Foye, R. L., and Baker, D. J. (1970). Design of Orthotropic Laminates. *Proc. Annu. AIAA Struct., Struct. Dynam., Mater. Conf.*, 11th.

Greszczuk, L. B. (1972). Stress Concentrations and Failure Criteria for Orthotropic and Anisotropic Plates with Circular Openings. *Conf. Compos. Mater: Testing Design*, 2nd STP-497, p. 363.

Griffith, A. A. (1920). *Phil. Trans. Roy. Soc.* **221A**, 163.

Grimes, G. C. (1971). Stress Distribution in Adhesive Bonded Lap Joints. SAE Paper 710107, published in *SAE Trans.*

Grimes, G. C. (1971). Joint Efficiency Techniques. Final Rep. on SwRI Project 03-2571, USAF Contract F33615-69-C-1572, Southwest Res. Inst.

Grimes, G. C., and Whitney, J. M. (1972). The Relationship between Design Allowables and Load Induced Micromechanical Damage in Composite Materials. *Proc. Colloq. Struct. Reliability: The Impact Advan. Mater. Eng. Design* (M. Swedlow, M. Cruse, and M. Halpin, eds.), p. 323.

Grimes, G. C., et al. (1967). Investigation of Structural Design Concepts for Fibrous Aircraft Structures, Volume III, Technology Appraisal-Experimental Data and Methodology, AFFDL-TR-67-29. Southwest Res. Inst.

Grimes, G. C., Francis, P. H., Commerford, G. E., and Wolfe, G. K. (1972). An Experimental Investigation of the Stress Levels at which Significant Damage Occurs in Graphite Fiber Plastic Composites. AFML-TR-72-40, p. 55.

Grimes, G. C. *et al.* (1972). The Development of Nonlinear Analysis Methods for Bonded Joints in Advanced Filamentary Composite Structures, AFFDL-TR-72-97.

Haddock, R. N. (1972). Joints in Composite Structures. *Proc. Conf. Fibrous Compos. Vehicle Design* AFFDL-TR-72-13, pp. 791–811.

Hart-Smith, L. J. (1972). Design and Analysis of Adhesive Bonded Joints, *Proc. Conf. Fibrous Compos. Vehicle Design,* AFFDL-TR-72-13, pp. 813–856.

Hawley, A. V., Lehman, G. M., *et al.* (1969). Investigation of Joints in Advanced Fibrous Composites for Aircraft Structures, AFFDL-TR-69-43, Vols. I, II.

Lekhnitskii, S. G. (1963). "Theory of Elasticity of an Anisotropic Body" (J. J. Brandstatter, ed.; P. Fern, translator). Holden-Day, San Francisco, California.

Lekhnitskii, S. G. (1968). "Anisotropic Plates" (S. W. Tsai and T. Cheron, translators). Gordon and Breach, New York.

Pagano, N. J., and Pipes, R. B. (1971). *J. Compos. Mater.* **5,** 50; AFML-TR-71-8 dated March, 1971.

Paris, P. C., and Sih, G. C. (1965). Stress Analysis of Cracks, ASTM STP-381, pp. 52, 70.

Petit, P. H., and Waddoups, M. E. (1969). *J. Compos. Mater.* **3,** 2–19.

Pipes, R. B. (1972). Interlaminar Stresses in Composite Laminates, AFML-TR-72-18.

Pipes, R. B., and Daniel, I. M. (1970). *J. Compos. Mater.* **5,** 255.

Pipes, R. B., and Pagano, N. J. (1970). *J. Compos. Mater.* **4,** 538.

Puppo, A. H., and Evensen, H. A. (1970). *J. Compos. Mater.* **4,** 204.

Ramberg, W., and Osgood, W. R. (1943). Description of Stress-Strain Curves by Three Parameters, NACA TN 902.

Rybicki, E. F. (1971). *J. Compos. Mater.* **5,** 354–360.

Rybicki, E. F., and Hopper, A. T. (1972). Analytical Investigation of Stress Concentrations Due to Holes in Fiber Reinforced Plastic Laminated Plates, Two Dimensional Models, AFML-TR-72-15.

Savin, G. H. (1961). "Stress Concentration around Holes." Pergamon, Oxford.

Waddoups, M. E., Eisenmann, J. R., and Kaminski, B. E. (1971). *J. Compos. Mater.* **5,** 446.

Wu, E. M. (1968). "Composite Materials Workshop." Technomic, Westport, Connecticut.

11

Design of Composite Structural Components

C. C. CHAMIS

NASA-Lewis Research Center
Cleveland, Ohio

I. Introduction

The advent of composite materials, in general, and filament (fiber) reinforced composites, in particular, provides the structural designer with

231

several degrees of freedom for efficient material utilization and creative design. The material degrees of freedom in conjunction with available optimization methods provide a means for the simultaneous structural component and material designs. Thus, the designer is able to specify the component geometry, the material composition, and, indirectly, the fabrication process.

The ultimate goal, then, in designing with composite materials is to specify: (1) types of constituents and their quantities, (2) the fabrication process, (3) ply sequence and orientation in angleplied laminates, and (4) the component geometry so that the final product is tailor-made for the specific objective. This is accomplished with the aid of available multilevel analyses and various design procedures.

The various analysis levels employed are parts described in Volume 7 and previous chapters of this volume. In this chapter the various design procedures are described which include: evolution of design, sources of design data and types of design data, conventional and automated design including structural synthesis, simultaneous component and material design, important factors to be considered in designing composite components, and some sample design cases. The chapter text is supplemented with pertinent illustrations to illustrate concepts, procedures, or structural response.

II. Evolution of Design

The evolution of any design results from a requirement or desire to satisfy either a known or agreed upon need. In this sense, design of structures is mission oriented even though the term mission has not been used by structural designers. Several decisions precede the definitization of any specific design objective. Some of these decisions are schematically illustrated in Fig. 1. For example, modular-type construction for low cost housing evolved from the need to have suitable but inexpensive housing for underprivileged families.

Selection of the material for the modules for low cost housing is governed by whether the material under consideration satisfies the specific requirements such as: local codes, inexpensive, ease of fabrication, human and environmental factors, conservation of natural resources, etc. To establish whether the material selected meets the specific requirements depends on the availability of the following and other information: resources available, necessary design data, design methodology, and fabrication technology. In the case of structural fiber composites, considerable design data have been accumulated and the design methodology has been generated as will

TABLE I

SUMMARY OF THE DISCIPLINES THAT MIGHT BE EMPLOYED IN THE DESIGN PROCESS

I. Multilevel analysis for structural behavior	II. Structural analysis	III. Design

1. Micromechanics
  a. ply thermoelastic properties
  b. ply uniaxial strengths
2. Ply combined-stress strength criterion
3. Laminate analysis
  a. force balance
  b. energy
  c. interply layer effects
  d. transverse shear effects
  e. coupling responses
  f. stress analysis
  g. edge effects
  h. residual stresses
	1. Classical methods
	2. Matrix methods
	  a. force
	  b. displacement
	3. finite-element methods
	4. buckling
	5. vibrations
	6. impact
	7. statistical
		1. Conventional methods
		  a. handbook and design guides
		  b. trial and success
		2. Probabilistic
		3. Optimization methods
		  a. parametric studies
		  b. structural synthesis
		  c. simultaneous material and structural design

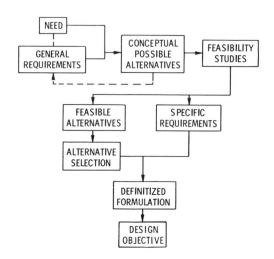

Fɪɢ. 1. Schematic of the evolution of the design objective.

be discussed subsequently. The fabrication and construction technologies are available as is evidenced from the achievements cited in Dietz (1972), Heifetz *et al.* (1972), Lynema (1972), McClelland (1972), Powell (1972, 1973), Winfield (1972), Gerin-Lajoie (1973). See also Volume 3, edited by Noton, in this treatise.

A schematic for designing structural components from fiber composites is illustrated in Fig. 2. In this schematic, all the essential parts of the design process: mission, constituent materials design criteria and controls, various analyses, and optimization are illustrated. The type of design illustrated in Fig. 2 is evolved using elaborate computer programs. The important point

TABLE II

Cᴏᴍᴘᴏsɪᴛᴇ Dᴇsɪɢɴ Dᴀᴛᴀ Bᴀɴᴋ

1. Constituent properties	7. Creep
2. Unidirectional composite properties	8. Stress rupture
3. Environmental effects	9. Impact resistance
a. temperature	10. Viscoelastic behavior
b. moisture	11. Statistical data
c. vacuum	a. mean
4. Material nonliniarities	b. variance
5. Fatigue resistance	c. Weibull parameters
6. Notch sensitivity	

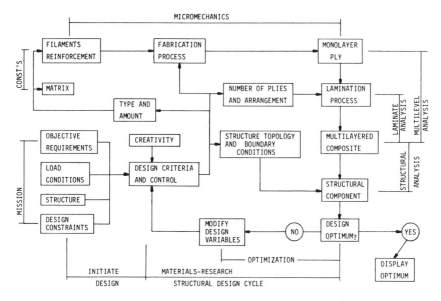

Fɪɢ. 2. Schematic of designing structural component from fiber composites.

to be kept in mind while studying Fig. 2 is that design is a strategic sequential process where feedback from previous steps in the sequence is required for selecting the best alternative for the next step in the design sequence.

The various disciplines that may be employed in designing structural components from fiber composites are summarized in Table I. The types of data needed in a fiber composite design data bank are summarized in Table II.

It is noted at this juncture that design for many composite components requires only small portions of the disciplines shown in Table I and the design data in the data bank of Table II. This will be illustrated in Section V where sample design cases of components are discussed.

III. Design Procedures

Conventional methods and optimization methods constitute the two general classes of procedures for designing structural components from fiber composites. Both of these are described in some detail in this section.

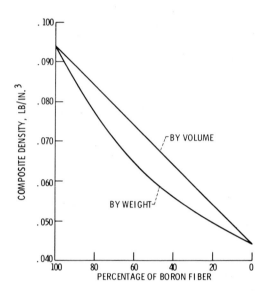

FIG. 3. Composite density *versus* fiber content (Structural Design Guide, 1968).

A. Conventional Designs

Conventional designs are evolved using a trial and success process with the aid of handbooks, design guides, material supplier's brochures, technical articles and reports, and other relevant data.

1. *Design Handbooks*

Several design handbooks are available: Baer (1964), Gibbs and Cox Inc. (1960), Grove and Pray (1964), Juveric and Rittenhouse (1968), Lubin (1969), MIL-HDBK-17A (1971), Oleesky and Mohr (1964), and White (1965). In addition to the handbooks, several books have been published which contain both composite design data and design procedures. Many of these books have been referenced in the previous chapters of this volume. See also the survey papers Chamis (1969b, 1972).

Handbooks and books contain information such as material properties, fabrication processes, analysis methods, design curves, environmental effects, and sample designs. The data from these sources are directly applicable when the material is a shelf item or is covered in the handbook (book). Mostly, handbooks and books have utility as design guides and are a valuable source for preliminary designs.

2. *Design Guides*

Design guides recognize the multitude of design variables in advanced fibrous composites. Their primary purpose is to be used as guides in any one facet of the design. The information in these sources covers the whole field of composites from material properties to test methods and design examples of special components. Design guides are usually organized for continuous updating so that relevant information is included as it becomes available (Structural Design Guide, 1973; NASA, 1973).

3. *Other Sources of Design Information*

The majority of design information is scattered throughout various publications. These sources include: books, technical journals, conference proceedings, professional society special publications, and government, university, and industry research reports. Some of these sources are included in the references cited herein. Extensive lists of design information sources are cited in the survey papers by Chamis (1969b, 1972). The literature surveys Beckwith *et al.* (1970, 1971) and Fleck (1972) are also good sources for available publications in composite materials.

Obviously there is a large amount of design information available and a good amount of it is continuously generated. Convenient accessibility to the majority of this information and proper interpretation are the major problems.

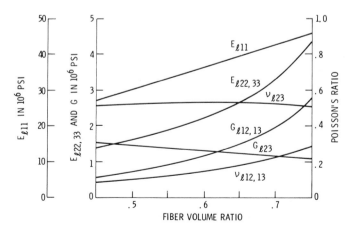

Fig. 4. Theoretical elastic properties for boron–epoxy unidirectional composites. E = Young's modulus, G = shear modulus, ν = Poisson's ratio. Subscripts 1, 2, and 3 are along the fiber, transverse, and through the thickness, respectively (Chamis, 1968b).

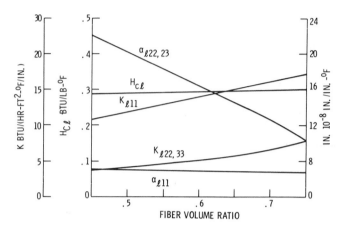

FIG. 5. Theoretical thermal properties for boron–epoxy unidirectional composites. K = thermal conductivity, H = heat capacity, α = thermal coefficient of expansion. Subscripts 1, 2, and 3 are along the fiber, transverse, and through the thickness, respectively (Chamis, 1968b).

4. *Typical Design Data*

Typical design data available in handbooks and other publications are described in this section for illustration purposes. The usefulness of these data in design will be illustrated in Section V where sample design cases are described.

Figures 3 through 6 provide design data on boron–epoxy unidirectional

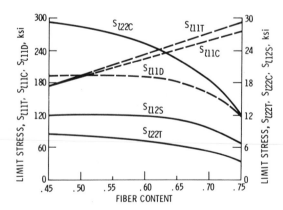

FIG. 6. Theoretical limit stresses for boron–epoxy unidirectional composites. S_{l11T} = longitudinal tensile, S_{l11C} or S_{l11D} = longitudinal compression, S_{l22T} = transverse tension, S_{l22C} = transverse compression, S_{l12S} = intralaminar shear (Chamis, 1969c).

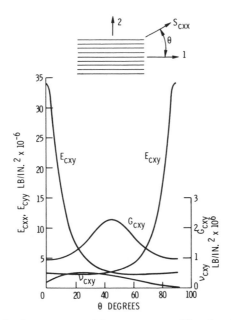

FIG. 7. Typical elastic constants of boron–epoxy unidirectional composites loaded off-axis (4-mil diameter fiber; fiber volume ratio ≈ 0.60). (Structural Design Guide, 1968.)

composites. Figures 7 and 8 show elastic constants and tensile strength data of unidirectional composites loaded at some angle to the fiber direction. Figures 9 and 10 show elastic constants and tensile strength data of various symmetric angleplied laminates. Figures 11 and 12 show analogous results for a specific symmetric angleplied laminate loaded at some angle to its axis of symmetry. For strength data on other composite systems and failure envelopes of unidirectional composites subjected to combined loadings, see Volume 7, Chapter 2, of this treatise.

Buckling coefficients of various orthotropic plates subjected to single loading and with different edge support conditions are given in Figs. 13–16. The parameters in Figs. 13–16 are given by (Grove and Pray, 1964)

$$c = \frac{2\nu_{cyx}E_{cxx}G_{cxy}(1 - \nu_{cxy}\nu_{cyx})}{(E_{cxx}E_{cyy})^{1/2}} \tag{1}$$

$$q = \frac{a}{b}\left(\frac{E_{cyy}}{E_{cxx}}\right)^{1/2} \tag{2}$$

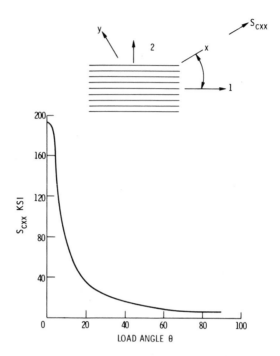

Fig. 8. Typical strength of a boron–epoxy unidirectional composite loaded off-axis (4-mil diameter fiber; fiber volume ratio ≈ 0.60). (Structural Design Guide, 1968.)

TABLE III

Buckling Loads of Simply Supported Homogeneous Anisotropic Plates[a]

Applied loads			Buckling load N_{cr} lb/in. material axes at $\theta°$							
$\bar{N}_x/N_{cr}$	$\bar{N}_y/N_{cr}$	$\bar{N}_{xy}/N_{cr}$	Al	0	15	30	45	60	75	90
−1.0	0	0	320	145	219	351	377	327	212	145
0	−1.0	0	125	36	55	101	155	203	237	249
−1.0	−1.0	0	100	29	44	81	124	162	156	116
−1.0	0	1.0	250	99	112	135	159	180	175	155
0	−1.0	1.0	120	35	48	79	114	165	209	237
−1.0	−1.0	1.0	97	28	40	66	94	128	123	111
−0.001	0	1.0	526	175	167	204	246	306	360	491

[a] 20 × 10 in. from boron–epoxy. Fiber volume ratio ≈0.50 and 0.10 in. thick. Note Al denotes aluminum plate with same thickness (Chamis, 1969f).

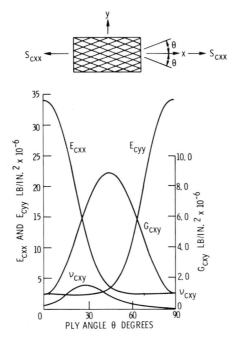

FIG. 9. Boron–epoxy angleplied laminate elastic constants (4-mil diameter fiber; fiber volume ratio ≈ 0.60). (Structural Design Guide, 1968.)

The buckling (critical) stress is obtained from

$$\sigma_{\mathrm{cr}} = k \, \frac{(E_{cxx} E_{cyy})^{1/2}}{1 - \nu_{cxy} \nu_{cyx}} \left(\frac{t_c}{b}\right)^2 \tag{3}$$

The notation in Eqs. (1) through (3) is as follows: E, G, ν are normal modulus, shear modulus, and Poisson's ratio, respectively; a, b, t_c are plate length, width, and thickness, respectively; k is the buckling coefficient from the figures; and x, y are plate structural axes.

Buckling load data of simply supported anisotropic homogeneous plates subjected to combined loads are given in Table III. Similar results for layered plates are given in Table IV. The effects of the ply sequence on the buckling load are illustrated in Table V.

Buckling loads of composite tubes subjected to axial and torsion loads are shown in Fig. 17. Note the strength cutoff lines in Fig. 17. The axial and hoop moduli of glass–resin pressure vessels with various ratios of longitudinal and hoop windings are shown in Fig. 18. The corresponding

TABLE IV

BUCKLING LOADS OF SIMPLY SUPPORTED LAYERED PLATES FROM BORON-EPOXY[a]

Applied loads			Buckling load N_{cr} lb/in. layer orientation θ							
$\bar{N}_x/\bar{N}_{cr}$	$\bar{N}_y/\bar{N}_{cr}$	$N_{xy}/\bar{N}_{cr}$	Al	20(0)	10(±15) 10(∓15)	10(±30) 10(∓30)	10(±45) 10(∓45)	10(±60) 10(∓60)	10(±75) 10(∓75)	20(90)
−1.0	0	0	320	145	226	429	504	405	225	145
0	−1.0	0	125	36	56	107	166	213	241	249
−1.0	−1.0	0	100	29	45	86	133	171	167	116
−1.0	0	1.0	250	99	144	263	351	318	196	155
0	−1.0	1.0	120	35	53	100	155	200	226	237
−1.0	−1.0	1.0	97	28	43	82	127	163	150	111
−0.001	0	1.0	528	175	249	443	643	706	591	491

[a] Plates are 20 × 10 in. Fiber volume ratio ≈0.50 and 0.10 in. thick. Note Al denotes aluminum plate with same thickness (Chamis, 1969f).

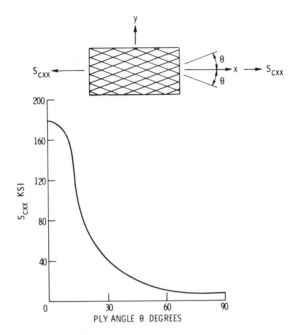

Fig. 10. Boron–epoxy angleplied laminate strength (4-mil diameter fiber; fiber volume ratio ≈ 0.60). (Structural Design Guide, 1968.)

axial buckling loads are shown in Fig. 19. Additional typical design data available will be described in Section IV.

B. *Optimization Methods*

Optimization methods in structural design seek to optimize some design evaluation criterion (called objective or merit function) in terms of the free design variables. The methods employed may be grouped into three general categories: parametric or trade-off studies, the structural index method, and structural synthesis. These methods are most conveniently used with the aid of electronic computers.

1. *Parametric Studies*

Parametric studies seek to optimize the objective function by the try-them-all method. This approach consists of making contour plots of the objective function *versus* pertinent design variables. These contour plots are used to select combinations of design variables which yield the optimum

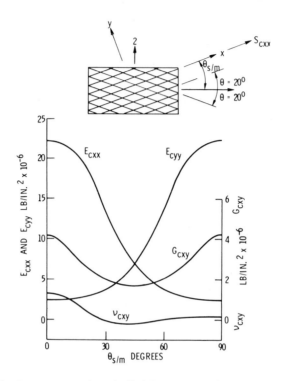

Fɪɢ. 11. Elastic constants of angleplied boron–epoxy laminate with noncoincident structural and material axes (4-mil diameter fiber; fiber volume ratio ≈ 0.60). (Structural Design Guide, 1968.)

value of the objective function. Results of this approach are illustrated in Figs. 20–30 for beams, strengths of off-axis-loaded and angleplied laminates, internal pressure vessels, plates subjected to buckling and vibrations, and built-up sections.

Considerable design information may be obtained from the curves plotted in Figs. 20–30. The following serve as illustrative examples:

(1) Beams from high-modulus graphite-fiber–resin composites have no optimum fiber volume ratio for minimum weight (Fig. 20).

(2) In general, geodesic isotensoid contoured domes provide the most efficient internal pressure vessel (Figs. 23–25).

(3) When subjected to buckling, boron–aluminum unidirectional plates are not sensitive to load direction (Fig. 26).

(4) Boron–resin square plates subjected to buckling possess an optimum fiber content (Fig. 28).

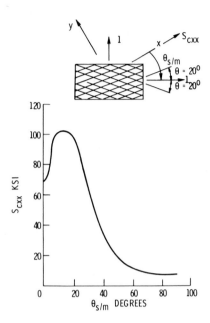

FIG. 12. Strength of angleplied boron–epoxy laminate with noncoincident structural and material axis (4-mil diameter fiber; fiber volume ratio ≈ 0.60). (Structural Design Guide, 1968.)

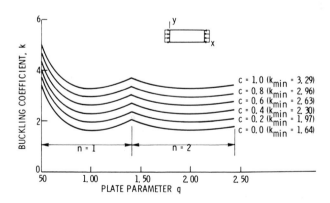

FIG. 13. Buckling coefficient of a simply supported orthotropic composite plate with coincident material and structural axes (Grove and Pray, 1964). n = no. half-waves.

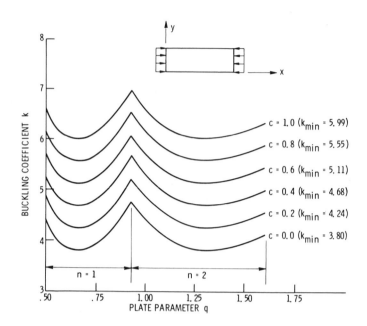

Fig. 14. Buckling coefficient of an orthotropic composite plate with loaded edges simply supported and the other two fixed. Plate loaded parallel to its material axes (Grove and Pray, 1964). n = no. half-waves.

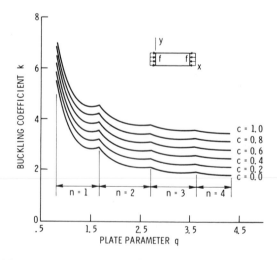

Fig. 15. Buckling coefficient of an orthotropic composite plate with loaded edges fixed and the other two simply supported. Plate loaded parallel to its material axes (Grove and Pray, 1964). n = no. half-waves.

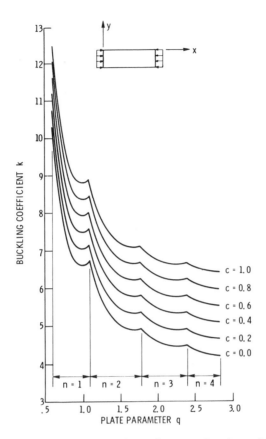

Fig. 16. Buckling coefficient of an orthotropic composite plate with all edges fixed and loaded parallel to its material axes (Grove and Pray, 1964). n = no. half-waves.

(5) An optimum stringer-flange area ratio exists for minimum weight in built-up sections (Fig. 30).

How the information in Figs. 20–30 may be used in specific designs will be illustrated in Section V.

2. *Structural Index Method*

The "structural index" concept relates the structural efficiency of members to load conditions and pertinent design variables. These relations are subsequently employed to generate plots where design parameters can be selected for efficient component utilization. The concept of structural index as applied to fiber composites is extensively discussed in Dow and Rosen

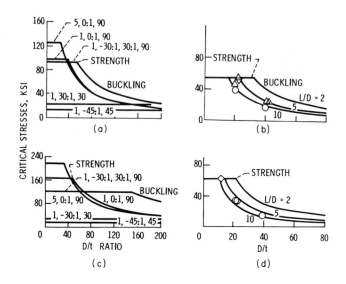

Fig. 17. Buckling strength of various composite tubes (Cole and Cervelli, 1968). (a) Axial compressive strength of composite cylinders, glass. (b) Torsional strength of round tubes; 1, -30: 1, 30: 1, 90. Ply pattern, glass. (c) Axial compressive strength of composite cylinders, boron. (d) Torsional strength of round tubes; 1, -45: 1, +45. Ply pattern, glass.

(1967). The results are usually presented in graphical form as is illustrated in Fig. 31.

3. *Structural Synthesis*

Structural synthesis optimizes some aspect of the component (weight, cost, efficiency, etc.) called the objective function. Structural synthesis examines the whole design space in a simultaneous fashion with complicated computer programs and reaches the optimum of the objective function which is the best compromise among the various influencing factors. The design space consists of the objective function expressed as a function of the various influencing factors. These factors are in the form of load conditions, design variables, behavior variables, and constraints.

To clarify the structural synthesis terminology, consider a beam component. The load conditions will be any set of loads on the beam such as concentrated and uniform lateral loads and axial loads. The design variables for a composite beam will be its width, depth, fiber content, and fiber orien-

TABLE V

LAMINATION ARRANGEMENT EFFECTS ON BUCKLING LOAD OF A SIMPLY SUPPORTED
ANISOTROPIC PLATE[a]

Lamination arrangement	Buckling load lb/in. load condition $\bar{N}_x/N_{cr}$; $\bar{N}_y/N_{cr}$; $\bar{N}_{xy}/N_{cr}$						
	100	010	110	101	011	111	$\sim0\sim01$
8(0)	74	36	29	64	34	27	133
8($\pm$15)	88	56	44	71	49	40	159
4($\pm$15), 4($\mp$15)	85	55	43	74	51	41	179
4($+$15), 4($-$15)	47	34	23	41	31	23	102
8($\pm$30)	115	108	58	92	88	53	209
4($\pm$30), 4($\mp$30)	112	106	56	97	96	54	245
4($+$30), 4($-$30)	46	46	23	40	40	22	103
8($\pm$45)	131	131	66	121	112	63	276
4($\pm$45), 4($\mp$45)	125	125	63	108	108	60	279
4($+$45), 4($-$45)	50	49	24	42	42	23	110

[a] Plate is 10 × 10 in. Boron–epoxy; fiber volume ratio ≈0.50, plate thickness ≈0.04 in. (Chamis, 1969b).

tation. The behavior variables are maximum lateral displacement, maximum stress, maximum horizontal shear stress, and, say, Euler buckling. The constraints constitute upper and lower limit allowables on both design and behavior variables. Some typical constraints for the beam are maximum deflection one-three-hundredth of the span, the normal stress lying in the

TABLE VI

STRUCTURAL SYNTHESIS FORMULATION IN OUTLINE FORM

Given: Preassigned parameters $(a_1, a_2, \ldots)$,
　　　Load conditions P,
　　　Design variables $\mathbf{D}$,
　　　Constraints $G_{ik}(\mathbf{D})$, i $\rightarrow$ constraints, k $\rightarrow$ load cond
　　　Objective function $W(\mathbf{D})$
　　　Required theories
　　　Efficient minimum (maximum) seeking algorithms
Find:　$\mathbf{D}^* \ni W(\mathbf{D}^*)$ is min,
　　　and $\ni G_{ik}(\mathbf{D}^*) \geq 0$

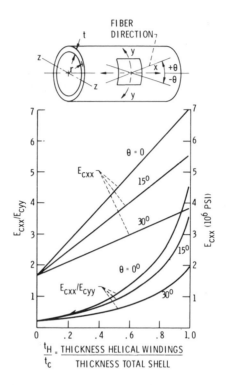

Fig. 18. Elastic moduli for a cylindrical shell with various combinations of helical and hoop windings (Ravenhall, 1964). $E_{l11} = 7.00 \times 10^6$ lb/in.^{2}, $E_{l22} = 1.57 \times 10^6$ lb/in.^{2}.

range $-S_{l11C} \leq \sigma_{l11C} \leq S_{l11T}$, and the beam depth being greater than zero but less than one-tenth the beam span ($0 < h \leq l/10$).

Applications of structural synthesis concepts to fiber composite structural panels are extensively described in Chamis (1967a, b). The formal structural synthesis problem definition is outlined in Table VI. Structural synthesis results for a plate subjected to three sets of normal loads are shown in Fig. 32. The design variables for this plate are fiber modulus (E_{f11}), number of layers (N_l), and orientation angle (θ_{li}). The objective function is cost of filament material. The behavior constraints are gross plate buckling, ply at combined-stress limit, and interply delamination in each load condition. As can be seen in Fig. 32, the optimum design for this case is a panel with fiber modulus of about 30×10^6 psi, 18 plies at ± 50, and at a unit area cost of 2.96.

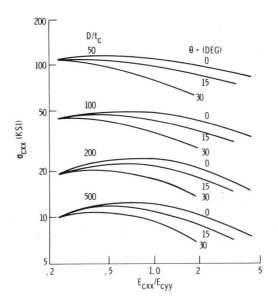

Fig. 19. Axial buckling load of a cylindrical shell with various ratios of hoops/longitudinal windings; see Fig. 18. (Ravenhall, 1964.)

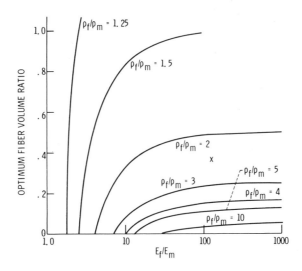

Fig. 20. Optimum fiber volume ratio for minimum weight rectangular beam with constant width and deflection limited. (Structural Design Guide, 1968.)

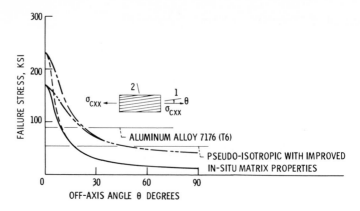

FIG. 21. Failure envelopes for off-axis loaded boron–aluminum composites with currently available strength properties, with improved fiber-loading efficiency, and with improved matrix properties. Fiber volume ratio = 0.5 (Chamis, 1970b). — Currently available; – – –, – – – –, – – – Improved values. The following unidirectional strengths in ksi correspond to these: S_{l11T}: 167, 230, 167, 230; S_{l22T}: 14.0, 14.0, 44.7, 44.7; S_{l12S}: 15.6, 15.6, 33.7, 33.7.

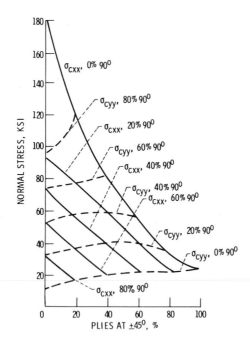

FIG. 22. Allowable stresses of a boron–epoxy angleplied laminate [0, ±45, 90]$_{sym}$ loaded along its material axes (4-mil diameter fiber; fiber volume ratio ≈ 0.50). (Structural Design Guide, 1968.)

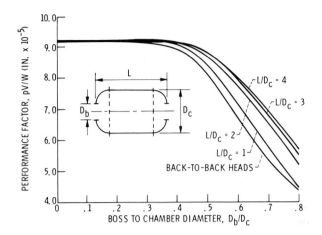

FIG. 23. Theoretical performance factor *versus* dimensional parameters, geodesic-isotensoid contour (S-glass–epoxy with fiber volume ratio ≈ 0.65). (Darms *et al.*, 1964.)

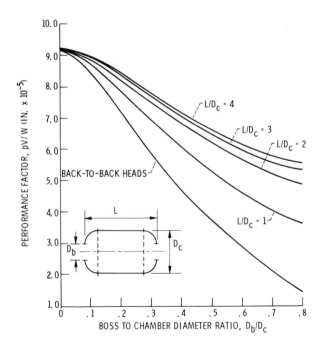

FIG. 24. Theoretical performance factor *versus* dimensional parameters, zero-hoop-stress contour (S-glass–epoxy with fiber volume ratio ≈ 0.65). (Darms *et al.*, 1964.)

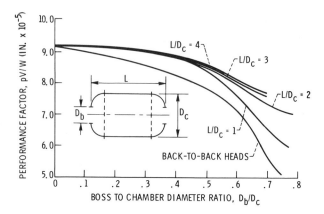

FIG. 25. Theoretical performance factor *versus* dimensional parameters, balanced-in-plane-wrap contour (S-glass–epoxy with fiber volume ratio ≈ 0.65). (Darms *et al.*, 1964.)

The structural synthesis design space for a wing box is illustrated in Fig. 33 after Foye (1967). The controlling design variables are the torsional stiffness and bending stiffness and are plotted as the ordinate and abscissa, respectively. The objective function (weight) and the various constraints are plotted as functions of the design variables in the figure.

Structural synthesis was used for the optimum design of a graphite-fiber–resin composite stiffened cylindrical shell (Kicher and Chao, 1970).

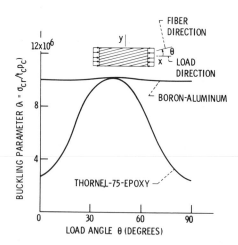

FIG. 26. Specific buckling stress of two fiber composite plates—simply supported four edges; plate aspect ratio (*a/b*) = 2) (Chamis, 1971b) (fiber volume ratio = 0.50).

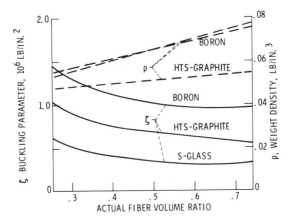

FIG. 27. Buckling parameter for simply supported square plate (Chamis, 1969a). $\zeta = 12 \, a^2 \, N_{cr}/\pi^2 \, (d_f N_l)^3 (N_f \pi/4)^{3/2}$; $\rho = W/d_f N_l (\pi N_f/4)^{1/2}$.

A schematic of the stiffened cylinder geometry and results of the optimized design variables are shown in Fig. 34. Additional work on the optimum design of fiber composite structures was reported by Hackman and Stotler (1966), Foye and Baker (1970), Waddoups *et al.* (1970), Verette (1972), Rand and Shen (1973), Card and Strout (1972), McCullers and Lynch

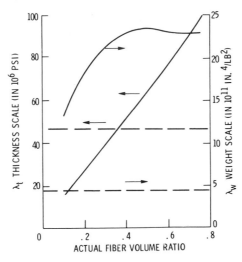

FIG. 28. Optimum fiber content for the buckling resistance of a simply supported square plate (Chamis, 1969a). $N_{cr} = \lambda_t \pi^2 t_c^3/12a^2$; $N_{cr} = \lambda_w \pi^2 W^3/12a^2$. — Boron–epoxy ($\pm 45°$); – – Aluminum (7075-T6).

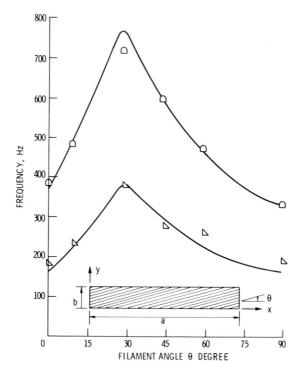

FIG. 29. Free vibration with filament angle of natural frequencies of first and second plate-types modes (a/b = 7) (Clary, 1972). Experiment Mode I, △; Mode II, □. — Analysis.

(1972), Purdy *et al.* (1972), Khot *et al.* (1973), Structural Design Guide (1973).

The key link in optimum design is efficient minimization (maximization) algorithms of linear or nonlinear optimization problems. A survey of the various minimum (maximum) seeking algorithms, including advantages and disadvantages of each, is given in Jacoby *et al.* (1972).

Structural synthesis may also be used to establish the sensitivity of the optimum design on the various design variables (Chamis, 1967a, b).

4. *Simultaneous Material and Structural Design Optimization*

Structural synthesis principles can also be applied for the simultaneous material and structural design optimization. This is discussed extensively in Chamis (1968a, 1969g). Results employing this approach to a heat shield

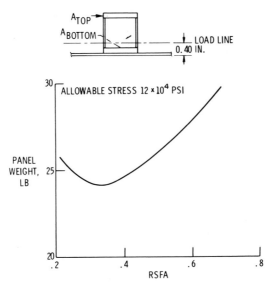

Fɪɢ. 30. Stringer-flange area proportion *versus* panel weight high-modulus graphite–fiber–epoxy composite (Fabrication Report, 1971). RSFA = $A_{top} + A_{bottom}$.

problem are illustrated in Figs. 35 and 36. The problem is defined in Fig. 35. In this problem is sought that combination of composite constituents, plate thickness, and orientation angle so that the plate weight is a minimum. The optimum constituent combination is obtained from Fig. 36.

The concept of simultaneous material and structural design is applicable to a wide range of problems. Its application to optimum burst chamber pressure as a function of resin content and processing variables is illustrated in Fig. 37. Still different applications are reported in Sandrock and Holms (1969) where the optimum combination of alloying elements is sought for improved material tensile strength. A comprehensive review of the formalisms of this approach is given in Holms (1969).

IV. Additional Important Factors

Several other factors need to be considered in designing composite components. These factors are composite thickness dependence of fiber volume ratio, interply relative rotation, interply delamination, excessively large and negative Poisson's ratio values, lamination residual stresses, edge

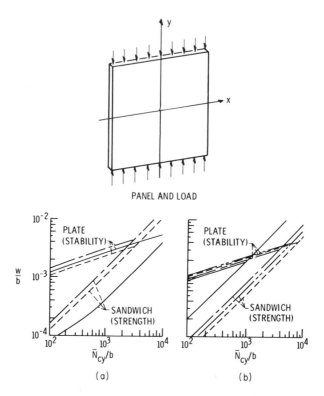

PANEL AND LOAD

(a)   (b)

FIG. 31. Structural efficiency, boron *versus* aluminum (MIL-HDBK-17A, 1971). $\bar{N}_{cy} = 10^5$ lb/in. (a) — 0° Boron–epoxy; – – – – Quasi-isotropic boron–epoxy; — – – 7075 T6 Aluminum. (b) — ±45° Boron–epoxy; – – – – 60%, 0°/40% ±45° Boron-epoxy; — – — 40%, 0°/60% ±45° Boron-epoxy; – – – – 60%, 0°/40%, 90° Boron-epoxy.

effects, environmental effects, etc. Several of these factors are discussed extensively in Chamis (1969a, d, e). Herein, the effects of fiber volume ratio on composite thickness, interply relative rotation (scissoring) effects, excessively large and negative values of Poisson's ratio, and lamination residual stresses are discussed in some detail. The remaining factors will be mentioned briefly, and references will be cited where additional information is available.

A. Composite Thickness Dependence on Fiber Volume Ratio

The composite thickness is the sum of its plies and interply layers' thicknesses. The ply thickness in functional equation form is given by

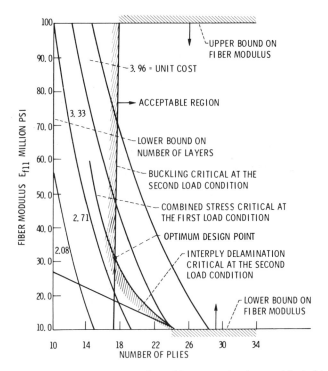

FIG. 32. Design space of a multilayered graphite–epoxy laminate subjected to multiple combined in-plane loads. Design space section at ply angle = 50. The optimum laminate for this case consists of 30×10^6 psi modulus, 18 plies at ±50 at a cost of 2.69 units per square inch of area (Chamis, 1967b).

Chamis (1969a, d) :

$$t_l = f(d_f, N_f, k_v, A, C) \tag{4}$$

where t_l is ply thickness, d_f is fiber diameter or the equivalent, N_f is the number of fibers per end, k_v is void volume ratio, k_f is the apparent fiber volume ratio, A is some regular *in situ* fiber array, and C is the *in situ* end aspect ratio (width to thickness).

For a square array Eq. (4) reduces to

$$t_l = \left[\frac{\pi N_f}{4(1 - k_v) C k_f} \right]^{1/2} d_f \tag{5}$$

The graphical representation of Eq. (5) is shown in Fig. 38 for three composite systems. As can be seen in Fig. 38 the fiber volume ratio effect

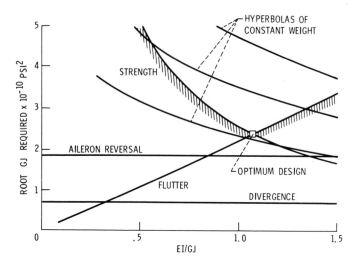

FIG. 33. Design space for a fiber composite aircraft wing (Foye, 1967).

on the ply thickness is more pronounced at low values (less than 0.5) of fiber volume ratio.

The interply layer thickness dependence on fiber volume ratio for a square array is given by Chamis (1969a, d):

$$\delta = \tfrac{1}{2}\big[(\pi/\bar{k}_\mathrm{f})^{1/2} - 2\big] d_\mathrm{f} \tag{6}$$

where δ denotes the interply layer thickness, $\bar{k}_\mathrm{f} = (1 - k_\mathrm{v})k_\mathrm{f}$, and k_v, k_f, and d_f were defined in Eq. (4). The ratio of Eq. (6) to Eq. (5) is plotted in Fig. 39 versus actual fiber volume ratio $\bar{k}$ for three composite systems. As can be seen in Fig. 39 the interply layer thickness is quite sensitive to the actual fiber volume ratio, especially at lower fiber volume ratios ($k_\mathrm{f} < 0.5$).

B. Interply Layer Effects on Elastic Constants

The plies in angleplied laminates (under load) undergo relative rotation in general. This relative rotation subjects the interply layer to torsional-type stresses and contributes to the laminates' structural response (Harrington *et al.*, 1964; Chamis, 1967a, b, 1969a, d).

The interply layer effects on the laminate structural response are intro-

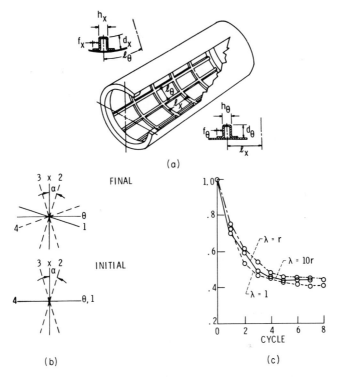

(a)

(b)

(c)

Fig. 34. Optimized design variables for an integrally stiffened cylinder with hat cross-section stiffeners (Kicher and Chao, 1970). $f_x = \frac{1}{4}(d_x + h_x); f_\theta = \frac{1}{4}(d_\theta + h_\theta)$. (a) Cylinder geometry. (b) Initial (90, 15, -15, -90) and final (110, 19.5, -19.8, -108) ply orientations in skin, 4-ply skin shell under axial compression. (c) Weight reduction at each cycle for various λ values, 2-ply skin, axial compression.

duced through the laminate-theory equation (Chamis, 1969a)

$$U_c = \sum_{i=1}^{N_l} U_{li} + \sum_{j=1}^{N_l-1} H_j \Delta \phi_j \tag{7}$$

where U_c is the laminate elastic strain per unit area and U_{li} is the ply elastic strain energy per unit area. Also H_j is the Harrington coefficient and for fiber–resin composites is approximated by (Chamis, 1969a, d)

$$H_j = 0.0186 G_m \left[1 - \frac{2\delta_{li+1}\delta_{li}}{\delta_{li+1} + \delta_{li}} \right] \tag{8}$$

where G_m is the matrix (resin) shear modulus and δ_{li+1} and δ_{li} are the inter-

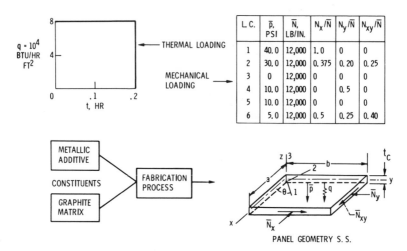

FIG. 35. Problem statement of a thermostructural composite panel (Chamis, 1968a).

fiber spacing distances in the adjacent plies. In Eq. (7) $\Delta\phi_j$ is the adjacent ply relative rotation and is given by (Chamis, 1969a, d)

$$\Delta\phi_j = \tfrac{1}{2}(\epsilon_{cxx} - \epsilon_{cyy})(\sin 2\theta_{li+1} - \sin 2\theta_{li}) + \tfrac{1}{2}\epsilon_{cxy}(\cos 2\theta_{li+1} - \cos 2\theta_{li}) \quad (9)$$

where the ϵ_c are the laminate structural axes strains and θ_{li} is the ply orientation angle measured from the structural x axis.

The contribution of the interply layers to the laminate modulus is

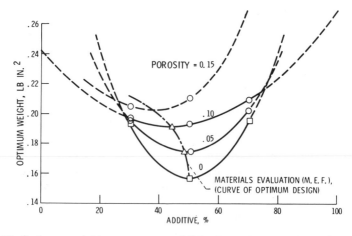

FIG. 36. Optimum weight *versus* percent additive for various porosity ratios, 36 in. ×
24 in. panel (Chamis 1968a). ○ Synthesis result, □ Extrapolated, △ Curve fit minimum
points.

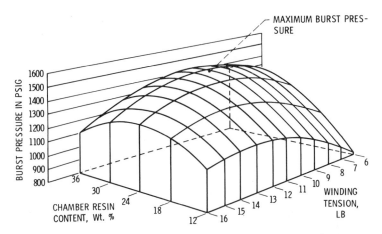

FIG. 37. Optimization of burst pressure of internally pressurized pressure vessel *w/R* to material and processing variables (Buxton and Weingart, 1965). Maximum burst pressure in 1470 PSIG at 29.5% resin content and 10.1 lb winding tension.

shown in Fig. 40 and to the laminate Poisson's ratio in Fig. 41. As can be seen from these figures, the interply layer contributions tend to increase the laminate modulus and decrease the Poisson's ratio.

C. Excessively Large and Negative Poisson's Ratio Values

It is possible to fabricate laminates which have Poisson's ratio values of greater than unity and even negative. These types of Poisson's ratio values are a direct result of the relative ply rotation, a large part of which is a kinematic contribution. These types of Poisson's ratio values may cause severe end restraints (Chamis 1969a, e).

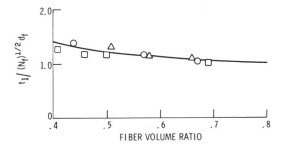

FIG. 38. Ply thickness *versus* fiber content (Chamis, 1969a). Experiments: △—Boron; □—Carbon; ○—Glass.

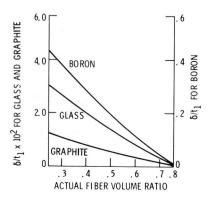

FIG. 39. Actual fiber volume ratio effects on interply layer (Chamis, 1969a). $\zeta/t_1 = [1 - 2(\bar{k}_f/\pi)^{1/2}]/(N_f)^{1/2}$.

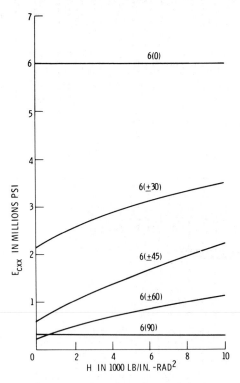

FIG. 40. Interply layer effects on composite modulus (E-glass–epoxy, fiber volume ratio ≈ 0.50). (Harrington et al., 1964.)

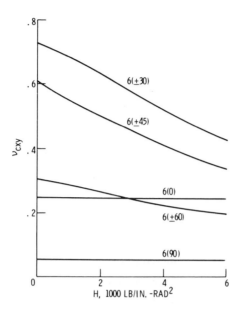

FIG. 41. Interply layer effects on composite Poisson ratio (E-glass–epoxy fiber volume ratio ≈ 0.50). (Harrington *et al.*, 1964.)

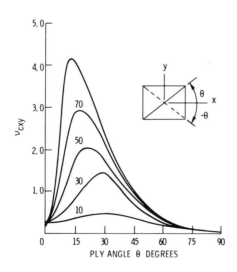

FIG. 42. Effects of fiber longitudinal modulus on the major Poisson ratio of symmetric angleplied laminates (Chamis, 1969a). 90×10^6 psi $= E_{f11}$ (thornel).

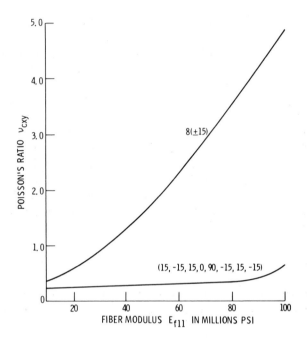

Fɪɢ. 43. Restraining effect on the Poisson ratio of angleplied laminate (graphite–epoxy composite with fiber volume ratio = 0.6 and zero voids). (Chamis, 1969a.)

Laminate Poisson's ratio values versus ply orientation are plotted in Fig. 42 for various fiber moduli. As can be seen in this figure, Poisson's ratio values of four and greater are obtained for laminates with fiber modulus about 90×10^6 psi. It is possible to reduce large Poisson's ratio values to relatively small values by sacrificing one or more plies oriented at

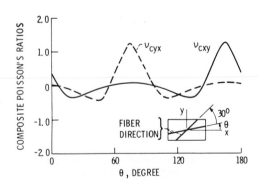

Fɪɢ. 44. Composite Poisson ratio for nonsymmetric ply lay-up (Chamis, 1969a).

0/90 from the structural x axis. The restraining effects of the 0/90 plies on the Poisson's ratio are illustrated in Fig. 43.

Laminates with zero and negative Poisson's ratios are also obtainable with suitable ply orientations. This is illustrated in Fig. 44 where the Poisson's ratio of a nonsymmetric laminate is plotted versus fiber direction.

The designer of either structural components or test specimens should keep in mind the wide range of Poisson's ratio values that may be obtained by suitable ply orientations. Large Poisson's ratio values produce severe restrained conditions at boundary edges and at load transfer points. An example of large Poisson's ratio values restraining edge effects is illustrated in Fig. 45. In this figure the buckling loads of laminates with various Poisson's ratios and two types of edge conditions are tabulated. As can be seen in the tabulated values the Poisson's ratio restraining effect can reduce the buckling load by as much as 24%.

D. Lamination Residual Stresses

Fiber–resin composites are cured at elevated temperatures in general. This curing process produces two types of residual stresses in the composite,

POISSON'S RATIO	BUCKLING LOAD		RATIO METAL TO TEFLON
	METAL STRIP	TEFLON STRIP	
0.32	583	661	0.88
1.63	533	662	.81
.84	477	602	.79
.22	379	394	.96
.44	327	433	.76
.36	316	372	.85

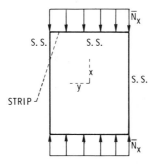

FIG. 45. Poisson ratio effects on the buckling load of a square simply supported anisotropic plate (boron–epoxy, fiber volume ratio $\approx$ 0.50, plate thickness $\approx$ 0.10 in.). (Chamis 1969b.)

namely micro- and macroresidual stresses (Chamis, 1970a). Microresidual stresses are present in the constituents within the ply. They arise primarily from the differences in the thermal coefficients between fiber and matrix. Macroresidual (or lamination residual) stresses are approximately constant through the ply. They arise from the differences in the longitudinal and transverse thermal coefficients of the ply.

The microresidual stress influence on composite structural response is integrated in the properties of the unidirectional laminate which are determined either by measurement or by micromechanics. These types of stresses are discussed in other treatise volumes which deal with the micromechanics of unidirectional composites. Herein, the discussion is restricted to macro- or lamination residual stresses.

The lamination residual stresses can be predicted readily using laminate theory since they are a form of thermal stress (Chamis, 1970a, 1971a). These stresses need to be calculated and superimposed on the applied load stress. Otherwise, the laminate will fail at considerably lower loads than the design loads which have been determined by neglecting the lamination residual stresses. Transply cracks produced by residual stresses have been observed in angleplied laminates made from high-modulus graphite–fiber–resin composites (Winters, 1970).

The laminate theory equation for predicting the ply residual stresses is given by

$$\{\sigma_{li}\} = [E_{li}]^{-1} \langle [R_{li}]\{\epsilon_{c0x}\} - z_{li}[R_{li}]\{\kappa_{cx}\} - \Delta T_{li}\{\alpha_{li}\} \rangle \qquad (10)$$

The reference plane strains $\{\epsilon_{c0x}\}$ and the curvature changes $\{\kappa_{cx}\}$ for a free composite (free of external loads and boundary constraint) are computed from

$$\begin{Bmatrix} \{\epsilon_{c0x}\} \\ \{\kappa_{cx}\} \end{Bmatrix} = \begin{bmatrix} [A_{cx}] & [C_{cx}] \\ [C_{cx}] & [D_{cx}] \end{bmatrix}^{-1} \begin{Bmatrix} \{N_{c\Delta Tx}\} \\ \{M_{c\Delta Tx}\} \end{Bmatrix} \qquad (11)$$

Equations (10) and (11) show that the ply residual stress is a function of the following factors: (1) the composite structural stiffnesses, $[A_{cx}]$, $[C_{cx}]$, and $[D_{cx}]$, (2) the ply spatial location in the composite z_{li} and $[R_{li}]$, (3) the ply stress–strain relation $[E_{li}]$, (4) the ply thermal coefficients of expansion $\{\alpha_{li}\}$, and (5) the temperature difference between the ply and the reference value ΔT_{li}. This difference equals the ply temperature minus the cure temperature in computing residual and thermal stresses. The previous discussion leads to the identification of the independent variables which influence the ply residual stress. These are (1) constituent materials'

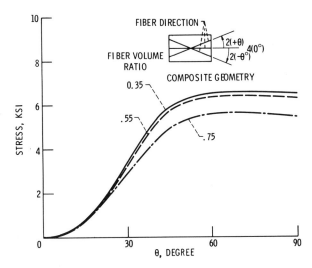

FIG. 46. ±θ-Ply transverse residual stress for boron–epoxy composite. Ply stacking sequence 8[2(0), 2(±θ), 2(∓θ), 2(0)]. Temperature difference = −300°F (Chamis, 1971a).

elastic properties, (2) constituent materials' thermal properties, (3) fiber volume ratio, (4) void content, (5) ply distance from reference plane, (6) ply orientation relative to composite structural axes, and (7) difference between ply temperature and cure temperature.

Ply transverse residual stresses as predicted by Eq. (10) for a boron–epoxy laminate 8[2(0), 2(±θ), 2(∓θ), 2(0)] are plotted in Fig. 46 versus θ and for three values of fiber volume ratio. Corresponding plots are shown in Fig. 47 for S-glass–epoxy laminates and in Fig. 48 for thornel–epoxy laminates.

A better appreciation of the lamination residual stresses in design is obtained by comparing the transverse ply residual stresses in Figs. 46, 47, and 48 to corresponding ply strengths. The transverse tensile strength for 0.55 fiber volume ratio unidirectional composite (ply) is: boron–epoxy ≈ 8.6 ksi, S-glass–epoxy ≈ 4.4 ksi, and thornel–epoxy ≈ 3.7 ksi. Comparing these values with the corresponding curves in Figs. 46, 47, and 48, it can be seen that transverse residual stresses can reach magnitudes comparable to ply transverse tensile strength. Similar plots for the other ply residual stresses are given in Chamis (1971a). In this reference, results are presented showing the effects on lamination residual stresses of pertinent variables such as resin modulus, resin thermal coefficient of expansion, void

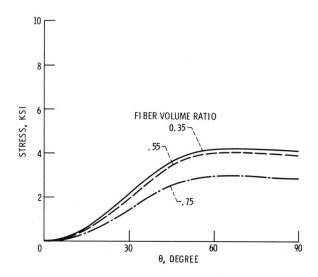

FIG. 47. ±θ-Ply residual transverse stress for S-glass–epoxy composite. Ply stacking sequence 8[2(0), 2(±θ), 2(∓θ), 2(0)]. Temperature difference = −300°F (Chamis, 1971a).

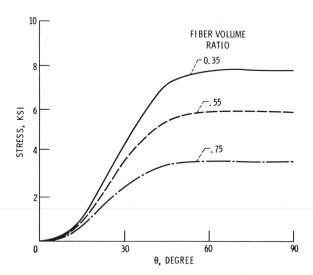

FIG. 48. ±θ-Ply residual transverse stress for graphite thornel-50–epoxy composite. Ply stacking sequence 8[2(0), 2(±θ), 2(∓θ), 2(0)]. Temperature difference = −300°F (Chamis, 1971a).

volume ratio, nonuniform fiber volume ratio through the laminate thickness, and the introduction of transitional plies. Also several alternatives for minimizing and/or eliminating lamination residual stresses are discussed.

E. Other Factors

Other factors which are important in designing composite components include: edge effects, environment (both temperature and moisture), material nonlinearity, creep, fatigue, notch sensitivity, and impact. For detailed information of the effects of these factors on angleplied laminate structural integrity, see Volume 5, edited by Broutman, in this treatise. For some selected references on these factors see Chamis (1972). Herein, the discussion is limited to a few brief but general comments.

Through the thickness shear and normal stresses arise near free edges of angleplied laminates which tend to cause ply separation. These stresses decay rapidly away from the free edge. They are predictable and means exist for designing to minimize their effects; see Chapter 10.

Both elevated temperature and moist environments tend to degrade the stiffness and strength of fiber–resin angleplied laminates. Lower temperature environments have the opposite effects.

Angleplied laminates exhibit material nonlinearity and high creep rates where the load direction does not coincide with the fiber direction. However, they exhibit linear material behavior to fracture and have negligible creep rates for coincident fiber and load directions.

Angleplied laminates from advanced fiber composites have excellent fatigue strength and are not notch sensitive. Advanced fiber composites have relatively low impact resistance when compared with metals. However, the methodology for designing impact tolerant composite components is available (Chamis *et al.*, 1971).

V. Sample Design of Components

Any structure, regardless of how complex, is an assemblage of basic structural components such as truss, beam, frame, membrane, plate, and shell. The design of the structure, then, consists of designing its constituent structural components and their respective joints. In this section, some guides are given on selecting constituent materials and sample designs of the aforementioned members are discussed. The design/analysis of joints was covered in Chapter 10 (by Grimes and Greimann).

TABLE VII

Design Requirement

Tensile strength	Stiffness	Elongation	Fiber
High	Low	High	S-glass, Kevlar-49
High	Moderate	Moderate	High-strength graphite
High	High	Low	Boron
Moderate	High	Low	High-modulus graphite

A. Constituent Materials Selection

The primary load-carrying constituent in the composite is the fiber. The fiber to be used is controlled by the design requirements. Some guidelines are given in Table VII.

Criteria for selecting resin matrices are given in Chamis *et al.* (1973). As a general rule, resins with higher initial modulus yield composites with higher mechanical properties.

B. Design of Truss Members

1. Simple Bars

A 1 in. $\times$ $\frac{1}{2}$ in. $\times$ 20 in. bar is needed to carry a tensile load of 50 ksi pounds. The axial extension of the bar should not exceed 0.05 in. when subjected to the load.

Solution. The only variables at one's disposal for this problem are fiber type and content. The governing equations are:

$$\sigma_{cxx} = \frac{P}{A} \qquad E_{cxx} = \frac{PL}{A\delta}$$

where $P = 50$ ksi, $L = 20$ in., $A = \frac{1}{2}$ in.^{2}, and $\delta = 0.05$ in. From this it follows that

$$E_{cxx} = \frac{50 \times 20}{\frac{1}{2} \times 0.05} = 40 \times 10^6 \, \text{psi}$$

$$\sigma_{cxx} = \frac{50}{\frac{1}{2}} = 10^5 \, \text{psi}$$

Since the modulus needed is high, consider a unidirectional boron composite.

From Fig. 4, $k_f = 0.68$. From Fig. 5, $S_{llT} = 28 \times 10^4$ psi at $k_f = 0.68$. $S_{llT} > \sigma_{llT}$; therefore the member is adequate. Use a unidirectional boron composite at 68% fiber content for this bar.

2. Tubular Members

Fabrication considerations require that a 2 in. diameter tubular truss member be made by laying up $\pm 30°$-oriented plies from boron tape at 60% fiber content. The load to be carried is 4000 pounds. Find the number of plies.

Solution. From Fig. 10, for a 60% $\pm 30°$ boron composite, $S_{llT} = 40$ ksi. Then, the wall thickness required is

$$t_c = \frac{4000}{40,000(2\pi)} \approx 0.016 \text{ in.}$$

The ply thickness is $t_l = 0.0045$ at $k_f = 0.6$ and the number of plies is

$$N_l = \frac{t_c}{t_l} = \frac{0.016}{0.0045} \approx 3.55 \quad \text{or} \quad 4$$

Therefore, use 4 plies as follows: $4(30, -30, -30, 30)$.

C. Frame Members

1. Panel Under Axial Tension

Design a $(0, \pm 45, 90)$ boron composite (at $k_f = 50\%$) panel to carry an average composite stress (σ_{cxx}) of 60 ksi.

Solution. Enter Fig. 22 with normal stress equal to 60 ksi and read several alternatives; some of these are:

(1) 40% 0, 20% ± 45, 40% 90
(2) 20% 0, 40% ± 45, 40% 90
(3) 40% 0, 60% ± 45, 0% 90

Assume the ply arrangement of alternative (1) is selected for this member.

2. Simply Supported Beam

Design a simply supported beam using boron composite with constant width and optimum fiber content.

Solution. $E_f/E_m = 100$ and $\rho_f/\rho_m \approx 2$ for boron–epoxy systems. Entering Fig. 20 with these values, the optimum fiber content is found to be approximately 50%.

D. Plate Members

1. Orthotropic Plates

Design a simply supported orthotropic plate from boron composite with average composite compressive stress $\sigma_{cxx} = 1000$ psi, $a = 20$ in., $b = 10$ in. Find thickness and approximate fiber content.

Solution. This is an iterative process. Only the first cycle will be given. From Fig. 28, the optimum fiber content for minimum weight is about 50%. Entering Fig. 4 with $k_f = 0.5$, it is found that $E_{l11} = 30 \times 10^6$ psi, $E_{l22} = 1.8 \times 10^6$ psi, $G_{l12} = 0.8 \times 10^6$ psi, $\nu_{l12} = 0.3$. From the reciprocal relation, $\nu_{l21} \neq \nu_{l12} \mp E_{l22}/E_{l11} = 0.02$ and the product $\nu_{l21}\nu_{l12} = 0.3 \times 0.02 = 0.006$, which is negligible when compared with unity. The required thickness can be calculated by using Eqs. (1) to (3) and Fig. 13. From Eqs. (1) and (2), respectively,

$$c = \frac{0.02 \times 30 + 2 \times 0.8}{(30 \times 1.8)^{1/2}} \approx \frac{2.2}{7.35} = 0.30$$

$$q = \frac{20}{10}\left(\frac{30}{1.8}\right)^{1/4} = 2 \times 2.04 = 4.08 \approx 4.1$$

Entering Fig. 13 with $c \approx 0.30$ and $q \approx 4.1$, it is found that $k \approx 2.13$ (minimum value).

Next, Eq. (3) is solved for the thickness; thus,

$$t_c^2 = \frac{\sigma_{cr}(1 - \nu_{l12}\nu_{l21})}{(E_{l11}E_{l22})^{1/2}} \frac{b^2}{k}$$

where now $\sigma_{cr} = \sigma_{c\alpha\alpha} = 1000$ psi is used.

$$t_c^2 = \frac{1000\ (1)}{(30 \times 1.8)^{1/2} \times 10^6} \frac{100}{2.13} = 0.0064$$

$$t_c = 0.080 \text{ in.}$$

The ply thickness at $k_f = 0.50$ is approximately 0.0047 in. Therefore, the number of plies is

$$N_l = \frac{t_c}{t_l} = \frac{0.080}{0.0047} \approx 17 \text{ plies}$$

Design 17 plies at 0 with 50% fiber content.
The weight of this plate per unit area is given by

$$w = \rho_c \times N_l \times t_l$$

Entering Fig. 3 with $k_f = 0.50$, one finds $\rho_c = 0.07$. Therefore

$$w = 0.070 \times 17 \times 0.0047 = 0.0057 \text{ lb/in.}^2$$

Additional trials would be required to establish whether this is the optimum fiber content.

2. Anisotropic Plates

Several 20 in. $\times$ 10 in. boron plates are required to carry the following edge load conditions:

Plate	$\bar{N}_{cx}$	$\bar{N}_{cy}$	$\bar{N}_{cz}$ (lb/in.)
1	500	0	0
2	0	160	0
3	150	150	150

The solution to this design problem requires a parametric study as is shown in Tables III and IV. From lines 1, 2, and 6 in Table IV, one finds, respectively: [10($\pm$45), 10($\mp$45)], [10($\pm$60), 10($\mp$60)], and [10($\pm$60), 10($\mp$60)] boron composites at $k_f \approx 0.54$.

E. Shell Members

1. Internal Pressure Vessels

An internal pressure vessel is required with $L/D = 2$ and $D_b/D_c = 0.4$. Here, L is the vessel total length, D_c is the cylinder diameter, and D_b is the boss opening diameter.

Find the most efficient dome contour.

Solution. From Figs. 23 through 25 it is seen that the geodesic-isotensoid contour is the most efficient.

2. Cylindrical Shell under Axial Compressive Load

A cylindrical shell is required with 20 in. diameter and 40 in. length to carry a 20×10^3 psi average composite stress. The shell is to be made from S-glass composite at 55% fiber content. Design the number of plies and orientation.

Solution. For this case, assume symmetric buckling controls. Entering Fig. 19 with $\sigma_{cxx} = 20 \times 10^3$ psi one has $D/t = 200$ and a range of E_{cxx}/E_{cyy} values and helical layers. Select $E_{cxx}/E_{cyy} = 3$ and $\theta_l = 15$. The numbers of layers required and stacking sequence are:

$$N_l = \frac{t_c}{t_1} = \frac{20}{200} \times \frac{1}{0.008} = \frac{0.1}{0.008} = 12.5$$

say about 13 layers. From Fig. 18, $t_{\text{helical/total}} = 0.9$ for $E_{cxx}/E_{cyy} = 3$ and $\theta_l = \pm 15°$. Therefore, the ply arrangement is $[3(\pm 15), 90, 3(\mp 15)]$ for a symmetric w/r to bending composite. Other orientations are possible.

Note, the buckling of cylindrical shells is more complex. The example given here serves only as an illustration of how to apply the available design data. See also Holston $et\ al.$ (1967) and Wang (1966) for additional data.

List of Symbols

A	Area, regular array, Eq. (4), axial stiffness array, Eq. (11)	N_l	Number of plies in the laminate or composite
a	Plate edge dimension parallel with x axis	P	Load
		$\bar{p}$	Pressure
b	Plate edge dimension parallel with y axis	q	Parameter, Eq. (2)
		R	Coordinate transformation array, Eq. (10)
C	$In\ situ$ end of fibers rectangle aspect ratio, Eqs. (4) and (5), coupling stiffness array, Eq. (11)	S	Strength, subscripts identify type, face, direction, and sense
c	Parameter defined by Eq. (1)	t	Time
D	Bending stiffness, Eq. (11)	t_c	Laminate or composite thickness
D_c, D_b	Chamber and boss diameters	V	Volume
d_f	Fiber diameter	w	Weight
E	Modulus, subscripts identify type and direction	Z_{li}	Distance from the reference plane to the ith ply
G	Shear modulus, subscripts identify type and direction	α	Thermal coefficient of expansion, subscripts identify type and direction
H	Heat capacity		
H_j	Harrington coefficient, Eqs. (7) and (8)	δ	Interfiber spacing, deflection
H_z	Frequency	ϵ	Strain, subscripts identify type, face, and direction
K	Heat capacity		
k	Buckling coefficient, Figs. 13–16	θ_{li}	Fiber direction in the ith ply measured from the structural x axis
k_f, k_v	Fiber, void volume ratios		
L	Length	$\theta_{s/m}$	Load direction measured from the laminate material x axis
$M_{c\Delta T}$	Thermal moments, Eq. (11)		
$\bar{N}$	Normal load, subscripts identify type and direction	κ	Curvatures, Eqs. (10) and (11)
$N_{c\Delta T}$	Thermal forces, Eq. (11)	λ_t, λ_w	Buckling parameters, Fig. 28
N_f	Number of fibers per end	ν	Poisson's ratio, subscripts identify type and directions

ρ	Density, subscript identifies type	f	Fiber property
σ	Stress, subscript identifies type, face, and direction	l	Ply property
		S	Shear
		T	Tension
$\Delta\phi$	Change in angle between adjacent plies, Eq. (9)	x, y, z	Structural axis coordinate directions
		1, 2, 3	Material axes coordinate directions (1 direction parallel to the fiber direction)
Subscripts			
C	Compression		
c	Composite property	0	Reference plane value

References

Baer, E. (ed.) (1964). "Engineering Design for Plastics." Van Nostrand-Reinhold, Princeton, New Jersey.

Beckwith, S. W., Schapery, R. A., and Webb, L. D. (1970). Literature Survey of the Field of Fiber-Reinforced Plastic Composites, Part I, 1958–August, 1970. Texas A & M Univ., College Station, CMR-1.

Beckwith, S. W., Schapery, R. A., and Webb, L. D. (1971). Literature Survey of the Field of Fiber Reinforced Plastic Composites, Part 2, August, 1970–July, 1971. Texas A & M Univ., College Station, CMR-2, N73 10585.

Buxton, R. W., and Weingart, O. (1965). Final Report on Development of Improved Processes for Filament-Wound Reinforced-Plastic Structures. Wright-Patterson AFB, AFML-TR-65-80.

Card, M. F., and Stroud, W. J. (1972). Current Langley Research Center Studies in Composite Structural Design Technology. *Proc. Conf. Fibrous Compos. Flight Vehicle Design* AFFDL-TR-72-130, p. 893. Wright-Patterson, AFB.

Chamis, C. C. (1967a). Design Oriented Analysis and Structural Synthesis of Multilayered Filamentary Composites. Ph.D. Thesis, Case Western Reserve Univ.

Chamis, C. C. (1967b). Micro and Structural Mechanics and Structural Synthesis of Multilayered Filamentary Composite Panels. Case Western Reserve Univ. SMSMD Rep. 9, Contract No. AF (615)-3110.

Chamis, C. C. (1968a). Thermostructural Response, Structural Synthesis and Material Optimization of Particulate Composite Plates. Case Western Reserve Univ. Rep. SMSMD 21, Contract No. AF (615)-3110.

Chamis, C. C. (1968b). Thermoelastic Properties of Unidirectional Filamentary Composites by a Semiempirical Micromechanics Theory. Science of Advanced Materials and Process Engineering, Vol. 14. Western Periodicals Co., Paper I-4-5.

Chamis, C. C. (1969a). Important Factors in Fiber Composite Design. *SPI Annu. Conf., 24th* Sect. 18-E.

Chamis, C. C. (1969b). Analysis Design and Research Trends in Structural Fiber Composites (A State of the Art Report). ASCE Pamphlet Structural Plastics, Properties and Possibilities, Louisville, Kentucky.

Chamis, C. C. (1969c). Failure Criteria for Filamentary Composites. NASA TN D-5367.

Chamis, C. C. (1969d). Important Factors in Fiber Composite Design, Part 1, *Modern Plastics.*

Chamis, C. C. (1969e). Important Factors in Fiber Composite Design, Part 2, *Modern Plastics.*

Chamis, C. C. (1969f). *ASCE J. Struc. Div.* **95,** No. ST10, 2119; (1971). **97,** No. ST3, 960.

Chamis, C. C. (1969g). *ASCE J. Eng. Mech. Div.* **95,** No. EMS, 1255.

Chamis, C. C., (1970a). Design and Analysis of Fiber Composite Structural Components. NASA SP-227, p. 217.

Chamis, C. C. (1970b). Characterization and Design Mechanics for Fiber Reinforced Metals. NASA TN D-5784.

Chamis, C. C. (1971a). Lamination Residual Stresses in Multilayered Fiber Composites. NASA TN D-6146.

Chamis, C. C. (1971b). Theoretical Buckling Loads of Boron/Aluminum and Graphite/Resin Fiber-Composite Anisotropic Plates. NASA TN D-6572.

Chamis, C. C. (1972). Design Considerations for Fiber Composite Structures. NASA TMX-68039.

Chamis, C. C., Hanson, M. P., and Serafini, T. T. (1971). Design for Impact Resistance with Unidirectional Fiber Composites. NASA TN D-6463.

Chamis, C. C., Hanson, M. P., and Serafini, T. T. (1973). Criteria for Selecting Resin Matrices for Improved Composite Strength. *Modern Plastics.*

Clary, R. R. (1972). Vibration Characteristics of Unidirectional Filamentary Composite Material Panel. *Conf. Compos. Mater. Testing Design, 2nd,* ASTM STP 497.

Cole, E., and Cervelli, R. C. (1968). Comparison of Composite and Noncomposite Structural Tubes. *AIAA/ASME Struct., Struct. Dynam. Mater. Conf., 9th, Palm Springs, California,* AIAA Paper No. 68-340.

Darms, F. J. *et al.* (1964). Improved Filament-Wound Construction for Cylindrical Pressure Vessels. Wright-Patterson AFB, ML-TDR-64-43, Vol. I.

Dietz, A. G. H. (1972). Reinforced Plastics in Building; Examples, Constraints, and Problems. *SPI Annu. Conf. Proc., 27th* Sect. 20-E.

Dow, N. F., Rosen, B. W., Shu, L., and Zweben, C. H. (1967). Design Criteria and Concepts for Fibrous Composite Structures. N68-14176.

Fabrication of ⅓ Scale Boron/Epoxy Booster Thrust Structure. (1971). Phase I Final Rept., Grumman Aerospace, NASA Contract No. NAS8-26675.

Fleck, J. N. (1972). Bibliography on Fibers and Composite Materials—1969-1972. Battelle Inst., MCIC-72-09.

Foye, R. L. (1967). Private communication.

Foye, R. L., and Baker, D. J. (1970). Design of Orthotropic Laminates. Paper presented at the *AIAA/ASME Struct., Struct. Dynam., Mater. Conf., 11th, Denver, Colorado.*

Gerin-Lajoie, G. (1973). An Architect's Experience in FRP Building and Housing Construction. *Proc. Ann. Conf. Soc. Plast. Ind., 28th,* Sec. 4-D.

Gibbs and Cox Inc. (1960). "Marine Design Manual for Fiberglass Reinforced Plastics." McGraw-Hill, New York.

Grove, C. S., Jr., and Pray, R. F. (1964). Materials Design Handbook Division 1 Structural Plastics, AD 604860.

Hackman, L. E., and Stotler, C. L. (1966). *SAMPE* **10,** C-1–C-11.

Harrington, R. A., Chamis, C. C., and Tatarzycki, E. M. (1964). Design Criteria on Filament Wound Structures Subjected to Combined Loading. B. F. Goodrich Res. Center, AD-451216.

Heifetz, S., Kushner, I., and Mandlebaum, G. J. (1972). Utilization of Standard Modules as Building Blocks in Construction of High Rise Structures. *SPI Annu. Conf. Proc., 27th,* Sect. 20-G.

Holms, A. G. (1969). The Design and Analysis of Optimum Seeking Experiments.

Lecture notes for a short course on mathematical and statistical analysis of laboratory data. Univ. of Tennessee Space Inst., Tullahoma.

Holston, A., Jr., Feldman, A., and Stang, D. A. (1967). Stability of Filament Wound Cylinders under Combined Loading. Air Force Flight Dynam. Lab. Rep. AFFDL-TR-67-55, AD 815 620.

Jacoby, S. L. S., Kowalik, J. S., and Pizzo, J. T. (1972). "Iterative Methods for Nonlinear Optimization Problems." Prentice-Hall, Englewood Cliffs, New Jersey.

Juveric, W. G., and Rittenhouse, J. B. (1968). Structural Plastics Applications Handbook, AD 840 585.

Khot, N. S., Venkayya, V. V., Johnson, C. D., and Thschler, V. A. (1973). Amplication of Optimality Criterion to Fiber-Reinforced Composites. Wright-Patterson AFB, AFFDL-TR-73-6.

Kicher, T. P., and Chao, T. L. (1970). Minimum Weight Design of Stiffened Composite Cylinders. *AIAA/ASME Struct., Struct. Dynam., Mater. Conf., 11th, Denver, Colorado* A70-27126, p. 129.

Lubin, G. (ed.) (1969). "Handbook of Fiberglass and Advanced Plastics Composites." VanNostrand-Reinhold, Princeton, New Jersey.

Lynema, L. (1972). A Revolution in Building. *SPI Annu. Conf. Proc., 27th*, Sect. 20-F.

McClelland, W. (1972). The Use of Structural RP Sandwich Panels in Housing and Building Construction. *SPI Annu. Conf. Proc., 27th*, Sect. 20-A.

McCullers, L. A., and Lynch, R. W. (1972). Composite Wing Design for Aeroelastic Requirements. *Proc. Conf. Fibrous Compos. Flight Vehicle Design* AFFDL-TR-72-130, p. 953. Wright-Patterson, AFB.

MIL-HDBK-17A (1971). Plastics for Aerospace Vehicles, Part I, Reinforced Plastics. Dept. of Defense, Washington, D.C.

NASA Space Vehicle Design Criteria (Structures) (1973). Advanced Composite Structures. NASA SP – –.

Oleesky, S., and Mohr, G. (1964). "Handbook of Reinforced Plastics of the SPI." VanNostrand-Reinhold, Princeton, New Jersey.

Powell, D. (1972). Reinforced Plastics in Building—The European Example. *SPI Annu. Conf. Proc., 27th*, Sect. 5-A.

Powell, D. (1973). New Contributions of FRP in the Construction Industry. *SPI Annu. Conf. Proc., 28th*, Sect. 4-E.

Purdy, D. M., Dietz, G. G., and McGrew, J. A. (1972). Optimization of Laminates for Strength and Flutter. *Proc. Conf. Fibrous Compos. Flight Vehicle Design* AFFDL-TR-72-130, p. 929. Wright-Patterson, AFB.

Rand, R. A., and Shen, C. N. (1973). *Comput. Struct.* **3**, No. 2, 247.

Ravenhall, R. (1964). *J. Spacecr.* **1**, 260.

Sandrock, G. D., and Holms, A. G. (1969). Statistical Design and Analysis of Optimum Seeking Experiments to Develop a Gamma-Prime Strengthened Cobalt-Nickel Base Alloy, NASA TN D-5587.

Structural Design Guide for Advanced Composite Applications (1968). Wright-Patterson AFB.

Structural Design Guide for Advanced Composite Applications (1973). 3rd ed. AFML, Wright-Patterson AFB, Ohio.

Verette, R. M. (1972). Stiffness Strength and Stability Optimization of Laminated Composites. *Conf. Compos. Mater. Testing Design, 2nd* ASTM STP 497.

Waddoups, M. E., McCullers, L. A., Olson, F. O., and Ashton, J. E. (1970). Structural

Synthesis of Anisotropic Plates. Paper Presented at the *AIAA/ASME Struct., Struct. Dynam., Mater. Conf., 11th, Denver, Colorado*.

Wang, C. S. (1966). Longitudinal Stability Problems of Filament Wound Shells. *SPI Annu. Conf. Proc., 21st* Sect. 14-E.

White, T. H. (1965). Engineering Design Data on Glass-Reinforced Plastics and Related Materials, AD 486 124. Part 1A. Admiralty Underwater Weapons Establishment, Portland, England.

Winfield, A. G. (1972). Forefronts of FRP in Building Applications (World Coverage), *SPI Annu. Conf. Proc., 27th* Sect. 20-D.

Winters, W. E. (1970). Thermal Anisotropic Behavior in Graphite Epoxy Composites. Paper presented in the *Annu. Int. Conf. Products Show, 15th* Palais Du Centenaire, Brussels, Belgium.

Author Index

Numbers in italics refer to the pages on which the complete references are listed.

A

Abbott, B. W., 115, *126*
Abelkis, P. R., 61, *70*
Adams, D. F., 95, 97, 104, *126*
Adams, E. H., 93, 103, 112, *129*
Adams, R. D., 122, *126*
Adsit, N. R., 88, *126*
Ahimaz, F. J., 97, *130*
Airhart, T. P., 85, *131*
Anderson, R. M., 93, *129*
Argon, A. S., 47, *71*
Ashkenazi, E. K., 84, *126*
Ashton, J. E., 76, 77, 82, 85, 97, 101, 114, 118, *126*, *131*, 155, 156, 168, *229*, 255, *279*

B

Baer, E., 236, *277*
Baker, D. J., 161, *229*, 255, *278*
Balaban, M. M., 99, *126*
Baldridge, K. G., 84, *130*
Barker, R. M., 152, 153, *229*
Barnet, F. R., 75, 90, *126*, *131*
Barton, R. S., 80, *126*
Batt, J. R., 2, *31*
Baucom, R. M., 111, *129*
Baumberger, R., 83, *126*
Beckett, R. E., 93, *126*
Beckwith, S. W., 237, *277*
Behrens, E., 120, *126*
Bell, J. E., 108, *133*
Berg, C. A., 84, *126*
Bergsträsser, M., 93, *126*
Berke, L., 12, *31*

Bert, C. W., 72, 76, 77, 80, 85, 87, 90, 96, 97, 100, 102, 105, 108, 109, 110, 111, 112, 113, 114, 120, 124, *126*, *127*, *129*, *130*, *132*
Bishop, R. E. D., 124, *131*
Bodnar, M. J., 174, *229*
Bombara, E. L., 57, *70*
Boresi, A. P., 114, *130*
Boutan, I., 35, *70*
Bowie, O. L., 139, *229*
Bracco, A., 104, *127*
Bronstad, M. E., 75, 80, *128*
Broutman, L. J., 75, 115, *126*, *127*
Brugger, K., 119, *127*
Bryan, E. L., 97, *127*
Burchett, O. J., 87, *127*
Buxbaum, R. S., 93, 103, 112, *133*
Buxton, R. W., 263, *277*

C

Card, M. F., 90, 100, 113, *127*, *132*, 255, *277*
Cervelli, R. V., 95, 100, *127*, 248, *278*
Chambers, R. E., 77, *127*
Chamis, C. C., 154, *229*, 236, 237, 238, 240, 242, 249, 250, 252, 254, 255, 256, 258, 259, 260, 261, 262, 263, 264, 265, 266, 267, 268, 269, 270, 271, 272, *277*, *278*
Chan, S. T. K., 45, *71*
Chang, S., 80, 124, *127*
Channon, S. L., 86, *127*
Chao, T. L., 254, 261, *279*
Chen, P. I., 46, *71*
Cheng, S., 113, *127*

281

Subject Index

A 5
B 6
C 7
D 8
E 9
F 0
G 1
H 2
I 3
J 4